The Master Musicians Series

MONTEVERDI

SERIES EDITED BY
SIR JACK WESTRUP,
M.A., Hon.D.Mus. (Oxon.), F.R.C.O.

MONTEVERDI IN OLD AGE
From the title-page of Marinoni's 'Fiori Poetici'

THE MASTER MUSICIANS SERIES

MONTEVERDI

by

DENIS ARNOLD

*With eight pages of plates
and music examples in the text*

LONDON
J. M. DENT AND SONS LTD

FARRAR, STRAUS AND CUDAHY INC.
NEW YORK

PREFACE

Two studies of Monteverdi's life and works, both based on recent research, are available in English. The preface for a third one must necessarily be an explanation for writing yet another. The main reason is simply that a series such as the Master Musicians can no longer neglect Monteverdi, whose greatness is now generally acknowledged; and the need for a book designed specifically for the English general reader is increased because the existing books were both intended for a somewhat different audience. Professor Schrade's *Monteverdi: the Creator of Modern Music*, with its detailed analyses, is best read with the complete edition to hand; Professor Redlich's *Claudio Monteverdi: Life and Works* was written originally for the German reader with a knowledge of Heinrich Schütz and Samuel Scheidt rather than for the Englishman who knows Byrd and Wilbye.

I have therefore tried to write a study which will introduce Monteverdi and his background to readers with a limited knowledge of Italian music of the time. In the musical examples the filling in of the *continuo* part has been made as simple as possible, both to save space and to facilitate performance. It in no way represents my views on the method to be used in the performance of Monteverdi's work. The time-values of certain examples have been reduced to conform with modern notation. The bibliography is also a guide for the general reader rather than for the scholar.

Bearing this in mind, I have deliberately avoided marshalling all the arguments about such matters as the authenticity of *Il ritorno d'Ulisse* and the meaning of *canto alla francese*. But in one matter I have ventured to state my views at some length. Previous writers have all stressed the revolutionary nature of Monteverdi's music. After a fairly

v

Preface

close examination of music by certain of his contemporaries, it seemed
to me to be more accurate to consider him as a moderate and progressive rather than an experimental composer. Since the music of
these other composers is not widely known, I have tried to give
sufficient background material to justify this new approach, though
not, I hope, at such great length that it distorts the broader picture
which the general reader requires.

Extracts from Einstein, *Essays on Music*, and Strunk, *Source Readings
in Music History*, are by kind permission of Faber & Faber Ltd
(London) and W. W. Norton & Co. Inc. (New York).

Two engravings of Venetian scenes are reproduced by permission
of the Trustees of the Victoria and Albert Museum. I have to thank
my colleagues Professor Philip Cranmer, Mr Raymond Warren and
Mr R. H. Semple for reading either the whole or part of this book in
manuscript and making some most helpful suggestions; Dr G. B.
Gaidoni for checking the translations from Italian; Mr Gordon
Wheeler for reading the proofs with a splendidly keen eye and com-
piling the index; and my wife, who not only typed the book from an
illegible manuscript, but encouraged me to finish it.

D. A.

Belfast,
  September 1962.

CONTENTS

ILLUSTRATIONS

CHAPTER I

CREMONA

'It is a beautiful and large town, whose precincts are at least 5,000 steps, surrounded by fine walls and defended by a castle which is very strong. . . . The houses of Cremona are beautiful, large and well constructed, so that one could say that all of them are palaces. There are several public squares, all very beautiful. The streets are wide and straight, and there are several beautiful public gardens in the town.'[1] In this way an eighteenth-century French writer describes Cremona, where Monteverdi was born. The town lies on the banks of the river Po, about fifty miles from Milan, in the heart of the great plain of northern Italy. It is a place comparatively unvisited today, except by tourists who wish to look at the cathedral and the splendidly tall clock tower. Indeed it seems an almost isolated town, distant from all the major cities of Italy with the exception of Milan, not even on a main road to the east or south.

Yet in the sixteenth century it was a good place for the musician or artist to be born in. If in itself Cremona was too small and too provincial to be very important, it was near several centres of Renaissance society. Milan, dominated by the Spaniard, was the least interesting of these. Parma, whose ruling family, the Farnese, was linked strongly with the Netherlands, was more important and provided a fitting setting for several great composers, including Cipriano de Rore and Merulo. Mantua, to the east, was ruled by the Gonzagas, rich, prosperous and cultured, for they too liked good music and painting. A little farther away were Ferrara, the most progressive court, musically speaking, in Europe; Venice, more conservative, but the heart of music publishing and full of fine composers, players and painters;

[1] *Les Délices de l'Italie*, Tome iv (Paris, 1707).

I

Florence; and the Transalpine courts of Bavaria, Innsbruck and Graz. This region in northern Italy, its ground fertile to the point of luxury, was the heart of artistic Europe, the equivalent of eighteenth-century Vienna or nineteenth-century Paris.

We are not sure of the exact day when Monteverdi was born. The first record to be found is of his baptism, which took place on 15th May 1567. He was the eldest child of Baldasar Monteverdi, a doctor, whose wife Maddalena gave birth to four more children, two of them girls. We know nothing of his earliest years. All that we can say is that his family must have been musical, since of the boys, both Claudio and his brother Giulio Cesare became professional musicians. It is usually assumed that Claudio became a choirboy in Cremona Cathedral, and this seems likely enough if we consider the musical institutions in a small town of the period.

Lacking the natural focusing point of patronage which a prince and his retinue provided for larger cities, the most important centre of music-making was undoubtedly the principal church of the town, usually the cathedral. This would normally have a small choir of about ten men and up to fifteen boys. Some of the men may also have played instruments, but the only professional player would be the organist. At the head of these was a director of music, or *maestro di cappella*. The cathedral chapter tried to find a composer for this post, since he was expected to provide music for the more important festivals. He was also expected to conduct the choir, and to instruct both priests and boys in the art of music. The priests for the most part only learned to sing plainsong. The boys, on the other hand, received a complete education in music, as well as being given the elements of a literary education by a teacher called the *maestro de grammatica*.

Compared with court musicians, the servants of the church were not very well paid, but they were comfortably enough off and a modest social status was accorded to them. Further down the social ladder were the town musicians, or *piffari*. These were wind-players, and were employed by the municipality for various purposes. They entertained the populace in the town square, as Montaigne found at Piacenza (in the Duchy of Parma, not far from Cremona) and wrote in his journal:

CREMONA CATHEDRAL
From Antonio Campo's 'Historia di Cremona'

'Morning and night they play for one hour on those instruments we call oboes, but which they call *piffari*!' At other times they accompanied the mayor and town dignitaries in processions to church. In some towns they had to teach anyone who wanted to learn an instrument. For such duties they were paid very badly, though in the end they probably made enough money from casual engagements—playing at weddings and banquets, or in church when hired by the *maestro di cappella* for a festival. Socially they were usually considered a cut below the more dignified musicians of church and court, but they were men of considerable skill. Some of them could play virtually any wind instrument and sing as well. Entry into their ranks was usually by apprenticeship, and in the manner of the guilds they were strict in the upkeep of their standards.

Finally, the musician could sometimes gain an education and a livelihood from the academies which were so important in the sixteenth century. These were not teaching institutions. They were associations of upper-class gentlemen who wished to discuss literary topics, learn a little music or otherwise follow the curriculum laid down by the courtesy books such as Castiglione's *The Courtier*. Some of these academies paid musicians quite well to instruct and entertain their members. Others employed them more casually. But whether employed full-time or not, these musicians were generally more intelligent and better educated than those of church or town. Their patrons often discussed the basic philosophy of music with them, and at least in some of them there was a very close relationship between musician and gentry.

Monteverdi must have learned his music from the church and its seminary. A boy from a doctor's family would never have been apprenticed to a town musician. And although we know that there was an academy in Cremona, Monteverdi was too accomplished a musician at a very early age to have picked up his knowledge amongst amateurs, for at the age of fifteen he was ready to publish a book of motets with the distinguished Venetian publishing firm of Gardano. The title-page tells us that they are sacred songs for three voices and that the composer is a pupil of Marc' Antonio Ingegneri. Ingegneri,

3

whose pupil Monteverdi was proud to acknowledge himself, was *maestro di cappella* at Cremona Cathedral. He was exactly the kind of man we should expect to find there. Educated (perhaps also born) in Verona, he started as a singer at Cremona before being promoted to be director of music. He had published some madrigals and church music by the time Monteverdi produced the *Sacrae cantiunculae*, and these reveal him as a sound rather than brilliant composer, inclining to the older methods of contrapuntal music which we associate with the Netherlands composers. Nevertheless he was not completely old-fashioned. He knew something of the newer style of Cipriano de Rore, and he must have been a good teacher, for Monteverdi's pieces show every sign of proficiency.

It is not surprising that a choirboy should set Latin words rather than attempt the madrigal style straight away; nor that this book was for three voices, which are easier to manipulate than the five or six voices usual for motets at this time. What is a little surprising, perhaps, is that the book appeared under the imprint of the most famous Venetian publisher, especially since the dedication is to a priest and not to a member of the nobility who might have provided a subsidy. The reason for Gardano's acceptance may well have been the easiness of the music for the performer, and the fact that it was suitable for domestic devotional singing as well as for churches with very small choirs. In any case we find Monteverdi continuing in this vein, for in the next year he produced a set of *madrigali spirituali* for four voices— again no mean achievement for a boy not yet sixteen. This time he had to rest content with a less distinguished publisher in Brescia, and since the dedication is to a Cremonese nobleman, this book almost certainly was subsidized. Continuing his career as a prodigy, Monteverdi in his eighteenth year saw yet another book in print. This time it was a book which broke away from the ecclesiastical traditions—a book of canzonets for three voices. This was a popular *genre* at the time, and the book was likely to sell. Monteverdi tried yet another publisher in Venice, the house of Vincenti and Amadino, which accepted the work. Whether they made any money out of it we shall never know, but Amadino's shrewdness was continually to profit him, for he published most of Monteverdi's later music, including the very popular books of madrigals which went through many editions.

Then comes a gap of three years in our knowledge of Monteverdi's life and works. Some writers have surmised that he attended the University of Cremona, but there is no evidence for this—rather the reverse, in fact, for later in life he was to say that he never understood the antique signs and notations of the Greeks, something about which he would surely have been less modest if he had had a normal education in classical thought. Certainly there is little evidence that he was widely read, or that his knowledge of the classical philosophers was any more than he might have obtained in discussions with members of an academy. It is more probable that he continued his studies to be a professional musician; on the title-page of his next book, his first book of madrigals, he still proclaims himself a pupil of Ingegneri. The dedication is again to a member of Cremona's nobility, Count Marco Verita, and so experienced does Monteverdi seem by this time that we are a little surprised to find in it a modest declaration: 'I must not expect for compositions so much the product of youth, such as are these of mine, other praise than that which can be given to the flowers of spring in comparison with those awarded to the fruits of summer and autumn.' Monteverdi was nineteen and had published four books in a little over four years. He was evidently an ambitious young man; we may note that in the secure surroundings of his later life he never published his work so eagerly.

His ambitions were certainly not to be fulfilled in his home town, and like other composers from Cremona he began to think of leaving it. Benedetto Pallavicino was now at the Mantuan court; so was Gastoldi, who had left nearby Caravaggio. Costanzo Porta had gone away to Padua, Massaino to Prague and Salzburg. All had improved their position by leaving Cremona; and the style of Monteverdi's madrigal book shows that now he could learn little more from Ingegneri. His first attempt at finding a post away from home apparently was directed towards Milan. His father had had dealings with the Milanese health authorities as the representative of the Cremona Doctors' Association and no doubt had friends there. Claudio

Monteverdi went up to the city in 1589 and tried to obtain the influence of Giacomo Riccardi, then President of His Catholic Majesty's most excellent Senate and Council in Milan. He was unsuccessful— luckily, since Milan, under the influence of the foreigner, was a backwater at this time and remained so during the seventeenth century. He seems to have made some friends who were to help him in his Mantuan years, but for the time being he had to return to Cremona.

Back there, he put his energies into the preparation of a second book of madrigals, which came out in the following year. This was dedicated to Riccardi, perhaps in the hope that something might still turn up in Milan. This madrigal book still acknowledges the teaching of Ingegneri on the title-page: its contents do not. On the contrary, the mature style of these madrigals reveals more clearly that Monteverdi was looking far beyond the confines of Cremona, and was studying the works of more famous and more modern masters than his old teacher.

The exact date, and even the year itself, when Monteverdi left Cremona are unknown to us. In one of his letters written in 1608 he writes of his nineteen years' service in Mantua, which, if true, means that he must have started his life there as early as 1589. Another of his letters, written in 1615, speaks of his 'twenty-one years of service in Mantua', and since he was deprived of his post there in 1612, this suggests that he went to his new post in 1591. Against this must be placed the fact that a list of musicians compiled by the treasurer at the Mantuan court in this later year [1] does not contain the name of Monteverdi. Perhaps the most reasonable explanation is that he went to Mantua in the two or three earlier years to take occasional and part-time engagements, of which there were plenty to be had, and then was given a permanent place in the latter part of 1591. Of one thing we can be certain. By the time he was ready to publish yet another madrigal book in 1592 he was *suonatore di vivuola* to Vincenzo I, Duke of Mantua, and in his first permanent post.

---

[1] Arch. Gonzaga *Busta* 395.

CHAPTER II

MANTUA

THE visitor to Mantua may find it hard to believe how great was Monteverdi's success. The town today seems rather forlorn, its huge palace a museum, its present *raison d'être* a market for the rich countryside by which it is surrounded. In the later years of the sixteenth century it was very different. Although never destined to be one of the greatest cities of Europe, Mantua was no mere provincial centre. The house of Gonzaga had brought the city to a fine prosperity, and encouraged by a succession of dukes who loved all the outward signs of richness, artists and musicians, actors and poets were glad to accept the bountiful patronage they were offered. Rubens, Tasso and Guarini are only three among many famous names in letters and painting that we find associated with the Mantuan court; and to these can be added a group of musicians just as distinguished.

By a singular act of good fortune, the prosperity of Mantua was assured by the sagacity of a duke who was both cultured and thoroughly educated. Duke Guglielmo, who came into power in 1550, had a flair for organization and was progressive in his methods of government. Tasso could write of him that he was 'a prince of high talent and culture and most just and liberal'. Under him Mantua achieved a rare stability, and music was perhaps his greatest love. Not content with being a patron of musicians, he was a composer himself and sent his compositions to Palestrina for comment and correction. It was not his fault that Mantua's music was not directed by Palestrina or Marenzio; both were too comfortable elsewhere. As it was, Giaches de Wert was Guglielmo's *maestro di cappella*, and he built up a group of musicians among the most famous of the age. Alessandro Striggio, Gastoldi, Pallavicino and Soriano were all wellknown composers;

7

Gastoldi and Wert indeed were world famous. Rome or Venice apart, Mantua's musicians could not be surpassed.

If Guglielmo was something near to the ideal of a Renaissance monarch, his son, who became Duke Vincenzo I in 1587, was nearer the normal. Fond of women and gambling, he was in his youth at best an inconsiderate and inconsistent ruler, at the worst a brute and a murderer. He had no compunction about divorcing his first wife, accusing her publicly of physical deformity; and when the countercharge of his impotence was made by her family, proposed a trial of his virility on a virgin girl in Venice. Yet he could be genuinely repentant, giving vast sums to churches and monasteries, or planning a pilgrimage to the holy places in Palestine (although this was prevented by his death). He also supported artists of all kinds. The ducal palace was further embellished in his lifetime. Music was encouraged, and drama was almost a passion with him. Was it a production of *Il pastor fido* by Guarini in 1591 which provided Monteverdi with one of his first engagements in Mantua? The music for this play was composed by Giaches de Wert, and the production was planned on a most sumptuous scale, to be given in the courtyard of the Palazzo del Tè. The customary interpolation of intermezzos was planned with vast scenic designs and continuous music. There were to be four, representing *Musica della terra, del mare, dell' aria* and *Musica celeste*. Typical for Vincenzo was the fact that all this vast trouble and expense was to please one of his mistresses, the Spanish beauty Agnese d'Argotti. The play was put in rehearsal and arrangements were made for a brilliant illumination of the courtyard by a thousand torches and for vast tapestries to cover the walls. Alas, the performance never came off. The official reason given was the death of Cardinal Gioanvincenzo Gonzaga in Rome; [1] more malicious tongues whispered that the true one was the disapproval of the duchess. We know that musicians were to have been brought from as far as Venice and Verona and Ferrara, and they must have spent some time in Mantua rehearsing. May not Monteverdi have been among them?

---

[1] *Vide* W. W. Grey, *Pastoral Poetry and Pastoral Drama* (London, 1906).

This interest in drama was enough to make Vincenzo keep an adequate musical establishment, since plays always involved music, quite apart from the intermezzos which were given between the acts, with great machines, splendid scenery, and singing and dancing. Vincenzo seems also to have been fond of music itself. Admittedly he seems to have had less perception than his father. The really famous composers of the court—Monteverdi excepted—were those left over from previous years. His performers, on the other hand, were excellent. The singers, especially, were the most famous of their age—and from all accounts such women as Adriana Basile and Caterinuccia Martinelli were superb. This was the beginning of the age of virtuosity, an age where the prestige of the princely court was felt to be more at stake in the quality of the performers than the composers.

Concerts took place every Friday in the great Hall of Mirrors of the Gonzaga Palace—so one of Monteverdi's letters tells us; and although we have no descriptions of them, we can imagine what happened from a description of a concert at the nearby court of the Estensi at Ferrara. The two courts were very similar, and their composers often visited each other. The performers were more jealously guarded, and there was a great deal of rivalry between the two cities. Mantua could hardly compete with the grand instrumental *ensembles* of Ferrara, but the Gonzagas did everything to keep up with the standards of virtuosity set by several of the Ferrara singers. So we may take the letter of the Roman ambassador at Ferrara as giving a lively account of the sort of evening which was so popular at Mantua also:

The day before yesterday the court returned from Belriguardo, where I had stayed for two days upon the invitation of the duke. . . . In the morning we rode in a small open carriage, as is the custom, until the duchess was ready to go to Mass. After that we had dinner, and this was immediately followed by a game of cards, at which were present the duke and duchess, Lady Marfisa and I. And I cannot refrain from mentioning, since it is an inevitable custom here, that at once the music began, and I was forced to admire all the florid passages, cadences and other ornamentations: of these bagatelles, the cards included, I understand very little, and I care for them even less. These festivities lasted not one minute less than four hours, for after several ladies had sung, there finally appeared Lady Perperara—that lady from Mantua about whom I wrote before, and on the pretext that I should hear her sing now this thing, now that, both solo and accompanied, with one or more instruments, she continued to perform beyond one's endurance....[1]

To come from provincial Cremona into this atmosphere of courtly service, to mix with these great singers and players, to work under a fine composer such as Wert, must have changed Monteverdi's life considerably. Certainly it changed and matured his music, for he published his third book of madrigals in 1592, and this was no work of a provincial composer. The music of the other Mantuan composers had clearly had its effect—and this more up-to-date style made Monteverdi's music more popular. The book must have paid his publisher Amadino, since it was reprinted within two years. In the dedication Monteverdi naturally offers the book to his master, Duke Vincenzo. For the most part it is written in that conventional and flowery language we meet in all dedicatory letters of the time; but there is a hint that Monteverdi regarded 'his most noble service of playing the viol', as he called it, more as a gateway into the world of the court music than as an end in itself. He was clearly hoping for the better things that befitted a composer. He was not disappointed, for the next news we have of him is that he has raised his status from player to singer; and by this time he was senior enough for his patron to take him on an expedition. Duke Vincenzo was called upon by the Emperor Rudolf to aid him in a war against the Turks. The Turks were now in possession of a great deal of south-east Europe, and were menacing Austria from Hungary. At first Vincenzo sent troops to be directly under the command of the Emperor. Shortly afterwards he decided to go himself, to be at the head of his own army. Following the custom of the day, he took a formidable retinue with him, and among them were some of his musicians.

Monteverdi was at the head of a little group of five musicians. The journey was no doubt exhausting but also beautiful: across the Alps

[1] Translation adapted from C. G. Anthon, *Music and Musicians in Northern Italy during the Sixteenth Century* (Harvard thesis, 1943), page 258.

MONTEVERDI IN MIDDLE AGE
Portrait by an unknown painter

to Innsbruck, then Prague and Vienna, before the plains of Hungary. The warlike activities were brief enough, and not particularly success-ful. After the assault of one fortress the duke returned home, having been six months away. Such an expedition would in the normal way be hardly worth mentioning; it can scarcely have added much to Monteverdi's musical experience. But it seems to have affected him deeply. He remembered it vividly nearly forty years later, and warlike scenes became one of his principal interests as an artist. It is no coin-cidence that his last book of madrigals contains *madrigali guerrieri*, nor that he chose to set the battle scenes from Tasso's *Gerusalemme liberata*.

He arrived home richer in experience but poorer in pocket. As he said in a later letter: 'If it was my good fortune that the Most Serene Duke graciously allowed me to serve him in Hungary, it was bad luck that I had additional expenditure on account of the journey from which our poor home suffers even at the present time.'[1] To make matters worse he seems to have been disappointed when, on the death of Giaches de Wert in 1596, Benedetto Pallavicino was promoted to be *maestro di cappella* to the duke. Certain biographers of Monteverdi have sought explanations for the appointment of this mediocrity, as they have called him, over the head of a genius. The truth is simple. In 1596 Monteverdi was still not thirty, and although admittedly a composer of merit had shown no signs of that overwhelming popu-larity which was to appear ten years later. Pallavicino was older, had published a great deal of music and in any case at that time was not considered a mediocrity. Two contemporary writers—Artusi and Banchieri—both had good words to say of his music, and some of it even today seems remarkably fine. So we have no need to assume any intrigues. Regarded in this light, it was merely a matter of seniority; and now Monteverdi headed the salary list of the singers at court and was next in line for promotion.

We hear nothing more of Monteverdi until 1599. Then he married a court singer, Claudia Cattaneo. It was a marriage in a modern tradition, for she presumably kept on working, as her salary was

[1] G. F. Malipiero, *Claudio Monteverdi* (Milan, 1929), page 135.

continued until her death, although she had had children. The pair were married on 20th May, but they had little time to enjoy themselves. Monteverdi again had to accompany his patron on a journey. In June 1599 Vincenzo set out for Flanders, to spend a month at the bathing resort of Spa, before visiting Liège and Antwerp, where he bought paintings and antiques, and finally Brussels. This must have been a more interesting journey to a musician. On such travels the court was not content merely to listen to its own performers. Local singers and players performed before the duke and were well rewarded for their pains. It must have been from these that Monteverdi learned 'the French style of singing' which his brother mentioned some years later in his preface to the *Scherzi musicali*. Again he returned home richer in experience and poorer in pocket:

If my good fortune called me into the service of His Highness in Flanders, on this occasion also it went against me in that Signora Claudia, remaining in Cremona, had to keep up the expenditure of our home, with maid and servant, yet had only forty-seven lire a month from His Highness, besides that which my father gave me beforehand.[1]

If Monteverdi was not happy, at least his fame was becoming more widely spread. In 1600 a theorist, Giovanni Maria Artusi, who lived in Bologna, produced a book, *L'Artusi, overo delle Imperfettioni della moderna musica*. The attack, as the title suggests, is on modern music, and although Monteverdi is nowhere mentioned by name, his works come in for the brunt of the assault. There are a number of quotations from some of his madrigals (not as yet published), all of them to show 'irregularities' of harmony or counterpoint. No one attacks mediocrities. There is no point in writing a book to criticize the work of someone completely unknown, and from the setting of the book, the private house of one of the Ferrarese gentry, we may gather that Monteverdi was a leading light of a circle of composers which included some of the most progressive of the day. For the moment this is more important news than the attack itself, for we have had no

---

[1] Ibid., page 136.

works from Monteverdi's pen published for eight years, and Artusi's evidence shows the way his mind was working and his standing in his middle thirties.

It is not very surprising, therefore, to find that when Pallavicino died in the following year Monteverdi applied to Duke Vincenzo for the post of *maestro di cappella*. The tone of his letter is interesting:

... if, when the world has seen my zeal in Your Highness's service and your graciousness to me after the death of the most famous Signor Striggio, and after that of the excellent Signor Giaches [de Wert], and thirdly after that of the most excellent Signor Franceschino [Rovigo] and finally after this the death of the capable Benedetto Pallavicino—if I failed to seek (on the grounds not of merit but of the faithful and singular devotion that I have always given in Your Highness's service) the ecclesiastical post now vacant, and if after all this I were not to ask with vigour and with humility for the said rank, it could be claimed with justice that I was negligent.[1]

This letter, the first we possess, is typical of Monteverdi's writing, especially when he feels strongly about something. The complete lack of punctuation (the first full stop comes nearly at the end of a very long letter) and the piling of clause upon clause gives us a vivid picture of the temper of the man. It requires little imagination to see him, now after about ten years at Mantua, rather jealous of others, conscious of every imagined slight on his worth and well aware that gossip could undermine his position. Mantua, with its enclosed atmosphere, had left its mark on Monteverdi's character. Who can wonder if he became considered a difficult man in this small community?

On this occasion, however, he had no cause to complain. He was made *maestro di cappella* with full control of both court and church music. The addition to his income must have been welcome, since he was now the father of Francesco, born in 1601. The elevation in his status, one would imagine, must have contented him for a time, for his new post was equal to any in Italy, except some in Rome or Venice. And now the tide began to turn, at least as far as his fame was

[1] Ibid., page 128.

13

concerned. In 1603 he published his fourth book of madrigals with his old publisher Amadino. The contents were the work of several years, as he suggests in the preface (Artusi's attack of 1600 helps in dating some of them), and his dedication is not to anyone in Mantua but to the members of the Accademia degli Intrepidi at Ferrara, whose musicians were probably more his friends than those nearer home. The book was an immediate success and went through a number of editions quite quickly. Artusi followed up with another attack, this time naming the culprit who perpetrated his crimes against the traditions of music.

Either the success of this volume, or the desire for an opportunity to reply to Artusi, made Monteverdi publish yet another collection of madrigals soon after this in 1605. Again the contents were the work of some years, and this time he wrote a preface in addition to the usual dedication:

Do not wonder that I am allowing these madrigals to be printed without first replying to the attacks which Artusi has made against certain short passages in them. Since being in the service of His Serene Highness of Mantua I have not the time which would be required to do so; I have nevertheless written a reply to make known that I do not compose haphazardly, and as soon as it is rewritten it will be published bearing the title Second Practice or On the Perfection of Modern Music, which will perhaps surprise those who do not believe that there is any other way of composition save that taught by Zarlino; but let them be assured that, with regard to consonances and dissonances, there is yet another consideration different from those usually held, which defends the modern method of composition while giving satisfaction to the reason and the senses, and this I have wished to say, so that this expression 'second practice' may not be used by anyone else and the ingenious may reflect upon other secondary matters concerning music, and believe that the modern composer builds upon the foundations of truth.
Farewell.

The book to which he refers occupied his thoughts until his last years, but it was never published. The reason was probably that he was conscious of his limitations as a writer and as a scholar. The apparatus of Greek philosophy which was expected of the writer on music was beyond him; and the fact that most of his contemporaries were equally in the dark but went on writing all the same did not encourage him.

Treatise or no treatise, this fifth volume of madrigals made Monte-verdi's reputation quite secure. Not only was it reprinted within a year; his publisher found it financially expedient to reprint all his earlier books as well. But his position at Mantua was no happier than before. The irregularity in the payment of his salary was, to say the least, very trying. In a letter written in October 1604 we learn of his plight:

As a last resort it is necessary for me to have recourse to Your Highness's most infinite generosity, so that the last word can be said about that pay that was granted by Your Highness's grace. I come, however, to your feet, with as much humility as I can, to ask you to look upon my plight, not because of my boldness in writing this letter but because of the very great need about which I am writing; I do not write to the president, who many times has said yes in a most friendly and polite manner, but then, however good his intentions, has never wished to pay me except when it pleases him, so that it becomes necessary to ask him almost as though I were indebted to him and not to the generosity of Your Highness, who has been full of grace even to servants of little merit. . . . This letter of mine has no other end than to come to your feet to ask Your Highness to give the order for my pay which is now five months in arrears, in which plight is also Signora Claudia, and my father-in-law, and the sum increases in this way so that I see no hope of having it in the future without a special order from Your Highness, without which all my labours will remain failing and ruinous since day by day I am running up debts and I cannot repay them.[1]

In other words the treasurer, with whom Monteverdi has quarrelled, was holding up his pay;[2] and Monteverdi's debts were mounting,

[1] Ibid., page 129.

[2] This letter and later ones seem to suggest that it was mainly the treasurer who refused Monteverdi's pay and that the dukes of Mantua were generous enough. However, there are a number of documents in the Gonzaga archives which show the continual reluctance of the dukes to pay up. Perhaps the most pathetic is a plea from the town musicians of Mantua:

in part because Claudia was again staying in Cremona with her father-in-law, having had her third child, a son, who was born in May and called Massimiliano.[1] Monteverdi himself went to Cremona, probably to be there at his wife's confinement, and a letter written to Mantua tells us something of the work he was engaged on.

Significantly enough it was stage music. Monteverdi must have had some experience in this *genre* as a performer, for Guarini's *Il pastor fido* had not only been put into rehearsal in 1591; it was finally given a full performance in 1598. But this is the first knowledge we have of his composition for the stage, and at once we see his interest in the practical details. His commission was to write dances for what appears to have been either a pastoral play in the fashionable style of Tasso and Guarini or an intermezzo. One dance is an *entrata* for the stars, another is for shepherds, and Monteverdi says in his letter that he cannot proceed until he knows the number of dancers involved, for he would like to plan the dance with a number of *pas de deux* intermingled with a refrain for the whole *corps de ballet*. So he has already written to the dancing master and when he has the information, he will immediately set to work.

This letter is interesting, for it shows Monteverdi already fully aware of the necessity to plan the stagework and music together; and thus fascinated by the possibilities of dramatic music, he must have welcomed the opportunity to write an opera. This came when the festivities for the Carnival season of 1607 were planned. The details of

---

'A reminder to Your Highness from the players who served you at the baptism at which there were seven festivals and seven days during which they had been in the service of Your Highness of Gonzaga, begging Your Highness to give them satisfaction for

They are poor men.'

Arch. Gonzaga *Busta* 402.

[1] For details of the birth of Monteverdi's children see C. Gallico, 'Newly discovered documents concerning Monteverdi' in the *Musical Quarterly*, XLVIII (1962). Only two of the three seem to have survived beyond early childhood.

the conception and the performance of the new opera are unknown to us. The idea of producing an opera must have been in Vincenzo Gonzaga's mind for some time, since he had seen the Peri-Caccini opera *Euridice* in Florence during the wedding festivities of Maria de' Medici and Henry IV of France in 1600. Vincenzo's sons Ferdinando and Francesco were also interested in such activities, and as no doubt these were the mainstays of the Accademia degli Invaghiti, it was only a matter of time before this body decided to become a rival of the Florentine academies where opera had been born.

Monteverdi's opera was on the same subject as the Florentine opera of 1600—the story of Orpheus and Eurydice; but the work was a local production. The Mantuan court chancellor Striggio, the son of the composer whom we have already mentioned, wrote the libretto. The Mantuan virtuosos were probably given the principal parts, although we know that at least one singer was brought from Florence. The first performance took place before the members of the academy (probably in the Palazzo Ducale);[1] and then the opera was given more performances in front of the court with its guests. The libretto was published for the occasion, the score of the opera two years later. No description of the production exists, but we can assume that, if it resembled other such entertainments for the Carnival, it was a sumptuous one. In any case it was a great success, so much so that the Mantuan court must have looked forward to another opportunity for opera in the following year.

Professionally, *Orfeo* was a triumph, yet Monteverdi had little chance to enjoy it. His wife had been ill since at least November 1606, which was worrying enough in itself, and worrying because, as Claudia herself wrote: 'My serious illness has made me spend money which I cannot afford.' In July of the following year we find Monteverdi in Cremona, where Claudia could be looked after by his father. Work still followed him there and the duke was wanting more music

[1] There seems to be no reason to assume, with H. F. Redlich, that it took place in the state rooms of the academy—if they had them. 'In the academy', the phrase on the title-page of the libretto, surely means 'in front of the members of the academy'.

from him. Monteverdi could only reply that he was doing his best but he was tired and unwell. In August some of his music was performed before the Cremonese Accademia degli Animosi, and the academy made him an honorary member. Later in the month he went to Milan to show one of his oldest friends the score of *Orfeo*. At about the same time his *Scherzi musicali* were published in Venice with a new reply to Artusi, this time (and understandably in the circumstances) written by his brother.

In spite of all these successes, the honour in his home town, the popularity of the new book, the praise of his Milanese friend and the publication of yet another book of madrigals (old ones turned into *madrigali spirituali* by another friend living in Milan), personal tragedy was overwhelming. Claudia Monteverdi died on 10th September and was buried at Cremona. Monteverdi was at this time forty years of age, and he had been married for eight of them. His surviving children were aged six and three. It is no wonder he was in despair. Ironically, now was the least convenient time to give way to it. Duke Vincenzo's eldest son, heir to the throne, was to marry Margherita of Savoy. The celebrations were to include as many magnificent *spettacoli* as possible, including a new opera by Monteverdi.

He had the desire neither to resume work nor to return to Mantua. Why should he return to where the envy of colleagues and the lack of appreciation of his talents had made his life a misery, and everything about him must remind him of Claudia? Only a letter from his friend Follino, court chronicler, could make him consent to leave his father's house at Cremona:

Signor Claudio,

I do not know how to dissemble nor am I a flatterer, so please believe me that I have seen in the eyes of the prince and I have heard from his voice such things in praise of your genius that I have good, even excellent hopes for you; I believe that in the past you have known me to be affectionate, even most affectionate to my friends, and in particular to you yourself in such matters; so accept my advice, which is to forget now all these troubles, to return here and quickly, since this is the time to acquire the greatest fame which a man may have on earth and all the gratitude of the Most Serene Prince.[1]

Monteverdi returned to Mantua to try to submerge his sorrows in work.

There was plenty of this. The entry of Francesco and his bride into Mantua after their wedding in Turin was to mark the beginning of a week of dramatic entertainment, which for splendour and expense even in its own day was exceptional. Royal weddings had to be accompanied by such costly rejoicing, for these were the occasions when the succession was assured (or at least so it was hoped). Elegant and prosperous festivity was reassuring to all parties, quite apart from providing the occasion for hero worship on the part of the lower orders. Given this custom and the newness of Mantua's discovery of opera, we can understand how the celebrations of 1608 took shape. There was to be the usual play—Guarini's *Idropica*—with intermezzos; a triumph or masque by the bridegroom himself, two ballets—one of them in the opulent French style—and of course the new opera. No expense was to be spared. Naturally some singers would have to come from elsewhere—from Florence. When it became evident that Monteverdi and the other Mantuans could hardly be expected to compose everything, another Florentine, Marco da Gagliano, was commissioned to write one of the ballets and an intermezzo to *Idropica*. Yet one more Florentine was involved, the poet Rinuccini, who had supplied the book for the earlier operas produced in Florence and who was now to write the libretti for the new opera and one of the ballets.

Monteverdi's share of the work was enormous. The new opera *Arianna* was his; so was the music for one of the intermezzos and one of the ballets. This was a staggering task, the more so since the wedding seemed likely to take place early in the new year, and the music had to be composed and rehearsed by the Carnival season. Monteverdi arrived back in Mantua early in October. On 9th October he had no libretto

[1] S. Davari, *Notizie biografiche del distinto maestro di musica Claudio Monteverdi* (Mantua, 1885), page 12.

and obviously felt the pressure of time, since Prince Francesco wrote to his father:

> Yesterday evening Monteverdi came to speak with me, and showing his desire to serve Your Highness well in the wedding festivities and especially in the pastoral play which is to be set to music, he insisted that should you wish him to write it, it would be necessary for him to have the words in the next seven or eight days so that he could begin to work, since otherwise it will not be enough for his spirit to do good work in the short time between now and Carnival.[1]

We know from other letters that Monteverdi was not a quick composer, and to have under four months to produce a complete opera, a *genre* in which he had had little practice, was nearly impossible. In November Ferdinando, Francesco's brother, was taking precautions to see that there would be an opera during Carnival, even if it was not Monteverdi's, and had written to Florence for Gagliano, who came to Mantua with the score of his *Dafne* (already composed though not as yet produced). This was put into rehearsal and performed in January. Nevertheless, Monteverdi had not failed his master. By the beginning of February *Arianna* was almost finished.

At this point there was a new disaster. The prima donna who was to sing the title role fell ill with smallpox. This was a severe blow for Monteverdi. It came so suddenly (the singer had taken part in *Dafne* a week or two earlier) that it completely disrupted the production of *Arianna*. More than that, Caterinuccia Martinelli was one of Monteverdi's closest friends. She had been brought to Mantua from Rome in 1603, aged thirteen. The possessor of a particularly fine voice, she was the pride of the court and had lodged with Monteverdi since her arrival. Although, as it happened, she did not 'create' the role of Arianna, it was certainly created for her, and her illness was the worst thing which could have happened at this time. At first it looked hopeless, then she improved; finally she died, after being ill for over a month.

[1] De' Paoli, *Claudio Monteverdi* (Milan, 1945), page 127.

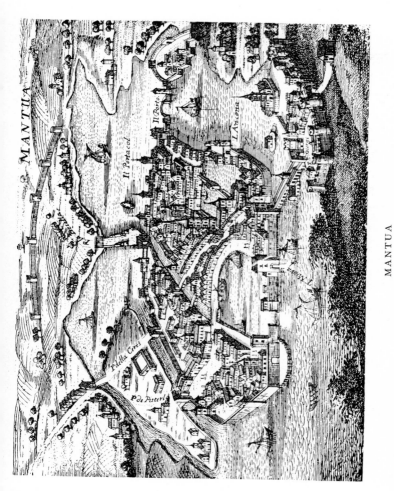

MANTUA

From a seventeenth-century engraving

By this time Carnival was over, but fortunately all was not lost. The ceremonial entry into Mantua had been put back into the spring, and the best thing to do was to postpone the performance of *Arianna* until the main marriage celebrations at the end of May. The first idea for a new singer was the daughter of Caccini, but she was singing another part and this would have meant two changes in the cast. Monteverdi then suggested a singer from Bergamo, who, however, would not come. Then someone had the brilliant idea of asking one of the actresses from the cast of *Idropica*. She turned out to be suitable and rehearsals went ahead. In the meantime, Monteverdi had still to write the music for one intermezzo and compose a long ballet, *Il ballo delle ingrate*.

The prince and his new wife arrived from Turin on 24th May with a train of guests from all over Italy. Four days later *Arianna* was given. There were some four thousand people—only a few of them from Mantua—packing the court theatre, and their enthusiasm is described by Follino in rapturous terms:

This work was very beautiful in itself both because of the people who took part, dressed in clothes no less appropriate than splendid, and for the scenery, which represented a wild rocky place in the midst of the waves, which in the furthest part of the prospect could be seen always in motion, giving a charming effect. But since to this was joined the force of the music by Signor Claudio Monteverdi, *maestro di cappella* to the duke, a man whose worth is known to all the world, and who in this work excelled himself, combining with the union of the voices a harmony of the instruments disposed behind the scene which always accompanied the voices, and as the mood of the music changed, so was the sound of the instruments varied; and seeing that it was acted by men and women who were all excellent singers, every part succeeded well, most especially miraculously in the lament which Ariadne sings on the rock when she has been abandoned by Theseus, which was acted with much emotion and in so piteous a way that no one hearing it was left unmoved, nor among the ladies was there one who did not shed a few tears at her plaint.[1]

As we have seen, Follino was a close friend of the composer, and

[1] De' Paoli, op. cit., page 139.

anyway, as court chronicler his account of *Arianna* would have had to record a great success. But there are many ways in which we can confirm his judgment. Time after time there are passages in Monteverdi's letters which refer to the power of the opera. The theorist Doni knew the score of at least the lament about 1640, a long time for any music to be remembered in the seventeenth century; nor must we forget that the opera was revived at least twice in the next thirty years, again unusual for a work which was written specially and hurriedly for a great occasion. As for the lament which Follino praised so lavishly, imitation certainly proved the sincerest form of flattery, for laments became the stock-in-trade of composers for half a century. They appeared not only in operas but also in the song-books and madrigal-books, written by bad, mediocre and good composers. Monteverdi himself was able to make money from his lament and published arrangements of it. In fact, the 'Lament of Ariadne' was the first great popular operatic *scena*.

After *Arianna* the music for the prologue for *Idropica*, and even *Il ballo delle ingrate*, must have seemed less important. The intermezzo was as ephemeral as most of these productions, and the music has disappeared. The ballet has survived, for later in life Monteverdi included it in his last book of madrigals. It is an important work, and clearly in its staging made a great effect, yet the music shows signs of the haste with which Monteverdi wrote it, and it remains little to console us for the loss of *Arianna*, the score of which has not yet been discovered.

'The greatest fame which a man may have on earth and all the gratitude of the Most Serene Prince'—these were Follino's inducements to return to Mantua. Both were Monteverdi's in June 1608. Neither could alleviate his misery. He returned to Cremona in a state of complete collapse. In November his father was desperate enough to write to the Duchess of Mantua to ask if Claudio could be released from his duties:

If he returns to Mantua the heavy duties and the unhealthy air will soon result in his death, and the burden of his two children will come upon me, which would be terrible on account of both my age and lack of money, since I have had to support his wife and others on behalf of the said Claudio when he went with His Highness to Hungary and Flanders and also when he came to Cremona with his wife, servants, carriage and children.[1]

If his father was worried by the prospect of his return to the court, Monteverdi himself was furious, and when a letter came on the last day of November, bidding him return, he replied at great length and with considerable heat. What has he ever gained from Mantua except hard work and debts, he asks. What has he gained from his splendid success at the recent wedding festivities? All that has happened is that his wife's salary has been stopped, and even the pension of a hundred scudi which the duke had promised him has turned out to be only seventy. No other Mantuan musician has had such bad treatment and certainly no foreigner. Bitterly he asks the court chancellor:

Do you wish, Your Excellency, for anything to be clearer; to give two hundred scudi to M. Marco da Gagliano who could be said to have done nothing new, and to me, who did all that I did, nothing at all? Knowing this, how ill and unfortunate I am in Mantua, I ask you, Most Excellent Sig. Chieppo, for the love of God, to help me to have permission to leave from His Highness, for I know that from this alone can come my well-being. Signor Federico Follino promised me in his letter asking me to return to Mantua from Cremona for work on the marriage celebrations, he promised me, I say, that which Your Excellency can see in this letter of his which I am sending, and yet in the end nothing has been done, and all that I have had is one thousand five hundred lines to set to music.[2]

Monteverdi was not accorded permission to leave. Instead his pay was raised to three hundred scudi a year, and his pension, 'for himself, his heir, and successors of any kind . . . of a hundred scudi each worth six lire of our Mantuan money', was formally granted to him.

When he actually returned to the court is unknown. His two surviving letters of 1609 were written from Cremona, but as they date

---

[1] De' Paoli, op. cit., page 150.
[2] Malipiero, op. cit., page 138.

from August and September it is possible that he had gone back to his father for the summer, after working again during the Carnival season. These letters and others in the next two years show us that the worst of his depression had passed by now. In 1610 he was working on a book of madrigals, including an arrangement for five voices of 'Ariadne's Lament' and another lament in commemoration of Cateri-nuccia Martinelli. Later in the same year he went to Rome to see if he could find a publisher for some church music which he intended to dedicate to the Pope, and also to try to obtain a scholarship to the Papal Seminary for his son Francesco. He could count on the influence of Ferdinando Gonzaga, now a cardinal, to whom Vincenzo's heir, Francesco, wrote in advance on behalf of the composer. Nothing came of either venture. The church music was printed by his Venetian publisher. His son was not given his bursary.

Was Monteverdi seeking a new post at this time? It seems quite likely. For a man not much given to travelling about, his Roman journey and one to Venice which followed immediately were unusual. Even less usual was his new interest in church music. We do not possess a note of his church music (as distinct from *madrigali spirituali*) before 1610. Then we find him writing a Mass in the Roman *a cappella* style, a Mass which cost him a great deal of study and hard work. We also have a letter which tells us that Monteverdi presented the duke with a *Dixit* for five voices and also a little motet for two voices to be sung at the Elevation and another for five voices in honour of the Blessed Virgin for Easter 1610. It is possible that the departure of Gastoldi—the official *maestro di cappella* of the ducal chapel of S. Barbara—to a post in Milan had caused this new activity. But it can scarcely be a coincidence that the principal posts in Venice and Rome demanded a knowledge of church music.

For Monteverdi was now at a difficult stage. He was so distinguished that, if he wished to move, posts which would be suitable for him were rare. As a court musician his chances were meagre. The court of the Estensi was now much reduced, following the secession of Ferrara and its province to the papal dominions on the death of Duke Alfonso. Parma, Turin and Milan were far less interested in music. Florence had its own composers. To accept an ordinary post as *maestro di cappella* at a cathedral was to retreat in social and financial status. Only St Mark's in Venice and the larger churches in Rome were of the right dignity for such a distinguished composer. The matter became more urgent in 1612. Vincenzo Gonzaga died. His son Francesco ascended the throne, and Monteverdi might well have been pleased about this, for Francesco had been especially keen on operatic entertainments. But some time in July he suddenly dismissed both Monteverdi and his brother Giulio Cesare. No reason is given in the documents. Perhaps it was something to do with the usual festival which was mounted on these occasions. There was certainly a public festival on 25th July to celebrate the election of a relative of Francesco Gonzaga as Holy Roman Emperor. The duke himself wrote a *torneo*, depicting the Rape of the Sabines; there were fireworks, and on the following Sunday some splendid music in S. Barbara.[1] Was Monteverdi ordered to write the music for church or *torneo*? If so, it would have had to be done at short notice, something which he always detested. He may well have refused to fall in with the duke's plans. In any case he left Mantua for good with just twenty-five scudi in his pocket as his savings after over twenty years in the service there.

He returned to Cremona, and having nothing to do, went to Milan in September, probably to visit his many friends there. Malicious tongues said that he was intriguing for the post of *maestro di cappella* of Milan Cathedral over the head of the incumbent, who was pleasing the authorities there well enough. This story was not true, as the Mantuan ambassador in Milan reported after making inquiries. After this we have no news of the composer for nearly a year. Then his luck changed. The *maestro di cappella* at St Mark's in Venice died in July 1613. The procurators of St Mark's, instead of merely advertising the post in Venice and its subject cities on the mainland, decided to make a wider search for a suitably distinguished musician, and wrote to the ambassadors and residents in Rome, Padua, Vicenza, Brescia, Bergamo, Milan and Mantua. The letter to Milan (for Cremona was

[1] Arch. Ven., *Dispacci, Senato III (Secreta), Mantova, Filza* 1 b, fo. 29.

in its province) shows clearly that they already had Monteverdi in mind:

On the death of the Most Reverend *maestro di cappella* of our church of St Mark there have been several people proposed, among whom is Signor Claudio Monteverdi, *maestro di cappella* to His Highness. We should therefore be very happy to have a report informing us of his worth and efficiency, and if you think of any other person we should be in your debt in having news about him.[1]

This letter left Venice on 16th July. The procurators must have received a favourable reply, for by 19th August Monteverdi was in Venice rehearsing some church music with the players and singers of St Mark's. The rehearsal took place in the church of S. Giorgio, after which the music was given in the basilica itself. It was a sumptuous work which needed twenty players and two portable organs in addition to the thirty or so salaried musicians; and it pleased the procurators. They appointed Monteverdi on the spot and gave him fifty ducats to show him how they did business.[2] Monteverdi went back home to Cremona to make arrangements for removing to Venice. On his way to take up his new appointment he had his last disaster. He was robbed by highwaymen and lost all his money. Then he crossed the lagoon to the city which was to be his final resting-place. Thereafter, in so far as he was capable of happiness, he was a happy man. Fame, prosperity and the better health which contentment often gives were to be his in the Most Serene Republic.

[1] Arch. Ven., *Proc. de Supra, Reg.* 193*bis*, fo. 64. See Appendix E (page 202).

[2] Arch. Ven., *Proc. de Supra, Cassier, Chiesa, Reg.* 10, 22nd Aug. 1613.

CHAPTER III

VENICE

THE procurators of St Mark's had made their choice with great speed. Usually they took their time in choosing a new *maestro di cappella*, with an interregnum of six months or more. They must have had unusual confidence in Monteverdi's reputation and demeanour. He was old enough, had experience in administration and was a famous composer. Someone of this stature was very necessary, since Monteverdi's predecessor had been a failure. Giulio Cesare Martinengo had come to St Mark's from Udine Cathedral. He left no mark on history as a composer, and worse still, he seems to have had unsatisfactory dealings with the procurators. The account books of the basilica show that he was constantly in debt almost from the moment he set foot in Venice. To pay his creditors he was continually asking for advances on his pay, and eventually died owing the treasurer several months' salary. To hasten the decline of Venetian music still further, the last of the great older school of composers, Giovanni Gabrieli, had died the year before Monteverdi's arrival. Given these circumstances, we can understand their welcome of an acknowledged master.

Monteverdi's new post was an onerous one. The musical establishment of St Mark's was large, perhaps the largest in Italy. There were about thirty singers, some of them *castrati*, and six players in regular employment, besides the boys of the choir school. In addition, on festival days it was usual to hire about fifteen extra instrumentalists, and to pay them *per diem*. There were two excellent organists, often composers of merit themselves, and a vice-*maestro*, usually a promoted singer, who helped to maintain discipline, and took on his shoulders the burden of teaching the boys and the younger priests the arts of plainsong and counterpoint. The minutes of the procurators' meetings show how much administration was involved in keeping the *cappella* routine in order. New singers to be tested and hired, music to be composed and copied, the players to be hired—all these and many other duties must have kept Monteverdi busy.

For a *maestro* like Monteverdi, appointed mainly on his reputation as a composer, the frequency of the Venetian festivals must have presented many problems. There were about forty festivals, all of them celebrated with the greatest pomp and involving music. These were days which we can relive today only at coronations, royal weddings, jubilees and the like. A great procession would form in the Doge's Palace—the clergy in their robes, the ambassadors and papal nuncio in their most brilliant regalia, the Doge and Senate in their brightly coloured gowns—and then would go round the great square to enter St Mark's by its west door. There Mass and vespers were sung and played, and the procession would retreat in all its glory. The whole populace would also be there, staring from the porticoes in the square, leaning out of their windows, even climbing on the roofs of the Procuratoria if they could find a way up. On Ascension Day the ceremonies were made even more picturesque by the use of the *Bucintoro*, the Doge's barge, which took the Doge and the Senate to a place near the Lido, where the Doge threw a ring into the sea, to 'wed' Venice to its mistress, the cause of its prosperity and glory.

This was all very well for the splendour-loving Venetian, but for the composer it meant a hardworking life from which there was no escape. For one thing, the liturgy used in St Mark's was unique, and therefore some of the motet texts were set only by Venetian composers. For another, the magnificence of the music required meant that the Masses and vesper psalms of composers outside Venice were rarely on a large enough scale. Sometimes works by recently deceased Venetians such as Croce and the Gabrielis were used, but new music was always needed. For Monteverdi it can scarcely have been easy, since there was no other composer in St Mark's in his first few years, nor had his duties in Mantua really prepared him for the rapid composition of church music. So his letters to Striggio at Mantua often have to apologize for a delay due to lack of time. In February 1615 he is sorry that he cannot leave Venice to fulfil a commission from the duke since 'I must serve

28

in St Mark's, because of the approach of Holy Week, at which time take place many functions attended by The Most Serene Signory [i.e. the Senate]'.[1] Four years later he was unable to compose a madrigal or cantata of some kind 'on account of the affairs of Holy Week that will occupy me at St Mark's, and the festivals, which are of no little importance to the *maestro di cappella*'.[2]

Yet it would be a mistake to interpret these as complaints, or even as meaning that he felt he was wasting time when he could have been writing opera. Certainly there was a great change in Monteverdi himself. From the tired, depressed, ageing man he seemed in the later years at Mantua he became a renewed, invigorated and thoroughly alive composer and *maestro*. The amount of work he did in his first few years at Venice was enormous. The Acts of the Procurators show that he thoroughly reorganized the *cappella*. He gradually brought the choir up to strength, hired more virtuoso *castrati*, and made them all work harder. Whereas in former years singers were needed only for the greater festivals (indeed this fact was used to attract good foreigners), Monteverdi insisted on sung Masses on the ferial days. He found that there was little music available for the choir, and persuaded the procurators to buy some part-books from the Gardano press, to build up a repertory of *a cappella* music by Palestrina, Soriano, Lambardi and others. He also regularized the position of the instrumentalists. Instead of paying the majority on a daily basis as they were required, he arranged to have them placed on the salary roll of the treasurer, so that they were paid bi-monthly, as were the rest of the staff of St Mark's.[3]

In spite of this he found enough time to compose and publish secular music. The contents of his sixth book of madrigals were certainly written at Mantua, but he saw the book through the press only in 1614, putting his proud new title on the front page. Then there were commissions from Mantua (now rapidly going downhill as a

[1] Malipiero, op. cit., page 157.
[2] Ibid., page 181.
[3] Arch. Ven., *Proc. de Supra, Chiesa Actorum* 135, fo. 9.

musical centre and having no composer of distinction any longer), including a ballet *Tirsi e Clori*, which was composed in 1615, and what amounts to an opera, commissioned in the following year. The latter, a *favola marittima* called *Le nozze de Tetide*, caused him a good deal of trouble before he finally abandoned it in January 1617. He seems to have spent over a month trying to make the libretto into something suitable, and perhaps had even composed parts of it by the time he gave it up. He also seems to have fitted into the literary circles of Venice quite happily. He sent a copy of his sixth book of madrigals to a minor poet, the Abbot Angelo Grillo, whom he had known a little in his Mantuan days. Grillo wrote back thanking him and referring to some manuscript works,

. . . in which you prove yourself such a great master, though you are given less support by the text; but even a mule looks like Bucephalus under a heroic rider. You have bestowed too much honour on my poems by your praise and by your music. Where my lines sound worst, there is the sweetest harmony in your composition.[1]

The procurators appreciated his hard work, and after three years we find a tangible expression of their approval in their minutes:

The procurators, knowing the worth and efficiency of D. Claudio Monteverdi, *maestro di cappella* of St Mark's, and wishing to confirm his appointment and give him the incentive to attend to the service of the Church to the honour of God with a whole heart, and in the desire that he will live and die in this service, have, by ballot, determined that he shall be confirmed in his post for ten years with a salary of 400 ducats per year with the usual perquisites.[2]

By this time he had settled the main problems in restoring the music of St Mark's, and had managed to tempt a most promising composer into Venetian service. This was Alessandro Grandi, *maestro di*

[1] A. Einstein, *Essays on Music* (1958), page 177.
[2] De' Paoli, op. cit., page 209.

L'Altra Parte della PIAZZA DI S. MARCO in Venetia.

T. S. Marco

ST MARK'S, VENICE

From a seventeenth-century engraving

cappella at Ferrara Cathedral, who was willing to enter St Mark's even as a singer. He was soon promoted, first to teach the boys in the choir school, then to be Monteverdi's deputy. Grandi must have been a great help, since he was a prolific composer with considerable experience in writing modern church music.

Monteverdi certainly needed another composer in the *cappella* during these years, since the ceremonial life of the Venetian Republic became as brilliant as it had ever been. In 1617 one of the most splendid of their processions took place, and it is worth while describing it in some detail, since it gives a fascinating idea of the atmosphere in which Monteverdi worked. During April workmen repairing the foundations of St Mark's found a casket with some relics in it. There was an investigation by the ecclesiastical authorities and one relic was declared to be part of the True Cross and to be stained with the blood of Christ. Such a discovery could not go by without a Mass of consecration and a procession, and the Master of Ceremonial in St Mark's, Cesare Vergaro, persuaded the Senate to provide money to meet the necessary expenditure. The preparations involved an incredible amount of work. New robes were made for the priests; new gloves for the people to carry the relics; the biers on which the relics were to be placed were made and covered with various rich stuffs; there was to be a new canopy for the relics. St Mark's Square was decorated by draping cloths from the windows of the Procuratoria, and carpets were hired to afford a dignified entry into the basilica.[1] Inside St Mark's a large platform (called 'a theatre' in the descriptions) was built into the middle of the choir, since it was here that the relics were to be exposed to view for three days. Four hundred copies of a booklet by Vergaro were printed and given to the nobility to explain how the relics were found and their significance. Hundreds of candles were made, and extra priests were invited to take part and were paid for the rehearsals of the ceremony.

On Sunday, 28th May, the procession took place. The relics were mounted on three biers, and the nobility came out of St Mark's to

[1] Arch. Ven., *Proc. de Supra, Cassier Chiesa, Reg.* 11.

hear an oration by the dean. Then, says Vergaro, 'there was sung the Mass of the Passion of Our Lord with most exquisite music, at the end of which a procession was formed which, passing in front of the high altar and in front of the Doge and Senate, went round the square'. After this procession the Schools, or religious confraternities, formed their own processions, each with a number of players and singers to precede the priests and brothers. Some of them had dressed floats, and the School of the Misericordia had one in which 'there was a most beautiful youth, dressed to represent the Virgin Mary'. Then came the brothers and monks from each order that had a foundation in Venice, and some of these had decorated floats too. After them came the main procession with the Doge and Senate and the relics, 'preceded by four singers who sang the Litany of the Saints, and after the relics and immediately before the Doge there was the whole body of musicians with their *maestro di cappella*'.[1]

The procession lasted an hour, and there were halts at three places in the square to adore the relics, with suitable music each time, after which the procession returned to St Mark's, where the relics were placed ceremonially on the newly erected platform. This was six feet high with steps up to it made of stone from Verona. In the middle of it was an altar on which the relics were to rest, while orations were given by various notable clerics.

> The singers retired to two platforms, one between the two large pillars . . . near the altar, the other directly opposite, singing divine praise. There was also singing from the theatre [the big platform] by a boy clad as an angel.[2]

On succeeding days there was music to accompany the exposition of the relics, and harp players were given a fee for performing this. The cost of the whole affair was about 800 ducats, an enormous sum.

What exactly Monteverdi had to do is not stated; but since in the following year he described his duties for a similar festival, we can

[1] G. C. Vergaro, *Racconto dell' apparato et solennità fatta nella Ducal Chiesa* (Venice, 1617).

[2] Ibid.

imagine his heavy burden. He writes to Striggio explaining why he cannot promise to send more of his opera *Andromeda*:

Next Thursday will be the festival of the Holy Cross . . . and it will be my duty to prepare a *messa concertata* and motets for the whole day, since the Holy Blood will be exposed on that day on an altar erected high in the middle of St Mark's, after which I must put in order [compose or rehearse?] a certain cantata in praise of His Highness, which they sing every year in the *Bucintoro* when he goes with all the Signory to marry the sea on Ascension Day, and also put in order a Mass and solemn vespers that they sing in St Mark's at that time.[1]

Hard work though it was, Monteverdi was happy. He was financially comfortable, he was famous, he was appreciated both by his employers and by the musical public at large. When an offer came from Striggio to go back (on presumably rather better terms than before) to his old job at Mantua, he contemptuously refused:

Your Highness must take into consideration how this Most Serene Republic, which never gave more than 200 ducats in salary to any of my predecessors, whether Adriano [Willaert], Cipriano [de Rore] or Zarlino, or anyone else, gives me 400 ducats, a favour which I must not lightly set aside without due consideration: since (Your Highness) this most Serene Signory never makes an innovation without due thought, I must regard this particular act of grace most favourably. Nor after this have they ever repented but have honoured me also in such a way that in the *cappella* they do not accept any report on a singer except that of the *maestro di cappella*; neither do they accept either organists or vice-*maestro* unless they have a report and opinion from the said *maestro di cappella*: there is no gentleman who does not esteem and honour me, and when I go to make either church or chamber music, I can assure Your Excellency, that the whole city runs to hear. And then my service is the more sweet since all the *cappella* is under temporal appointment except the *maestro di cappella*: on the contrary it is up to him to appoint and dismiss the singers, to grant leave of absence or not; and if he does not wish to go into the chapel, no one will say anything to him; and his position is certain until he dies, and is not made different by the death of

[1] Malipiero, op. cit., page 177.

33

Monteverdi

the procurators or of the prince provided that he gives faithful and reverent service; and his salary, if he does not go to collect it at the right time, is sent to his house, and this is only his basic income. Then there is some extra money which I obtain from outside St Mark's, amounting to 200 ducats a year, having been begged and begged again by the wardens of the Schools, since anyone who wishes to have the *maestro di cappella* to make music for him must pay 30, 40 and up to 50 ducats for two vespers and a Mass, and is glad to have his service and thank him very heartily afterwards.[1]

How different it had been at Mantua, Monteverdi goes on angrily. There, the death of a prince or a change in his favour could make a very real difference. There the *maestro di cappella* was treated with no more respect than a favoured singer, either financially or otherwise. Nor had his pay even been very regular when he had had

. . . to go to the treasurer every day to beg him for what was mine by right. As God sees me, I have never in all my life felt a deeper abasement of the spirit than when it was necessary (almost for the love of God) to beg the treasurer for what was mine.

Was it really so bad at Mantua, we are tempted to ask. Were all these slights real or were they imaginary, at least in part? Surely it was not all so depressing there? But what is important is that after the small court atmosphere the change to Venice must have seemed like heaven to Monteverdi. It was a change from a dying civilization to one capable of new life.

New life is to be found everywhere in the musical activity around Monteverdi. In secular music the popular song-books by Florentine and Roman composers give way to the lively new ariettas of the Venetians. The Vincenti catalogues now contain works not only by Monteverdi and Grandi but also by lesser known composers such as Pesenti, Rovetta and Berti, all of whom were part of the Venetian musical scene. When one of the *castrati* of St Mark's, Leonardo Simonetti, made an anthology of solo motets in 1625, he could include

[1] Malipiero, op. cit., page 198.

works by no fewer than fifteen composers, all living in or around Venice. Six of them were in the employ of the basilica itself. Nor are these pieces perfunctory make-weights; they are written most competently in the latest style.

The manner and quality of the music at St Mark's in the early 1620's are described by Giulio Strozzi in a small pamphlet in which he tells of the memorial service for the late Duke of Tuscany in 1621. The Florentines living in Venice commissioned the music, which was performed in the great church of SS. Giovanni e Paolo on 25th May of that year:

> The music of the Mass and the responsories was composed and performed for the occasion by Claudio Monteverdi, whose fame makes the fine quality of the work easily understandable. In these compositions he has given expression to a particular emotion, which in transporting our princes with delight makes them honour him for his genius. The ceremonies began with a plaintive sinfonia which brought tears to the eyes, imitating the ancient Mixolydian mode rediscovered by Sappho. After the sinfonia Don Francesco Monteverdi, son of Claudio, sang with the sweetest voice the words *O vos omnes attendite.* . . . The *Dies irae* and the delicate *De profundis* were also composed by Claudio, the latter, as it were, a dialogue between souls in purgatory and angels visiting them.[1]

Unhappily, Monteverdi's music and that of his colleagues has been lost, but even the description is invaluable to us since it shows us the way his mind was working. One thing we notice is that his church music is as modern as ever—apparently a dialogue in the dramatic manner. Yet more significant is the mention of the ancients, which suggests that Monteverdi is still under the spell of the academies. This is quite remarkable, for Venice had never been a centre of academies, at least not those of the kind found at Mantua, Ferrara and Florence. Nor were his younger pupils really interested in interpreting Plato and Aristotle; and even in other centres the composers of opera and monodic madrigals and songs had turned away from these now old-fashioned ideas. This description of his requiem music shows as ever

[1] De' Paoli, op. cit., page 241.

the mixture of the modern and old-fashioned in Monteverdi's music, possible now only for a man of increasing middle age.

Another fruit of his fifty-odd years is the veneration which was accorded to him abroad. In 1620 he visited Bologna to settle his son Francesco's future. After a little time studying law at Bologna Francesco had decided to enter the order of Carmelite friars and came back from Bologna to Venice. There his voice was enough to procure him a post as singer in St Mark's. He had sung in the basilica as early as 1615, and the account books record a payment on 22nd April 'to Signor Claudio, *maestro di cappella*, fifty ducats of gold, and ten ducats of gold to Francesco his son for having lent his services on the days of Holy Week and Easter'.[1] Francesco had received a further payment from the procurators in 1618: '15th March: ten ducats paid to Francesco Monteverde, son of the *maestro di cappella*, for having sung the lesson at matins on last Christmas Eve.' His permanent appointment as singer took place in the 1620's and he eventually earned eighty ducats a year, which denotes that he was one of the better singers. But to settle all this in 1620 meant a journey to Bologna. Banchieri, the doyen of the Bolognese musicians, remembered several years later how 'on the day of St Anthony in the year 1620 your eminence honoured us with your presence: attending the meeting of the Florid Academy of S. Michele in Bosco'.[2] Perhaps while Monteverdi was there he discussed his other son's future, for in the following year he made arrangements for Massimiliano to study medicine at Bologna University, carefully writing to the Duchess of Mantua to use her influence with Cardinal Montalto to obtain a place in the Cardinal's College, where Massimiliano would live free from the dangers of bad company and the traditional licentiousness of Bolognese student life.

With his sons' education well organized, and the music of St Mark's running smoothly, Monteverdi was free to follow his outside interests. As he was now at the home of music-publishing we find him

---

[1] Arch. Ven., *Proc. de Supra, Cassier Chiesa, Reg.* 11.

[2] *Lettere armoniche* (Bologna, 1628).

writing motets for the various anthologies of church music which were so popular. His greatest music for St Mark's was composed for large resources and was not readily saleable; he therefore composed solo motets, duets and other works which could be performed more easily. Another source of income was directing the music at the school of San Rocco, which he did on the day of its patron saint in 1623 and 1628. The accounts of the school tell us that he was paid 620 lire in 1623—a huge sum—but out of this he must have had to pay the other musicians from St Mark's. More revealing is the payment for the second year, when he received a personal fee of 146 lire, or just about the amount shared among the sixteen singers of St Mark's and nearly four times the fee of even the most treasured virtuoso singer.[1]

All this activity as a composer of religious music was counter-balanced by the composition of dramatic works. Monteverdi continued his relationship with the Mantuan court. The *favola marittima* had proved no stimulus to his imagination; in its place his friend Striggio suggested another subject, Alceste. This was to be a true opera, sung throughout. The only trouble was that he had no libretto early in January 1617, and had only until Easter to complete it. The composer was keen enough to go on with the idea and even obtained leave of absence from Venice to go to Mantua for a fortnight; but even as he made his preparations a letter came cancelling the whole affair. In the autumn of the same year a commission came from Parma to compose an intermezzo to words by the duchess. We do not know whether anything came of this, either, but the project again shows the composer's reputation and the interest which others took in him.

The next libretto sent him from Mantua was *Andromeda* by Ercole Marigliani. It arrived early in 1618, and quite obviously the idea was to produce it at some time during that year. This was highly optimistic, and from the letters between Monteverdi and Striggio we can gain some idea of why the relationships at the Mantuan court had been strained during the opera festival of 1608. Monteverdi was a slow

[1] See Appendix E (page 202).

composer, especially of a large-scale work. His first letter to Mantua, after apologizing for delay because of his daily work in St Mark's, shows clearly that he is thinking of the practical details—how many women singers he can count on for the chorus and who is going to sing the part of the nuncio, since he must think about how best to write for his voice? These questions suggest that Monteverdi is about to begin composition in earnest.

Alas, the next letter, two months later, is full of apologies. The main festivals have gone, so his work in St Mark's is no excuse. This time he has been suffering 'a little from headaches caused by the heat which suddenly followed the rains', which caused him to lack ideas, and he refuses to send quick but mediocre work rather than good music a little later. In any case he has finished some pieces—a chorus of fishermen, for instance—and has planned huge sections. Then there is a large gap. More apologies follow in March 1619, when he has had the libretto for over a year; more apologies still in December. Finally, when pressed to finish the work in time for a performance during the Carnival of 1620, he writes:

I should have sent the enclosed music to Your Excellency with the last mails but Signor Marigliani at the instance of Signor D. Vincenzo asked urgently in a letter addressed to me to finish the play *Andromeda* of the said Sig. Marigliani which I had begun already, so that it could be presented before His Highness during the coming Carnival on his return from Casale. But just as I shall be forced to write it badly in order to finish it in a hurry, so I am convinced that it will be badly acted and badly played on account of the very short time, and I wonder how Sig. Marigliani is willing to commit himself to such a dubious enterprise. For there would not have been time enough if they had started rehearsing—not to mention learning—the piece before Christmas. Now what does Your Highness think it possible to do, since there are still more than four hundred lines of verse to set to music? I cannot imagine any other end than bad acting, bad playing and a bad musical *ensemble*. These are not things which can be done in such a hurry— remember *Arianna*, where it was necessary to have five months of strenuous rehearsal after they had learned their parts perfectly by heart.[1]

[1] Malipiero, op. cit., page 185.

No wonder he was considered difficult! Even if he had found the libretto to be not to his taste, he might have turned it down earlier. The only excuse there can be for his injured innocence is that at least he had not received his pension from Mantua recently. After many letters asking for it, he dedicated his seventh book of madrigals to the duchess, obviously with an eye to gaining her influence in the matter. All he received in return was a necklace, a perfectly suitable token of her appreciation, no doubt, but not what he wanted. It is a wonder that he ever did anything for Mantua again, although this can scarcely excuse him for his dealings over *Andromeda*.

In all probability he kept on working for the Gonzagas, because in Mantua he could go on producing operas and intermezzos. At Venice there was no opportunity as yet to write dramatic music—or at least only occasionally, for in 1624 he had the chance to have his *Il combattimento di Tancredi e Clorinda* produced. This took place in the Palazzo Mocenigo, but we have no means of knowing whether the work was commissioned by Count Girolamo Mocenigo, or whether Monteverdi composed it first and looked round for a chance to perform it. One thing is certain: this time there were no embittering negotia-tions with a librettist. The poem was by Tasso, a scene from *Geru-salemme liberata*, and Monteverdi had known it for years. This in itself put it outside his normal development as an opera composer, for it was not meant as an opera libretto at all. The result is curious. The work is not really an opera or a ballet. It was performed by only three people, of whom one was a narrator and commentator. Instead of the festival orchestra of Mantua only a group of strings was used. The massive scenic designs were also not available. From this it is clear that Venice had little to offer even the most famous opera composer of the time.

His next commission, then, had to come from elsewhere—from Mantua again. Duke Ferdinand died in October 1626 and was succeeded by Vincenzo II, who was so ill that he spent most of his days in bed. Was it, as has been suggested, that Striggio as court chancellor was really in charge of affairs and could indulge his taste for Monteverdi's operas? Or was it that there was the usual desire for a festival when a new duke came to the throne? Whatever the reason, we find Monteverdi sending to Striggio a play (or a libretto) by Giulio Strozzi that he had been reading. It was called *Licori finta pazza inamorata d'Aminta* (Licoris who feigned madness, in love with Aminta), and it is significant that the idea of the opera came from Monteverdi himself. Moreover Strozzi, although a Florentine, was staying in Venice and was willing to adjust his play according to the composer's ideas. This time inspiration visited Monteverdi. He sent the original play to Mantua early in May 1627. By the end of the month he had permission to begin composition, but had to wait for the return of Strozzi from Florence to revise the libretto. Strozzi came back about 3rd June and work started. Monteverdi already had the part of Licoris planned to fit Margherita Basile, and was thinking of the other virtuosos. By the 20th the play was reorganized into five acts instead of the original three. By the end of July work was well advanced, and in spite of trouble with his eyesight and the sickness of the copyist, the score was dispatched to Mantua on 10th September, less than five months after its conception and not much more than three from the start of the composition. What happened after this is not known, and we have no record of a performance. The score is lost—a pity not only for the scholar but also for the musician. A work written at such a pitch of inspiration must have been a fine one.

The speed of composition would have been surprising in a young man, and Monteverdi was now sixty. Nor was *Licori finta pazza* the sum total of his work for the year. He set more of Tasso's *Gerusalemme liberata,* probably in some madrigalian form. And even before he had sent *Licori* to Mantua, he had received a commission from Parma to write music for an intermezzo to be performed during the celebrations of the marriage of Duke Odoardo Farnese to Margherita de' Medici. This time the libretto was sent to him from Parma. The subject was the strife between Venus and Diana, and Monteverdi saw the possibilities of the text at once. As usual, he found difficulties of detail, and since he was not conversant with the resources at Parma, nor was he a friend of his librettist, as he was at Mantua, he decided to go to Parma to discuss the problems at first hand. He already had an invitation from Striggio at Mantua, and having sought leave of absence from the procurators of St Mark's he left Venice immediately after the procession of the Doge and Senate to S. Giustina on 7th October. By the end of the month he was busy at work in Parma and was writing not only intermezzos but also music for a *torneo* or masque to be done during the wedding festivities. He was so busy that he wrote home asking for an extension of his leave. But the procurators were not pleased and wrote back on the 27th of November, demanding that he should 'come back to the duties of his post' at the earliest opportunity.[1]

No mean year's work, this, and possible only to a composer at the height of his powers. Monteverdi's cup of happiness must have been full when he received yet another invitation to return to Mantua as *maestro di cappella*. The composer's reply is especially revealing if we compare it with his angry refusal of seven years earlier. The anger now has gone. He even leaves his reply to the middle of his letter. No, he says, he is not going to move from Venice where he is secure and happy, where he has no burden of teaching and where his pay is regular and can be augmented with only a little extra work. If Duke Vincenzo really wishes to help him, perhaps he could use his influence to gain for him a canonry at Cremona so that he could return to 'his own earth' in his old age. It is a gentle letter and shows Monteverdi growing more graceful as he grows older. Such happiness was not to last. Even before Monteverdi was home in Venice to direct the Christmas music in St Mark's, disaster had happened. The composer tells us the story in a frantic letter to Striggio:

My son Massimiliano is in the prison of the Holy Office for having read three months ago a book which he did not know to be prohibited; but accused by the possessor of the book, who was already imprisoned and who had told him that the book contained only matter about medicine and astrology, he was immediately imprisoned by the Holy Father Inquisitor and wrote to me that if I gave a security of a hundred ducats as bail he would be released immediately.[2]

[1] Arch. Ven., *Proc. de Supra, Reg.* 194, fo. 40v. See Appendix E (page 203).

[2] Malipiero, op. cit., page 280.

With the aid of his Mantuan friend, Ercole Marigliani, Monteverdi found the bail and Massimiliano was soon out of prison. But the proceedings were by no means over. It was to be more than six months before the final examination proved the younger Monteverdi to be innocent—six months of fear and nervous waiting, with the threat of torture and imprisonment constantly overhead, six months of attempt-ted wire-pulling by the young man's father. In the meantime there was work to be done. Monteverdi went back to Parma in the New Year to finish off the intermezzos and the *torneo*. With the blessed fortune of a composer of festival music he was able to start rehearsing certain pieces and to try over anything that was doubtful months ahead of the actual performance. This finally took place in December 1628 at the ceremonial entry of Odoardo and his bride. Alas for the careful preparations—it rained. The firework display planned to take place in the main square was ruined, and Tasso's *Aminta* with Monte-verdi's intermezzos was performed there with a huge cloth acting as a roof.[1] Little wonder that observers have nothing to say about the music, although, as usual, the machines and the *balletto a cavallo* took the eye.

Any way Monteverdi was not there to hear how his music sounded under such conditions. Again he had tried to stay in Parma for Christmas. Again the procurators refused their permission. They were not going to have any inferior music since 'days of such solemnity cannot be celebrated without your presence', as they told Monteverdi.[2]

Back in Venice life changed but slowly. In 1627 Monteverdi's deputy at St Mark's, Alessandro Grandi, left to take charge of the music at Santa Maria Maggiore in Bergamo. In his place Giovanni Rovetta, a young man who had been first an instrumentalist and then a singer, was appointed. Less intimately concerning Monteverdi was the death of Duke Vincenzo at Mantua. His death was hardly unexpected, since he had been ill for some time. What was not so easily foreseen were the consequences. There was no male heir to the dukedom, and the son-in-law of old Duke Francesco Gonzaga

[1] A. Saviotti, 'Feste e spettacoli nei seicento', in *Giornale storico della letteratura italiana*, XLI (1903), pages 42 ff.

[2] Arch. Ven., *Proc. de Supra, Reg.* 194, fo. 50. See Appendix E (page 203).

assumed the title. Spain and Savoy both protested against the usurper, as they considered him. The Duke of Guastalla also pressed his claims to the throne. The 'usurper' relied on papal influence and Venice. France also took his part. In no time northern Italy was in an uproar. The bitter war which followed needs no description here. It culminated in the invasion of the imperial troops from north of the Alps and the sack of Mantua, with the cruel destruction of the Gonzaga treasures. After this Mantua was no longer a noble and important city. Its days of glory were over.

Monteverdi must have been doubly thankful that he had not returned there. In Venice, at least for the time being, things continued as before. Life seemed stable enough for the German composer Heinrich Schütz to come and learn the new art of opera and church music from Monteverdi. Monteverdi himself continued to practise his peaceful art. In 1628 he set to music some verses of Giulio Strozzi for a banquet given by the Venetian state to the visiting Grand Duke of Tuscany in the Arsenal. Two years later he collaborated again with Strozzi (who now seems to have become Striggio's successor as Monteverdi's librettist). This time the work was an opera, *Proserpina rapita*, produced on a grand scale in the palace of the Mocenigo family, with the usual machines and elaborate *décor*. In the same year Monteverdi collaborated with Manelli and produced an opera in Bologna.[1]

The political stability of Venice had protected her citizens from the effects of the war, and life was normal there as late as the summer of 1630. But the imperial troops had not only sacked Mantua; they had brought the plague into northern Italy. Venice took its usual stringent quarantine precautions and this delayed the arrival of the disease. The first cases appeared in the autumn and then it spread rapidly and fearfully. Soon no one would venture out of doors. The procurators of St Mark's even forwent the rents from their houses, for no one would

[1] Wolfgang Osthoff's recently published paper, 'Zur Bologneser Aufführung von Monteverdis *Ritorno di Ulisse* im Jahre 1640' (Vienna 1958), suggests that this is in fact not true, but that *Il Ritorno di Ulisse* was performed in Bologna ten years later. This information came too late for inclusion in this book.

collect them. The fathers of the church of SS. Giovanni e Paolo shut themselves up in their monastery. All their novices had died, and the organist Cavalli sought leave not to attend Mass on festival days for fear of the disease.[1] The school of San Rocco gave up its processions and no longer hired musicians to celebrate Masses for the souls of past wardens. Nor were the musicians of St Mark's spared. Several died, others were broken in health but survived. Monteverdi himself lived to see the end of the plague. So did his son Francesco (we have no news of Massimiliano). Both were almost certainly in St Mark's on 28th November 1631, when the Doge and Senate gave thanks for release from the scourge and 'there was sung a solemn Mass, composed by Sig. Claudio Monteverdi, *maestro di cappella*, the glory of our century, in which during the Gloria and Credo the singing was joined by loud trumpets (*trombe squarciate*) with exquisite and marvellous harmony'.[2]

After the strain of these times, it is not surprising that Monteverdi became ill, even though he had avoided the plague. He was well over sixty, and emotional strain affected him physically. A letter from the procurators tells us that in 1632 he went away from Venice for a time, perhaps to clear up affairs at Cremona after the destruction of the war. The address to which the letter was sent has been lost, but Monteverdi clearly had overstayed his leave:

To Sᵣ D. Claudio Monteverdi, *maestro di cappella* to the Serene Signory of Venice.

MOST EXCELLENT AND REVEREND SIR,

We have received yours of the 7th instant, but no other letter, and we sympathize with you in your past illness, and the disturbing crimes which have happened in those parts; but it would please us to know that if you have recovered and brought to an end and put right your affairs, when would be the earliest at which you could return to the service of the church and to your post.[3]

[1] Arch. Ven., *SS. Giovanni e Paolo, Reg.* 12, fo. 206.

[2] E. Vogel, 'Claudio Monteverdi', in *Vierteljahrsschrift für Musikwissenschaft*, III (1887), page 89.

[3] Arch. Ven., *Proc. de Supra, Reg.* 194, fo. 81v. See App. E (page 203).

The plague and the war which had devastated the two cities where Monteverdi had made his home marked the end of an era, and at first sight it must have seemed like the end of the composer's activity. For the time being there was little enough opportunity for producing opera. Count Alessandro Striggio was still at Mantua, it is true, but the musical establishment there was sadly reduced. In the 1620's there had been no fewer than thirty musicians, including some famous singers. The roll of employees in 1637 shows that only eight singers were there—mediocrities of no lasting or wide fame.[1] In Venice things did not sink to this level. Monteverdi gradually brought the choir of St Mark's up to strength again, and the records show that the singers were on the whole paid rather better than before the plague. Even so the distinction of these musicians could not approach that of the previous decade. The flourishing school of church music composers had disappeared. And Monteverdi himself seems to have been more lax. Whereas at the beginning of his service in St Mark's he had been keen on daily services attended by the organists and all the singers, we find that several of them now took on outside engagements. One of the organists, Carlo Fillago, even took on the post of organist of SS. Giovanni e Paolo in addition to his own work in St Mark's, for which a few years earlier he had been reprimanded by the procurators.[2]

There are other signs of increasing age. Admittedly Monteverdi allowed his publishers to collect a volume of his works, the first for thirteen years; but this is a very slim volume of, for the most part, light fashionable airs, popular with both the Venetian presses and the public. On the title-page (as from the letter sent by the procurators in this year) we learn that Monteverdi has become a priest, a surprising step for a man of great independence—and one who, after the affair of Massimiliano, had every right to feel a little aloof from clericalism. The only two of his letters from these years which have come down to us show us that his thoughts on music were old-fashioned and had scarcely changed since his youth. The book promised by Giulio Cesare over twenty-five years earlier still occupied his mind:

[1] Arch. Gonzaga *Busta* 395.
[2] Arch. Ven., *SS. Giovanni e Paolo, Reg.* 12.

The title of the book will be: Melody, or the Second Musical Practice: by 'second' I mean considered in the modern manner, the First Practice being according to the old style. I divide the book into three parts corresponding to the three parts of Melody. In the first I discourse about the treatment of the words: in the second, about the harmony: in the third about rhythm. I think the book will be appreciated by the public because I discovered in practice when I was writing the *Lament of Ariadne*, not finding a book which explained to me the natural way of imitation, nor one which could show me that I should compose 'imitatively' except Plato, from which came so dim a light that I could hardly see it with my poor eyes, I discovered, I repeat, how great a fatigue one must undergo in doing what little I did of imitation, and therefore I hope that my work will not go unappreciated.[1]

We may be reasonably sure that he never completed this book. If he had, one wonders how many people would have been interested in this antiquated academicism.

Just as Monteverdi and Venetian music seemed to be peacefully declining, new life came into both. The immediate inspiration was the arrival of two composers and singers from Rome. Manelli and Benedetto Ferrari had been producing operas in Rome when political circumstances made it advisable to seek patrons elsewhere. With the illness and approaching death of Pope Urban VIII war looked very likely, and a stable society where opera could be treasured and supported seemed far more probable outside the Papal States—in Venice, in fact, where the two of them came with certain friends late in 1636. Monteverdi, who knew talent when he saw it, snapped them up for the choir of St Mark's,[2] although he must have known that their principal interests were not in church music.

In 1637 an opera house was opened with Manelli's *Andromeda*. The audience was mainly patrician, but since boxes were hired by various nobility and it was possible to buy tickets of admission for the pit, the S. Cassiano theatre can truthfully be said to be the first of the public opera houses. The idea caught on quickly and several others were

[1] Malipiero, op. cit., page 293.

[2] Arch. Ven., *Proc. de Supra, Chiesa Actorum* 144, 3rd October 1638.

VENETIAN SERENADERS

From a sixteenth-century engraving

opened in the succeeding years. Naturally Monteverdi was not to be left out of this feast of dramatic music. *Arianna* was revived in 1639 and he wrote a series of new works—*Adone*,[1] *Le nozze di Enea con Lavinia* and *Il ritorno d'Ulisse in patria*. As if to show that his energy was completely up to any demands upon it he wrote a *balletto* for the Duke of Parma; and published his eighth book of madrigals and a collection of church music. Neither of these books was a slender achievement. The contents of these thick volumes may have been composed earlier, but even the business of seeing them through the press must have been arduous and time-consuming. Finally, at the age of seventy-five, he composed an opera which we may well consider his masterpiece, *L'incoronazione di Poppea*.

What the public thought of these works of Monteverdi's astonishing old age we shall never know. Tangible appreciation of his genius can be found only in the proceedings of the procurators, who twice made him a present of a hundred ducats and finally gave him leave of absence to revisit his old home at Cremona. He spent about six months in 1643 travelling to the places where he had spent his earlier years, not only to Cremona, but to Mantua, where perhaps there were still friends. He returned to Venice only to die. He was taken ill on 20th November and on the 29th the registers of the Public Health tell us of his death: 'The most illustrious and Reverend D. Claudio Monte Verde, *maestro di cappella* of the church of S. Marco, aged 73 [*sic*], of malignant fever of 9 days duration: Doctor Rotta.' To quote the obituary written by Camberlotti: '. . . the news of such a loss upset and turned all the city to sadness and mourning, and was accompanied, not by singing from the choir of singers of St Mark's, but by their tears and weeping.'[2] He was buried in the church of the Frari, in the chapel of S. Ambrogio, after a requiem with music conducted by his pupil Giovanni Rovetta.

Even in an age which looked to the present rather than the past for its music Monteverdi's music and reputation were too great to die

[1] First attributed to Monteverdi in the early eighteenth century. The libretto does not mention the composer's name.

[2] Malipiero, op. cit., page 61.

immediately. His publisher, Vincenti, collected the manuscripts of his unpublished church music and any secular music which could be reconciled with modern taste, and published them in 1651. *L'incoro-nazione di Poppea* was performed in Naples in the same year. The procurators of St Mark's found that it was not so easy to replace such a distinguished man. They were careful to make inquiries all over Italy before making their appointment, and tried to persuade a distinguished middle-aged composer, Orazio Benevoli, to come from Rome, before being content to give the post to Rovetta.[1] But gradually memories faded, tastes changed. By the end of the century Monteverdi was for-gotten. It is the pride of the modern historian that now we can justly write of his reward; for the reward of the composer of genius is immortality.

[1] Arch. Ven., *Proc. de Supra, Busta* 90, fo. 43.

CHAPTER IV

THE EARLIER MADRIGALS

THE heart of Monteverdi's music lies in his madrigals. There he tackled and solved what he conceived to be the problems of the composer. It is in his madrigal-books that we can observe his spiritual and technical development from his earliest youth to his old age. Just as Haydn's soul is laid bare in his string quartets, so is Monteverdi's in his madrigals; and this fact should make us cautious. No composer works in a medium for fifty years without taking it very seriously. The fact that the madrigal is by its nature a smaller-scale work than an opera or much of the church music does not mean we can dismiss it lightly.

The matter is further complicated by the very nature of the madrigal. The string quartet at least remains for a distinct grouping of players and has a certain unity of purpose from the beginning of its history to the end. The madrigal has not. Some madrigals were written, as we commonly imagine all of them were, for the intimate performance of amateurs, who played or sang their parts for the pleasure of *ensemble* performance. Others were destined for singing by virtuosos who were made to show off their voices to a highly critical audience. Others were meant as attempts at the revival of the glories of ancient Greece, aiming at the closest of unions between words and music, to be listened to by *literati* and sophisticated intellectuals. Nor have we exhausted the list. Some madrigals were essentially grandiose choral music, to be performed on a great festival day. Some were the choral episodes in plays and must be accounted dramatic music. Some were essentially light music, using dance rhythms and simple repetitive structures. All could be called madrigals; or, for the lighter music,

canzonets. If, then, we are to understand Monteverdi's secular music
we must do more than analyse it in an abstract way. It must be related
to the audience or purpose for which it was designed.

Monteverdi's first audience at Cremona can hardly have been made
up of the sophisticates and connoisseurs of the larger centres. It wanted
pleasing and elegant music rather than anything profound or complicated; and this is precisely what we find in Monteverdi's earliest books
of secular music. His first publication, which came out in 1584, was
a slender book of canzonets for three voices—just the thing for a
beginner, not only because its smaller forces made contrapuntal
manipulation easier, but because the form was short and clear-cut.
By this time the canzonet had lost its earlier connotation of parody and
had become virtually a light-hearted, small-scale madrigal—with one
difference. Morley tells us what it had become by the 1590's:

> The seconde degree of gravetie in this light musicke is given to Canzonets
> that is little shorte songs (wherin little arte can be shewed being made in
> straines, the beginning of which is some point lightlie touched, and everie
> straine repeated except the middle) which is in composition of the musick a
> counterfet of the *Madrigal*.[1]

The repetitive nature of the form is very important, for, combined
with its small scale, it virtually confined the composer to a simple
melodic growth with no complicated counterpoint and to a decidedly
harmonic style. There is no room for word-painting or any complication, nor for the tears and pathos of the serious madrigal.

Monteverdi's canzonets are, as we should expect, very like hundreds
which were written in the last two decades of the century. Typically
enough for a young man, he made his canzonets as complicated as he
dared. Out of the score of numbers only two or three have the simple
homophony which the more mature or less scrupulous masters of the
time used. The close imitations which end *Io son fenice* are typical of
his slightly academic attitude:

[1] *A Plaine and Easie Introduction to Practicall Musicke* (1597), page 180.

Che per an - co mo - rir, che per an - co mo - rir,

Che per an - co mo - rir ri - tor - no in vi - ta

Che per an - co mo - rir

Conventional 'points' of the sort which filled the textbooks are also common, and Monteverdi does not hesitate to provide some teasing rhythms occasionally, either to express the words or for purely musical excitement. But although these things may indicate his provincial origins, the canzonets are charmingly traditional. Since they are short, the cadences occur frequently and give a clear diatonic harmony. The rhythms of the words suggest a music which constantly repeats short rhythmic patterns, and gives a pleasingly regular structure to each piece. Virtually no difficulties are given to either singer or player, and it can only have been the composer's lack of fame and the rivalry of scores of similar volumes which prevented the book from receiving a reprint.

The same charm appears in Monteverdi's first book of madrigals for five voices, which appeared three years after the canzonets. 'Madrigal' sounds more ambitious than 'canzonet', and from a technical point of view the manipulation of five voices involves a larger scale of writing and a greater challenge to the composer. Emotionally, how-ever, there is no great advance in this book. The beginnings of the madrigals often remind us of the canzonets. *Se nel partir* has an opening phrase identical with *Chi vuol veder*; *Ch' io ami* is very like *Già mi credea*. The canzonet form seems to have remained in the composer's mind too. The traditional repetition of the last line of a madrigal is often interpreted by Monteverdi to mean a fairly strict repetition of a whole lengthy concluding section. Another reminder of the canzonets is the rhythms of the phrases. The gay, regularly accented fragments of melody are constantly used, and sometimes (as in *La vaga pastorella*), the whole madrigal seems to be centred on the rhythm of the music used for the opening words—another sign of small-scale, neat working.

Light-heartedness is the main mood of the madrigals, and the attitude to the poems reflects this. The verse either follows the pastoral convention, with the usual nymphs and shepherds, or it is lyrical, written in the first person with the sighs and tears of (as yet unrequited) love. None of it, except some poems of Tasso and Guarini, can claim any real distinction, and Monteverdi treats it for what it is worth: artificial and pleasing rather than profound. He has obviously learned all the tricks of conventional word-setting, such as the chromatic change to express *lasso*, triple time for *gioia*, the rest which represents a sigh before *deh* or *sospiro*. More than this, he has learned the art of contrast and has begun to explore the use of dissonance to express the pains of the lover. The strings of suspensions, without ever departing from traditional practice, nevertheless seem rather more prolonged and intense than is usual in madrigals of this time:

This passage from *Baci soavi* is magical in the way it excites us with its dominant sevenths, stiffens the tension with the major seventh, frustrates our feeling for tonality with an F♮, and makes it worse by turning this F into a dissonance before sinking helplessly into the cadence.

Such passages are quite common in this book, yet we still feel that the composer has not explored the possibilities of the poems fully. The reason is that the scale of the madrigal is hardly large enough to bear the strength of the passionate sections. He has not succeeded in using the variety of the five voices to develop his phrases to their full power. Too often a voice enters and disappears after a bar or two without doing anything more than repeat the opening of a motif; and Monte-verdi repeats rather than develops. In short, these madrigals are charming but little more, and it is not really surprising that the book had to wait for a reprint until 1607, when the composer's fame would ensure interest in his earlier music.

The second madrigal book also had to wait until 1607 for reprint-ing, but there is much less justification for this neglect. It came out in 1590, and it is remarkably mature and personal compared with the earlier works. It is not so much that the musical material is different. The canzonet rhythms and phrases permeate many of the madrigals also. The actual harmonies of the pieces contain nothing which cannot be found in his earlier music. Yet everything is slightly changed and more emotionally alive. What has happened is that Monteverdi has seen how to use the full *ensemble*, how to use the five voices to expand the phrases and sections. The beginning of *Non giacinti o narcisi*, for example, takes two short lines of the poem, opens with the first, overlaps it with the second and finally leaves the second in command. The cadence comes, and the third line takes up and expands the section with duet texture before yet another cadence. At this point Monteverdi would have rested content in his first book; in this one he is just beginning. He takes the melodic fragments already used and expands them. The first phrase, which had lasted only two bars at the beginning of the madrigal and was sung by two voices, is now given to the whole group of five. The phrase is spread over five bars and given a twist which takes it into a foreign key. The same thing happens to the second phrase and the third. A climax comes by bringing in the full group in a homophonic phrase, which is interrupted by two voices and then is itself repeated, slightly altered to make it more powerful. A little polyphonic working-out of new material follows, and then, canzonet-like, the opening phrase comes back and is developed in yet a new way, mingling with the middle section. Canzonet-like in principle this may be; but no canzonet on this scale was ever written, nor of this subtlety. The slight, anacreontic verse is given a new and more powerful meaning by the musician.

This madrigal is typical of the whole book, every number of which gives to its material and form the exact and inevitable working-out needed. To achieve this certainty of form Monteverdi has had to learn about two things. The first is the modern use of harmony. Instead of being little more than a by-product of counterpoint, it is now a very definite part of the musical structure. One symptom of this is the role of the bass part. In the earlier madrigals the bass had taken its place with the others, weaving the imitative fragments into the texture. This happens also in the second book; but there are long passages where the bass fills in harmonically and does nothing else. In *Non sono in queste rive* only twice does it take part in the imitation. The rest of the time it provides a foundation to the harmony in a way not very interesting for the singer but absolutely essential for the general effect.

The other development of skill is shown in the way the composer uses the variety of tone colour. Rarely do the voices enter one after another with their melodic points, except for special effects. Instead, Monteverdi brings them in to sing in pairs or threes, using the fifth voice to give a delicious unevenness and unexpectedness. The homophonic *tutti* nearly always comes as the first climax of a madrigal, and is used very sparingly thereafter. More usual are longish homophonic trio sections (such as we find at the beginning of *Dolcemente dormiva* or *Intorno a due vermiglie*).

Such technical developments are of the utmost importance, for they are precisely what makes possible a new certainty in matching the words. This time Monteverdi was more careful in choosing his poems. Eleven of the madrigals are settings of verses by Tasso, and this provided a great stimulus to the composer's imagination. Instead of the rather insipid and negative imagery of inferior lyrics, Tasso nearly always uses concrete images which can suggest music equally picturesque. How much better is the line 'Non si levava ancor' than 'Baci soavi, e cari'. It is no coincidence that the most famous madrigal of the book is a nature study where every line has an image in it. *Ecco mormorar l'onde*, indeed, is a gift to the composer. The murmuring of the waves, the rustling of the leaves, the height of mountains are things which naturally give an imaginative composer opportunities. If we quote some fragments of the tenor, we see how Monteverdi was inspired:

Equally vivid is the suggestion of a hunting scene in the opening of
S'andasse amor a caccia, with its close canons and quasi-military
rhythm. We may recall that the chase, with its opportunities for
realism, had been a favourite Italian subject for musical setting as early
as the fourteenth century:

The dawn setting of *Non si levava,* the calm of *Dolcemente dormiva* similarly inspire the composer to fluent and naturally imitative settings.

With this second book of madrigals Monteverdi spiritually left Cremona; and the difference between it and the first book makes us wonder whether the composer has not been studying more up-to-date models than his teacher Ingegneri could provide. The most probable explanation is that some of Giaches de Wert's madrigals had come into his hands, especially Wert's eighth book of madrigals for five voices which had appeared in 1586. There are too many similarities between these two sets of madrigals for a coincidence. Wert was a great friend of Tasso and set many of his poems. He also liked concrete images to make for easy tone painting, and in fact one of his madrigals, *Vezzosi augelli,* resembles *Ecco mormorar l'onde* very closely, even to the opening phrases setting the words 'mormora l'aura' and the melismas for 'cantan':

In another, *Qual musico gentil,* Wert sets *sospir* in exactly the way that we find in *E dicea.* The trio sections which Monteverdi finds useful are also clearly derived from Wert's works, as it was he who developed them in writing for the three ladies of Ferrara (see pages 9, 59). The very mood of Wert's madrigals is like those of Monteverdi's second book, never having the artificial gloom of the dissonant passages of the early works, but light, witty and very competent.

More than this, Wert about this time was developing something in which Monteverdi was to interest himself more and more. Wert was an academic composer in the sixteenth-century sense of the word, and was one of the favourite composers of the Accademia degli Intrepidi of Ferrara. We do not know much about the discussions of this body, as we do about those of the Florentine academies. What is certain is that it too was interested in interpreting the Greek theorists and that it had decided that the vital element in the creation of a modern music was a close relationship between words and music. Although in searching for audibility of the words it did not go so far as advocating monody, there can be no doubt from Wert's madrigals that some form of choral recitative was favoured. So in this eighth book we find constantly lines which repeat notes, less to give musical rhythms than to give exact declamations, and lengthy passages of homophony, not for musical effect, but to allow for the complete clarity of the words to the listener. The results are melodic lines which are quite the opposite of those required by polyphony. Not very interesting in themselves, they are explicable only in terms of the general effect as it appears to the listener.

In addition to these declamatory passages Wert was experimenting with other ways of verbal expression. Unlike many of the Ferrara composers, he had little interest in chromaticism and dissonance. Instead, he sought new effects by deliberately disobeying the tenets of smooth vocal writing and giving the singer huge awkward leaps which naturally conveyed great emotional tension. Sometimes he uses ninths and tenths in this way; at other places he merely arranges ordinary intervals into angular shapes which seem freakish and severe:

So - lo_e pen - so - so_i più   de - ser - ti   cam - pi

In these new paths Wert was one of the great pioneers, and the musical language of the later madrigal was much indebted to his work.

This extended discussion of Wert's style might seem superfluous if its influence on Monteverdi was as slight as it is in the second book of madrigals. The third book is so indebted to Wert that without some knowledge of his work it is impossible to see where Monteverdi was going. The young man's new book was published in 1592. Monteverdi had been about two years at Mantua, and suitably enough the book was dedicated to the duke as a thank-offering. Monteverdi now had a new and more musical audience, a group of composers of the most competent sort to put him on his mettle and more practised singers to perform his music. This perhaps explains the speed of production of this book. Normally Monteverdi was slow to gather enough works to publish; two years to complete twenty madrigals meant that he was working unusually quickly.

Only two of the madrigals seem to be Cremonese. *La giovinetta pianta* and *Sovra tenere herbette* are both in a light canzonetta style, with texts by unknown poets, treated with the gay rhythms and repeated sections we have noticed earlier. The rest are quite different in mood and treatment. The poets are Tasso or Guarini—both extremely fashionable at Mantua. The musical settings have obviously been influenced by Wert's declamatory technique. Almost all the madrigals in the book have some motifs which are based on a *parlando* monotone. Some begin with a solo voice declaiming the words:

In *Vattene pur, crudel* we can see Wert's awkward leaps giving rise to a line which yet reminds us of Monteverdi's most mature writing:

In fact, throughout the whole of this madrigal and its two succeeding parts Monteverdi is merciless to the singer, using leaps of the octave and of the sixth both ascending and descending, the upper registers of the voices and chromatic changes both in regular scale-wise passages and in sudden false relations. Add to this the onus on the singer to make the *parlando* phrases alive, and we see how far virtuoso singers have stimulated his imagination. In one madrigal particularly Monteverdi is writing for the virtuosos. This is *O come è gran martire*, inspired (no less a word will do) by the three ladies of Ferrara. The form, with its trio opening and repeated *tutti* sections in the middle, is very like that of *Non giacinti o narcisi*. But Monteverdi's obvious enjoyment of three virtuoso ladies' voices is reflected in the declamatory phrases, the falling sixths, the top A's for the first soprano, the constant delight in crossing the parts to give the same chords new colours:

One thing we notice in this third book is the widening of the emotional range. Monteverdi still clearly likes the concrete image to give a nature picture. *O rossignol*, with its song of the nightingale, suggests delicate melismas; the waves which are the concluding image of *Vattene pur, crudel* give a charming swirl of sound. But to go with the declamatory lines and chromaticism the dissonant passages have returned. They are not more astringent than in the first book but they are much more effective. With the expansion of the scale these expressions of pain no longer seem exaggerated and out of place. In *Stracciami pur il core*, for example, there are two extended sections of slow-moving dissonance. The first one comes immediately after the beginning and is ushered in while the first, rather gay theme is still going on. The whole passage is held together by an ascending scale in the bass and the tautest chord involves merely a minor seventh. The atmosphere is relaxed in gentle counterpoint until the words 'Non puo morir d'amor' insist on passionate setting. Again we have the rising scale in the bass, and the passage is much shorter than the first one. But this is the climax of the madrigal, and minor seconds and double suspensions give an added burst before the composer finds the cadence and a happy ending.

In this madrigal and others Monteverdi shows how he can move from one emotion to another and mingle them together in a short space of time. This is something that all the great madrigalists of the later sixteenth century could do, Wert included. There is one great difference, however, between Wert and Monteverdi. Wert is more literary, Monteverdi more 'musical'. That is, Wert expects his words to make an appreciable part of the total impression, and music may at times be secondary. Musical forms are less important than the relentless pushing forward of the recitative. Monteverdi, on the contrary, makes the music express the words. He tries to find a musical equivalent, and words are important only in so far as they inspire him to musical forms and textures. A good example of this difference can be found in their two settings of *O primavera*, from Guarini's *Il pastor fido*. Wert takes a long section of Guarini's verse and sets it in a recitative-like manner with scarcely a repetition of the words. There is no attempt at finding the image of the poem and setting it in equivalent music. If you cannot hear the words you are lost. Monteverdi's setting, on the other hand, is practically a canzonet. He writes a huge eleven-bar opening on two lines of the verse, and then, in a magical way, gives sixteen bars of expansion and development, using all the possible permutations of motif, phrase and voice combination. One is lucky to hear the words at all—but this does not matter in the least. We know precisely what it is all about from a verbal fragment or two and the very expressive music. Of the two, Wert is the more advanced, Monteverdi the more attractive; and in spite of all Monteverdi's theorizing about the words being master of the music, even at this early stage it is possible to see that it is the composer's musicality which makes his art alive, not his capacity for putting words and music on an equal footing.

The third book today not only seems a great advance on his early music; it was also a success in its own day. It was reprinted in 1594 and 1600, no mean achievement for a book which clearly was not meant to be popular in the same way that Gastoldi's ballets were; and after Monteverdi had achieved real fame it went through five more editions. His publisher, Amadino, must have been waiting for another collection to send to the press. He had to wait eleven years before the fourth book of madrigals was ready. Why, one wonders, did the composer delay? Would it not have been better to keep his name before the public? Was he too busy to compose? The answer to the mystery seems to be that Monteverdi was peculiarly reluctant to publish his music at this time. When the fourth book did come out he mentions in the preface that he had hoped to dedicate some madrigals to Duke Alfonso d'Este II of Ferrara. Alfonso had died in 1597, so Monteverdi must have been composing before this. We know also from Artusi's criticisms that at least two of the madrigals in the book were composed as early as 1600. This suggests that he was composing continuously in these eleven years. Why, then, was he so loath to see his music in print?

The only explanation we can offer is that Monteverdi felt within himself a sense of progress and movement which made him unsure of his music. Certainly his fourth book is in an 'advanced' style which, although firmly rooted in his older manner, was likely to shock the conservatives. For these eleven years were amongst the most turbulent in the history of music. At Florence the monodists had finally been able to produce an opera, Peri's *Dafne*, and to follow it with the *Euridice* of Peri and Caccini. The latter composer's *Nuove Musiche* came out in 1602, and thereafter the monodic movement was securely launched. Monteverdi must have known all about these events; but we have no need to go even to Florence to find a change of mood and a new revolutionary fervour. In madrigal books published in these vital eleven years both Giaches de Wert and Benedetto Pallavicino showed how they too were concerned in the academic attempt to 'move the affections'. Wert's eleventh book is a remarkable achievement for a man of his years. In several numbers, and especially in *O primavera*, he takes a declamatory style as far as it will go. There are harsh dissonances, and in *Udite lagrimosi spirti* a knowledge of chromaticism which we would hardly have expected from him.

More interesting still is Pallavicino's sixth book of madrigals, which came out in 1600. Here a man who had been a reasonably conventional madrigalist a few years earlier suddenly explores chromaticism and dissonance. Many settings are of poems by Guarini also set by Monteverdi; and the older composer shows himself every bit as up to date as the younger. Without ever really doing anything which goes against established practice, Pallavicino manages to express the emotions of the poems with great force. The beginning of his setting of *Cruda Amarilli* is most powerful:

And he shows in the succeeding bars that he understands the way of building a climax which Monteverdi used in the earlier books, and by different combinations of voices gives breadth to the scale of the madrigal. His use of chromaticism is less satisfactory, for he is more rarely consistent in its use, and, we feel therefore, more experimental. But he is obviously trying to gain something of the quick emotional change of modern music. These are only two of the advanced traits of Pallavicino's madrigals. A further search reveals that the declamatory technique of Wert, the wide intervals of melody (he is even quite fond of the falling sixth we associate with Monteverdi), are also used to fulfil the demands of the verse. He is indeed a composer of the *seconda prattica*.

Did Pallavicino influence Monteverdi or was it the other way round? Or perhaps Wert was the real teacher of them both. We do not know. What we do gain from our knowledge of the work of these Mantuans is a sense of a musical world in turmoil. We need not even think of the work of Gesualdo in Ferrara (he had married the Este princess in 1594 and must have started his experiments at this time), or Marenzio, to realize that there was a great deal to make Monteverdi unsure of the value of his music, to make him wonder if he was working on the right lines, and so to make him delay the publication of his madrigals. If he had such fears, there was little need of them. His fourth book is perhaps the most superb and consistent of all of them: it is the work of a complete master. Although the book's

greatest achievement may seem to be the added power which dissonance and chromaticism give to the deeply felt sad numbers, there
are a number of bright, happy pieces which are superb. Even a sense
of quiet bitter-sweet irony can be heard in *Ohimè*. There is a complete-
ness of emotional power which touches life at many points, and in
each madrigal Monteverdi has a control of the words which means
that he can follow their images and feelings in an incredibly exact
way.

To show this at work we may take *A un giro*. At first sight it looks
like a frothy piece in the manner of the Tasso settings of Book II. The
word 'giro' (turn) produces a picturesque motif, and we begin with
a little duet for sopranos with the bass filling in the harmony. The next
line of verse is built round the word 'ride' (smile) and is worked out
accordingly. The next section is an image of the sea and winds lightly
moved (most reminiscent of *Ecco mormorar l'onde*), and Monteverdi
again paints delicately. The mood changes: 'Only I am left to pine.'
A sudden change of motion and the harmony is again conventional.
Then Monteverdi pushes the shaft home, as the poet does: 'My death
is born from your cruelty.' The dissonance here is as harsh as it is
unexpected. A declamatory line with two voices on the same note
suddenly becomes a slow line of continuous suspensions:

This movement from unison to dissonance merely by moving the line
up a tone or semitone is a favourite device in this book, and always
surprises because of its sudden change from the most perfect of consonances to one of the keenest discords. Nevertheless, both in this
madrigal and in others, after its use as a weapon of surprise the scale
of the piece gradually allows the section to expand, and with its

repetition the dissonant phrase loses its sharpness and evaporates into another motif and the peace of the word 'death'.

Technical perfection, and especially perfection of form, gives Monteverdi a command of this kind; but it is an insight into musical imagery, a knowledge of where to place the emphasis and how to find an equivalent of the inner meanings of words, which gives this fourth book of madrigals a delight hard to find in any madrigal book by any other composer. *Sì ch'io vorrei morire* is an indecent little piece of verse, in which the love kiss (veiled as usual in the image of 'death') and the way to its climax—now sweet and almost restful, now passionate and energetic—are hinted at, until a state of rest comes at last. It is not a distinguished poem by any standards—little more than a play on words which scarcely arouses our feelings at all. It is indeed a standard of Monteverdi's mastery that he has managed to give added meaning to a poem without any concrete images to inspire him. The neutral opening does not attempt to paint 'morire'—quite deliberately because it is a point of rest. A *tutti*, by a chromatic twist, increases the tension; and then there is a huge section on the 'cara e dolce lingua' in which the lingering weakness and tenseness of love are given memorable expression by the continuous dissonance (usually with three adjacent notes of the scale sounded together), after which comes a falling section of more conventional suspensions as the lover feels himself 'dying'. He has a sudden return to life with a short rhythmic motif, and a feeling of haste is conveyed by a canon at the half-beat and a string of suspensions, repeated in one form or another three times, with a third voice finally exclaiming ecstatically 'Ahi bocca! Ahi baci! Ahi lingua!' until the great climax; and, with a touch of mastery, the peace of the aftermath is given perfect expression by a repetition of the opening.

Sì ch'io vorrei has an emotional life which could in 1603 be found only in the most intense modern madrigals; yet there is nothing in it which is revolutionary. Even the passage with the three adjacent notes of the scale held together simultaneously can actually be justified by conventional rules. This cannot be said of *Ohimè*. The very opening of the madrigal contains harmonies which are impossible by ordinary standards:

The effect is splendid. Again the subject is the spurned lover; and this time dare we take his sighs too seriously? The dissonance is not extended enough and therefore does not sound too severe. There is merely a tang of desire in these strange unaccented chords. This is carried through the madrigal in a magical way. When we arrive at the climax, 'Alas, why do you wish him who sighs to die?' the dissonances, far from being the astringencies of *Si ch'io vorrei*, are accumulations of passing notes which do not always arrive at their destination and which therefore attract attention to themselves; and they are never prolonged, never harsh. Nor is the ending full of the passion which Monteverdi has at his command. Instead the 'thousands and thousands of sighs' are given life by a series of false relations which convey a sense of indeterminate tonality. A pedal note in the final bars gives some light dissonance, and the concluding 'ohimè's' gently remind us of the opening. The mood of the music is again the exact mirror of the words. The bantering, never too passionate love of both is a typical offshoot of the pastoral conventions. It is often difficult to believe in the grand amours of Thyrsis and Cloris. Monteverdi has gone one better: he has written the music of flirtation without becoming purely artificial (for his motifs are anything but conventional), while at the same time remaining always full of feeling.

If I have discussed the emotional life of these madrigals in detail, reading into them perhaps—as is always the danger—things which are not really there, the reason is that the technical resources of this and the fifth book of madrigals are so interesting for the development of music that Monteverdi's masterful psychology is sometimes forgotten. But I cannot leave this book without commenting on its musical resource too, for the volume is a key to Monteverdi's subsequent development. One thing we notice is that the 'academic' traits come to their full expressiveness in these madrigals. Chromaticism, for example, is nowhere better integrated into the madrigal than in the last number of the book, *Piagne e sospira*. The rising chromatic scale of the opening acts almost as a *canto fermo*, around which the different emotions and different musical motifs are wrapped. At the end, when the final chromatic fragment is no longer used, a chromatic change in a chordal passage is as expressive as any harmonic use of chromaticism could be. There is none of the enigmatic suddenness of Gesualdo's chromatics. Everything is musically developed to its fullest extent.

Similarly, Wert's experiments in *parlando* declamation are used perfectly here and no longer seem at all experimental. A great deal of *Voi pur da me* is written in homophonic, quickly moving declamation in which the words are perfectly audible. What Monteverdi has done is to make every harmonic change significant, every change of texture contribute to the ebb and flow of tension. More than that, the expressiveness of melody now can be heard at its clearest, for the top lines (usually two of them) use the slides and ornaments, the capacity to hold notes, to make expressive pauses, all of which Monteverdi had learned from the virtuoso singers of Mantua. In *Sfogava con le stelle* he uses the declamatory style in yet another way. Here is the extreme of verbal clarity in the *ensemble* madrigal; in six places he does nothing but indicate the chords to be sung, leaving the rhythms to the singers, who must chant them as they would the psalms written in *falso bordone*. Nothing could be simpler; but this is used not just to give clarity to the words, but to make the succeeding passages in counterpoint more overwhelming. As one acute observer has found, the neutral words, the words which have no direct expressive power, are left in chant. Those which are personal, evocative and emotional are given the full power of expressive music—all the modern harmonies, the nervousness of ornaments and strange leaps in melody.

These two madrigals are typical of the whole book in this way. The power of harmony—not necessarily dissonance, but of chromatic changes and modulation—and virtuoso melody have now in fact done away with real counterpoint. There are many passages which could be performed by a solo voice with a keyboard accompaniment—even more by two voices and keyboard. Something would be lost, because the colouring of the voices and the changes of texture are important. Yet the essentials would be there. There is no doubt that Monteverdi is now writing music for the aristocratic listener rather than the aristocratic performer. No groups of dilettantes could possibly perform it adequately. The older ideal of the madrigal is as dead as it is in the madrigals of Gesualdo or the monodies of the *camerata* composers.

The fourth book of madrigals was successful and had to be reprinted in 1605 and 1607, to go no further (it is interesting to note that a great deal of 'modern music' was seemingly popular, for Pallavicino's sixth book also went through several editions quickly). Perhaps it was this that encouraged Monteverdi to bring out another book soon after. The fifth book appeared in 1605. At least one of its numbers had been composed five years earlier and another had been known to Artusi in a manuscript copy for some time. So it seems that part of the contents of the fifth book was composed about the same time as those of a previous collection. There are two changes to note, the first of which might appear a purely technical one. A *basso continuo* part is supplied. For over half the contents it is not necessary; for the remaining ones it is essential, and these are therefore rather different in technique. We must not exaggerate the immediate effects in sound. Probably madrigals of earlier volumes were performed with instrumental accompaniment and with soloistic decorations such as we find in these new madrigals. Nevertheless the conscious use of a keyboard accompaniment leads to very new conceptions, and these madrigals are original enough to open a new chapter in the history of the form. The other novelty for a Monteverdi madrigal book was the complete elimination of the canzonet style. Even the highly serious fourth book had its lighter numbers, for instance, *Io mi son giovinetta*. The 'conventional' madrigals (as we may call those which do not use the *basso continuo* as an essential ingredient) of Book V are all sad. Some of them seem almost emotionally overwrought. The laments of the various lovers in Guarini's *Il pastor fido* are the main choice of verse, and they are treated as vehicles for great musical intensity, without any suggestion of that teasing not-too-serious pastoralism of which Monteverdi is sometimes capable.

The immediate result of this emotionalism is that the harmony of some of the madrigals is more dissonant, and stranger in the way it uses false relations; and it was these things that Artusi attacked in his various books and pamphlets. It was to be expected that he would direct an attack on *Cruda Amarilli*, for there is one bar which is very unconventional:

Even so, Artusi's attack is more on a paper reading than on the actual sound. If we compare Monteverdi's opening, it is much less dissonant than Pallavicino's. It is unusual for its ornaments, fully written out; but Artusi must have heard things like that many times from singers adding improvisatory *gorgie*. There are other pin-pricks of harmony, but again they are more 'difficult' on paper than in sound. For the most part, the madrigal is more conventional than many in the fourth book, both in its melodic motifs and in its treatment of them.

More worthy of Artusi's attack, for it is one of the greatest of Monteverdi's madrigals, was *Era l'anima mia*. Guarini's first image is of the soul at its last hour. Its double meaning is so ordinary in the verse of the period that we hardly think about it. Monteverdi seems to take it at its face value, and using the lower voices (and the lowest registers of them) gives a picture of frightening intensity. Long-held pedal notes, over which two voices in thirds give the effect of modern dominant preparation, and frequent false relations never allow the tension to drop. If we wish to feel how intense this is, it is only necessary to compare the passage with a setting by Pallavicino:

The Earlier Madrigals

The soul is reprieved by a glimpse from a more blessed spirit and Monteverdi brings in his upper voices with almost angelic effect. Thereafter the verse proceeds by a series of double meanings, by sighs and threatened deaths. The music breathes life into the conventions, and by long pedals and dissonant passing notes comes to a memorable climax. These two madrigals could well have come from the fourth book; in psychological power and emotional grandeur they seem to complete a phase in Monteverdi's work.

The other 'conventional' madrigals, with one exception, seem less interesting and, for Monteverdi, more experimental. There are two long cycles of linked madrigals to verse from *Il pastor fido*, both of which seem to have gone back to the ideals of Wert. Both are obviously concerned less with madrigalian expressiveness than with the audibility of the words. Almost the whole of the first part of *Ecco, Silvio* is written in homophonic declamation. There are varied groupings of voices and some striking harmonic changes; but the sacrifice of expressiveness has been great. In the subsequent sections the texture is adhered to less severely, but nowhere in the works is there anything of the sheer magic we find in some of the earlier madrigals. What we do notice is a great interest in the development of the melodic line—by now the upper melody throughout. The lower parts often consist of filling in of little independent interest. Monteverdi is developing a definite attitude to this, and a number of personal mannerisms have appeared. One is the use of a descending leap of a sixth which comes at moments of crisis. It is possible to find this in earlier works (even in Book III), but it now happens so often as to become almost a cliché. Another is a suspension which resolves irregularly and draws attention to itself by leaping to an unexpected note of the new chord. Another is the use of sequence to press home a phrase; and another an occasional expressive ornament. The beginning of *Dorinda, ah dirò* is a good example. First a short phrase; then a repetition of it higher up; then an ornamental repetition and an obsessional development of the three notes of the scale before the section is complete—these are the stages of melody building:

Do·rin·da, Do·rin·da_ah di·rò mi·a, ah di·rò

mia Se mia non se·i

This is more skilful and more deeply felt than anything we find in Wert's recitative madrigals; yet it is little compensation for the splendours of Monteverdi's natural madrigal style. There is, however, one exception. This is *O Mirtillo*. It is certainly written in the recitative madrigal style, and with little trouble it could be reduced to a monody, for the important melody is always in the top part and there is always a clear bass part, even in the trio sections. The melody is of the most expressive kind of declamation. The downward sixth leap begins the madrigal and sets the atmosphere at once. The suspension which resolves irregularly comes several times. But more than this, Monteverdi uses the complete resources of the madrigal. The chains of suspensions which we have seen in earlier books now dominate the first climax. Words and phrases are repeated to give scale to the madrigal, which never seems restricted or in the least experimental. As several observers have pointed out, it is the first of the great laments and the true model for the *Lamento d'Arianna*, which was in turn to set a fashion for many years and many composers. Although rather simpler in psychology than some of the madrigals of the fourth book, it is a good example of what can be done with the new manner.

The continuo madrigals seem to demand a new chapter. Typically enough they start in the middle of a madrigal book, for Monteverdi's music progresses so naturally that any division is artificial. The division of his madrigals into two is merely for our convenience, since the introduction of the *basso continuo* is a suitable place for us to recapitulate the excitement of the 'new music' which had been so proudly proclaimed by the Florentines a few years earlier, and which used this new device as an integral part of its nature. Yet if the glories of Greece had been re-created by anyone it was by Monteverdi, using the older techniques or extensions of them. His claim to be a descendant of Rore and the rest was quite justified, and already he could claim to be by no means the least of the moderns.

As a writer of conventional madrigals Monteverdi stays somewhere between Marenzio and Gesualdo. He is a less polished composer than the former, whose music is often the accurate mirror of the anacreontic verse he sets. Monteverdi is too rugged, too interested in human beings to be able to believe in the pastoral convention. Yet he is too much a musician to be a purely psychological composer like Gesualdo, who seems to have no interest in musical device. In one way he excels both of them. In his range of emotion he is greater than either. He can be passionate and pessimistic, gently ironic or supremely gay in turn. We have no right to be surprised when he turns out to be a great opera composer. His madrigals, with their range of human interest and their variety, from introversion to almost pure objectivity, have prepared the way thoroughly; and if at times we seem to undervalue these works, the only reason can be that we do not devote to their performance the virtuosity which their composer expected. There is no other barrier to our understanding.

CHAPTER V

MADRIGALS WITH BASSO CONTINUO

THE *basso continuo* was one of those inventions which had an influence on the history of music far beyond any expectations of its originators. It came out of the specific needs of certain composers. Some of them were mundane. Viadana, *maestro di cappella* at Mantua Cathedral, had the need for a notation which would allow the organist to fill in gaps in the harmony when the singers were few. Motets written deliberately for one or two or three solo voices required a well-organized accompaniment if the music was not to sound thin and weak. A notation which allowed for the cheap production of keyboard parts was a godsend to him and many another musician working in difficult conditions.

There were also more noble reasons, especially those of the Florentine academics, who, in their attempt at reviving the glories of Greek music, came to the conclusion that the decadence of modern music was really caused by polyphony, since it 'lacerated the poetry' (as one of them put it), and that the only way of uniting words and music on equal terms was for a single voice to be used. The words would then be clear and the singer could 'move the spirit', or appeal to both the intellect (through the words) and the emotions (through the music). Unwilling to sacrifice the power of harmony altogether, they too sought a notation which would make quite clear the subordinate role of the accompaniment. Their attempt was a revival of Greek music; their success, a new kind of music for the court. It is no coincidence that some of the first composers of the new music were singers. The very nature of monody was to glorify the virtuoso, and since for some

74

time the tastes of Ferrara, Mantua and the other courts had been for
the nimble throats of Laura Perperara, Adriana Basile and the rest, it
is no wonder that the new music became fashionable. The first song-
books came out in 1602, and within ten years monody was in constant
demand.

The earliest books contained two types of song. One, the most
important in the first fifteen years or so, preserved the name 'madrigal';
and with good reason, for it followed the main principle of the later
polyphonic madrigal—that the words were to be expressed in the
greatest possible detail. The new methods were admittedly a little
different, although they too had their origins in the older style. In some
madrigals the conception was to provide an exact declamation for
most of the song, repeating the words little, if at all, and saving
expressive music for important words or phrases. This expressiveness took the form of virtuoso ornamentation, which now became
surpassingly involved and demanding. In other madrigals exact
declamation was sacrificed a little for a continuous *arioso* movement
with climaxes brought about by jagged intervals and dissonant
harmonies. Some of these *arioso* madrigals are really very like the more
advanced madrigals in Monteverdi's fourth and fifth books, in that
these would have sounded very similar if performed with a single
voice and instrumental participation. But the newer style, as it was
first conceived, had several disadvantages. Whereas the lightly contrapuntal texture of Monteverdi enforces both a fairly strict rhythm
and a sense of formal development, these *continuo* madrigals had a
tendency to be a little amorphous and uninteresting, especially if sung
with the free *rubato* which some of the composers advocated. Admittedly this followed up the ideas of the theorists in so far as it threw
emphasis on the words; but as time went on the music conquered,
and the repeating of verbal phrases, the use of refrains and other
devices began to give a new attractiveness.

The *continuo* madrigal was inconceivable without the taste for
splendid virtuoso singing. The second type of monody was designed
for broader popularity. The aria, as it was called, had nothing to do
with the ancient Greeks. It was the natural descendant of the ballett

and the canzonet, both of which were sold by the score (Monteverdi's among them) in the latter decades of the sixteenth century. The simplest arias are sharp in rhythm, clear-cut in harmony and tonality, and—so that they should be unforgettable—strophic in their treatment of the words. They set verse which one writer has aptly characterized as 'amorous baby talk' to the lightest of tuneful music. Some arias were, it is true, a little more complicated. These were written in the form which we know as the strophic variation. Each verse of the poem was set to slightly changed music, but the bass is kept the same throughout—a tether by which the melody maintains its general shape. The composer may manage to get in more detail of tone painting, but the general mood is still gay and it is no surprise that these two types of aria eventually defeated the more serious madrigal and drove it from the song-books.

What had Monteverdi to do with such new ideas? Not much, is the answer: or rather, not much while the ideas were really new. Certainly he was interested in the Greek philosophers and in the possibilities of monody. But the glories of the ancients were not necessarily to be found in this music of singers and dilettantes. Like most professional composers, he was slow to take to the solo madrigal and aria. When he did use the *continuo*, it is typical that it should interest him more as a new technical means, rather in the practical way of Viadana than in the experimental way of the Florentines; typical also that when he finally took the plunge, in the last six madrigals of Book V, the general effect is perhaps more conservative than some of the daring numbers of his Book IV. The first of the *continuo* madrigals, *Ahi, come a un vago sol*, is a masterpiece. The poem belongs to the usual kind of love verse, with all the conventionally affective words—sighs, wounds and so on. Monteverdi writes music which gives them vivid expression. In a *continuo* madrigal, melody is especially important, and the opening duet for tenors uses all the resources of florid ornamentation in much the same way that Caccini's madrigals of his *Nuove Musiche* use them. With a second voice to enrich both harmony and sonority, the effect is superb and much more powerful than anything Caccini ever wrote:

The phrasing, too, is magical—now long and sustained, then suddenly quickened emotionally with short, more broken fragments of
melody. The bass moves comparatively slowly as the interest lies
completely in the tenor parts, but because of the continuous movement
in these there is never any feeling that the rhythm has collapsed, as
there sometimes is in early operatic monody. This tenor duet is in four
sections, the first very long and culminating in a splendid decorative
climax, the second still decorated but somewhat shorter, the last two
becoming progressively more direct in melody and more concentrated.
To separate them is a *tutti*—a refrain which happens four times in all,
slightly altered each time in texture but otherwise the same, with the
final *tutti* extended by a coda using harmonies over a pedal note,
reminiscent of earlier madrigals. Indeed, the refrain is altogether like
part of one of the madrigals from the fourth book, contrasting with the
tenor duet by its rhythmic directness and mobile bass. Nor is any part
of the madrigal very different from the earlier madrigals which use the

trio texture freely. There are just two significant changes. One is the rondo form—a form which is clearly melodic, and much more obvious than the earlier developments from the canzonet. The other is the sectionalism which results from giving all the trio sections to one group of voices and from decisive cadences at each change of texture. This interest in forms, which derives from Monteverdi's earliest days, stands him in good stead. We have only to look at the motets of his Mantuan colleague Viadana, who was trying to solve the same prob-lems at the same time, to see how well Monteverdi has avoided the amorphousness which was the trouble in much early *concertato* music.

In *T'amo, mia vita* we find the same inventiveness in the face of this problem. The verse is simple enough. The beloved says 'I love you', and the lover is happy. Here Monteverdi gives the words of the beloved to a soprano, who sings them several times, while each time the lover, represented by the three lower voices, gives a different cry of joy and tenderness. The sections are short and the bass is more consistently in motion, so that everything sounds quite conventional. Yet the way the upper voice is used leaves no room for doubt that a soloist is needed, a soprano who can hold a note and make it expres-sive. The lower voices are full of chromatic changes, effective if perhaps less subtle than those used in Book IV; and the declamatory chattering in quavers, although at first sight not interesting in itself or very exactly matching the rhythm of the words, is psychologically right. The amplification of the opening motifs into a concluding *tutti* rounds off the piece perfectly.

After these successes (the fifth book went through seven editions in ten years) we might expect another madrigal book to follow; but between the opera and his emotional troubles Monteverdi can have had little time, and indeed the only volume of any sort was a collection of trios made by his brother, Giulio Cesare. These are called *Scherzi musicali* and came out in 1607. Scholars have devoted a great deal of attention to the volume, mainly in trying to find out what Giulio meant by referring in the preface to the *canto alla francese*—a term which turns up again in some of Monteverdi's motets. To relate these slight trios to *musique mesurée* and French academic ideas is to take these songs too seriously. They belong to an Italian tradition—a Mantuan tradition even. They are the natural successors of Gastoldi's *balletti*, which were popular as early as the 1580's. In particular, Gastoldi's *Balletti a tre voci*, which came out in 1594, are very near in atmosphere, texture and phrasing to Monteverdi's *Scherzi musicali*; and since they were designed for playing and singing together, they may well have sounded like the later works. Typically, Monteverdi is rather more complicated. He likes the *hemiolia* rhythms, which indeed intrigued some of the writers of the monodic ariettas and were to become increasingly fashionable:

Monteverdi also provides a short instrumental *ritornello* between the verses of each song, in most pieces seeming to develop the themes of the song lightly. Some of the songs are very charming, especially *Lidia spina* with its appealing little ending alternating between major and minor. Others are too regular and too short-breathed to satisfy. In this sort of light music many composers were as good as Monteverdi, and we must look elsewhere for his true development.

The sixth book of madrigals appeared in 1614 when Monteverdi was firmly installed in Venice, but its contents are the work of his Mantuan years. A madrigal book for five voices looked old-fashioned in 1614, even if there was a *basso continuo* part; and it is not surprising that there was not the tremendous success for it that there had been for the fifth book. Even so, it is a splendid volume. The two main works are a madrigalesque arrangement of the *Lamento d'Arianna* and the lament of a shepherd on the death of his nymph. There are also two Petrarch settings, both in a reasonably conventional, almost *a cappella* style, and a number of *concertato* madrigals after the manner of the last six in Book V.

The laments are both examples of Monteverdi's finest music. The *Arianna* arrangement was criticized by Doni on the grounds that it spoiled a work which was essentially expressive solo music. Be that as it may (and we must remember that we have neither seen the opera nor possess the complete score of the *scena*), it is easier for us to understand the popularity of the piece from the madrigal version than from the monody. The scale of the madrigal is nearer our expectations; the monody, as printed by Gardano, with its chorus interpolations cut out, seems too small. Again, the harmony which the composer uses in the madrigal is more powerful than any we can conjure up from the *basso continuo* part of the monody, if only because the sustaining power of the voices is so much greater than on any accompanying instrument; and this is important, for the madrigals are clearly very much in the tradition of Book V. Moreover, the arrangement is a great deal more than a thickening out of the monody. In the very first section, for example, the refrain, 'Lasciatemi morire', with its acid dissonance, comes twice in the monody to make up a neat *da capo* form which is entirely satisfactory. In the madrigal version, it bursts in yet another time. After the opening (slightly lengthened to allow all five voices to enter and expand the phrases) the second section, 'E chi volete voi' acts as an episode for three voices with a dissonant climax of its own. Then the first phrase of 'Lasciatemi morire' returns, but is never allowed to complete itself, as 'E chi volete voi' comes in with renewed tone on the full *ensemble*. Only then is a *da capo* allowed to bring a state of despair and rest. In a way this is more expressive than the original, and although the very rhythms of the later parts of the lament hardly seem appropriate for domestic music-making, it is one of the heights of Monteverdi's madrigal writing.

Monteverdi's arrangement of the piece is so good that there is only one thing which might make us suspect that the lament is part of a longer work. It is too intense. From its dissonant beginning to the turbulent final section there is scarcely a relaxed moment, and this robs the piece of some of the pathos which may well have been part of the original *scena*. In arranging the lament Monteverdi has clearly kept the moments of highest tension and cut away the rest. From this point of view, the other lament, *Incenerite spoglie*, is formally better, for it works towards its climaxes from points of rest and alternates the tragic exclamations with less subjective phrases. Several observers have pointed out that it would be possible to arrange the piece as a monody without much alteration, and this is certainly true of the first section, in which the tenor stands out against the *tutti* and in declamatory phrases sings of the shepherd's grief.

But this, after all, is something which would be said of many of the declamatory madrigals of Wert and a number of the madrigals from Monteverdi's earlier books, and it is as the successor of these that we must discuss *Incenerite spoglie*. It opens rather like *Era l'anima mia* with a chant setting the scene—the shepherd weeping beside the tomb of his beloved. His cry 'Ahi lasso' breaks in on the chant with a madrigalian symbol which is all the more effective for its context:

Then in a manner very similar to the madrigals in Book IV the declamation returns, but with varied vocal colouring in different trio combinations. In one way these trios are very different from the earlier madrigals. There is no attempt to make the words clear, and often the bass part of the trio sings a completely different phrase from the others.

The mastery of Book IV, however, is in evidence. Using but a single line of the poem, Monteverdi builds up a tense atmosphere, now allowing the phrase to complete itself, now breaking it off, now giving it a new ending or speeding it up to bring it to the cadence. In the later sections Monteverdi adds a device most affecting in its simplicity. While most of the voices declaim continuously, one or two voices break off to exclaim 'Ahi morte' or 'Ahi Corinna', so insistently that the other voices too in the end take up the plaint. Also unlike the earlier madrigals is the comparative lack of dissonance. Nor is chromaticism used a great deal, either for sudden changes or large-scale modulations. Only towards the end of the fourth section is there anything like the harmonic astringency which is often associated with Monteverdi, and here again the very restraint in the rest of the cycle makes the moment of anguish even more agonized, as the double suspensions and pedal notes bring the musical climax. The result is very different from the *Lamento d'Arianna*. Less obviously powerful, the cycle is by no means inferior, and it is as moving in its pathetic helplessness as any of Monteverdi's madrigals.

These two laments, with two shorter numbers in much the same mood, take up about two-thirds of the book. It is tempting to see reflected in them the emotions of Monteverdi's later troubled years at Mantua. But just as Beethoven could write an *Eroica* and a fourth symphony together, so we find in this sixth book of madrigals a lighter vein which shows that Monteverdi was still the complete master of all expressive music. In one of the conventional madrigals he even returns to the development of the canzonet. *Zefiro torna* goes back to Petrarch for its poem, and an *a cappella* texture for its music. Conventional, however, is not quite the word for it, because its first section is in triple time, something very rare in *a cappella* madrigals, and the decorations in the upper voices which round off each section never happened in former times. Both are reflections of the newer monodies—the triple time now a favourite for ariettas, the ornaments conventional for all music. All the old skill is there, with the contrasts of the poem brought out between lengthy sections as always, and the ending 'Sono un deserto e fere aspr'e selvagge', is a recollection of Wert's setting of another Petrarch sonnet, *Solo e pensoso*.

There are no such backward glances in the style of *Qui rise Tirsi*, a joyous *concertato* madrigal and a proper successor to *Ahi, come a un vago sol*. The form again is a series of duets and trios separated by the *tutti* singing an ecstatic refrain, 'O happy memory and happy day'.

This little refrain is in the style of the *tutti* sections of the madrigals of the earlier books (it is very like *O Mirtillo*). The duet sections, on the other hand, are modern and show an increasing grasp of the new medium. Instead of the mainly declamatory style of *Ahi, come a un vago sol*, Monteverdi enjoys the resources of florid melody to the full, using dotted rhythms and roulades with the greatest freedom. These orna-ments appear consistently throughout the phrases, forming sequences which give a firm shape to the melody. The duet texture itself is used splendidly. Plain writing in thirds and sixths which fills out the harmony is the staple fare; but instead of the rather dull results which come through the excessive use of these cloying intervals in the *Scherzi musicali*, Monteverdi now knows exactly how to offset them by breaking forth into counterpoint. How effective, for example, is the following climax to a duet section for tenors after about eight bars of movement in thirds; it comes about not just because of the florid melody but also because the second tenor has simply moved one beat later than the first:

In spite of this more cheerful music the total impression of the volume is one of tragic power, which seems to be Monteverdi's more familiar vein. To this period we must also ascribe yet another lament, a monody called *Lamento d'Olimpia*.[1] Written in three sections to words inspired by a scene in Ariosto's *Orlando furioso*, it is clearly an offshoot of the success made by the *Lamento d'Arianna*. The same short, memorable phrases, the same use of emotional falling intervals, the same tendency for the harmony and melody to be slightly at odds make it a fine piece. It is a worthy companion to the similar laments of contemporary composers such as d'India.

Yet pure monody of this sort still seems to have interested Monteverdi comparatively little. Admittedly the title of the next madrigal book is *Concerto. Settimo libro de madrigali a 1, 2, 3, 4 & 6 voci, con altri generi de canti*. We might expect now, only seventeen years after Caccini's *Nuove Musiche* appeared, to see Monteverdi's contribution to the history of monody. The contents reveal that we are likely to be disappointed. Only four out of over thirty works are for solo voice and only two of these are works for the simple combination of voice and keyboard. The other two demand some form of instrumental accompaniment or intervention. The rest of these madrigals are duets, trios and *ensemble* music of various kinds, including the ballet *Tirsi et Clori*, which, as we shall see in a later chapter, belongs to the madrigalesque *genre* only in the way that some of the great choruses for plays which appeared in other composers' madrigal books throughout the sixteenth century did. The very shape of the book is most unusual, and although we can find a similar *mélange* in the work of another senior composer— Marco da Gagliano's *Musiche* (1615), which also contains monodies, duets and a *balletto*—even in this there is not quite the rich diversity of Monteverdi's set.

The works for solo voice are emotionally the least significant, although all are interesting in some way. The two most difficult for the twentieth-century musician to understand are the *lettere amorose*,

[1] Printed in W. Osthoff, *12 composizioni vocali . . . (inedite)*, Milan, 1958.

written in the *genere rappresentativo* (or recitative style) and designed to be sung in a free rhythm. These are 'academic' monodies of the most severe kind, and it is rather surprising to find that they are so different from the climaxes of the operas. More ingratiating is the first work in the volume, *Tempro la cetra*. This is an aria in the sense that the word had been used by the Florentines—a set of strophic variations. There are four verses to be set, and the bass part of each is kept roughly the same (there are minor changes of rhythm). Over this the singer develops his theme. He has taken the lyre to sing to the glory of Mars, but as the first verse ends, he declares that all he can sing of is love. Each verse contrasts the images of war and love and gives the singer the opportunity for varying the melody. In each verse he increases the expressiveness of the ornaments, until the last stanza brings forth the *trillo* and the whole repertory of *gorgie*. To offset this, Monteverdi provides a little *ritornello* for five unnamed instruments, in the manner of *Orfeo*. As it is repeated between the verses, it seems little more than a conventional device; and then, as it seems to be about to bring the piece to an end, Monteverdi adds a little dance which is given twice before the *ritornello* finally does end the piece. The work is obviously an offshoot of Orpheus' aria to Charon, although more simple in its decoration and less intense, more playful in mood.

The fourth solo work is unique. *Con che soavità* is written for a soprano accompanied by three groups of instruments. The first consists only of *continuo* instruments—two *chitarroni*, a harpsichord and a spinet; the second, two violins, viola and a harpsichord; the third, viola and cello (or two viols) and *contrabasso* with an organ. The conception is based on the dialogues which were so popular in both church music and chamber monody; but instead of a voice with each group of instruments Monteverdi gives the words to a single voice, which sings virtually continuously. As usual when he grafts a new idea on to old forms, his inspiration runs high. The comparatively slow-moving harmonies traditional in dialogues, to accommodate the large forces performing them, fit exactly the work's mood suggested by the word 'soavità' (sweetness) in the opening phrase. But then the passion of the lover's kisses comes to life suddenly and powerfully in the contrasts which can be conjured up with the three instrumental groups. The vocal melody, by using the repetitions which are so much part of the dialogue form, is magically organized, always *arioso* rather than recitative in its steady rhythms and tight phrase structure. There is no need for extravagant decoration or severe dissonance. As a result the piece is one of the most contented of love madrigals, never violent yet never frivolous. It is a pity it is not more widely known, though perhaps understandable since the resources needed for its performance are not easy to come by.

The most notable masterpieces of the book, however, are the duets. They take up about half the volume and several of them seem in their emotional richness to hark back to the greatness of Book IV. It is not surprising that Monteverdi took to the medium so well. As we have seen, much of his earlier work had used the duet texture for long stretches even though it retained the variety inherent in larger resources; and duets suited him better than pure monodic writing. Fullness of harmony and expanded forms came out of the duet more easily than from the solo. Monteverdi borrowed what he required from the monody, but these duets are essentially a development of his earlier quasi-contrapuntal style. This will be clearer if we compare his duets with some by Gagliano. There are several in Gagliano's *Musiche*, and they divide quite naturally into slightly built strophic songs and more serious and complicated *continuo* madrigals. The strophic songs are clearly ariettas, with a melody, a bass and the second voice filling in. Short phrases and regular harmonic changes give a pleasant tunefulness, and variety is worked in by the instrumental interludes, which, however, never break up the phrase structure and seem to belong to the melody of the voice. The serious duets are another matter. They are declamatory, use the *gorgia* for the normal monodic expressiveness and have slower moving harmony. Here again, there are repeated sections where the voices change parts as had been customary in canzonets and balletts for a long time.

To compare Gagliano's slighter duets with Monteverdi's *Chiome d'oro* is perhaps unfair since Monteverdi's work seems on a so much more extended scale; but the works are similar, and *Chiome d'oro* is really an extension of the style of the *Scherzi musicali*, which certainly are comparable. The idea of instrumental *ritornellos* has been taken from the *Scherzi musicali* and the actual form of the duet also reminds us of them for it is in essence a strophic song with everything repeated twice. But there are some important differences. The *ritornello* is quite a complicated piece with three closely related strains, and instead of using all of it between the sung verses, Monteverdi uses the strains separately in between various lines of the poem. The vocal melody itself is superb, using the dotted rhythms which had previously been ornaments so consistently that they became the whole spring-board of the tune. Typically for Monteverdi, though much of the time the voices sing in thirds with one another, they interchange occasionally and add little roulades which mean that both are entirely necessary and that the piece is thus a genuine duet. Typical too are the two little cadenzas, as they seem to be, at the end of each stanza—typical, for they insert into a song of flirtation a touch of deeper feeling, without ever being heavy or sentimental.

The more serious works explore the resources of the duet even more thoroughly. The one which at first sight seems nearest to monody is *Interrotte speranze*; and yet this is a work far away from Florence. It is a song of a spurned lover whose hope and faith merely raise his desire. It begins with a pedal note in the bass. Over this two tenors begin the plaint, chanting on the same note. In a way which Monteverdi had used in his earlier madrigals, dissonances are produced by the upper part moving up a tone and thrusting the lower part down. These dissonances and the rise in the melody, the sustained pedal note, the broken phrases, the low *tessitura* for the voices, all establish the psychology of the despairing, desiring lover in a very powerful way. And then, when the pedal note has changed and the cadence has provided relief, Monteverdi repeats all this nervous material, only with altered, even more intense declamation. This cannot be kept up, and the music relaxes with a dialogue and more sober thoughts about the beloved. Only at the end are the dissonances resumed to twist the knife in our hearts:

In this duet it is the declamatory opening with the static bass that gives the appearance of monody; and it is possible to find many similar places in the duets of this volume. The expressive ornamentation also seems 'monodic' at first sight, and so do the sudden changes of harmony. But in fact the real power of these emotionally rich works lies in their derivation from older sources. The scale is achieved essentially by the methods of the older madrigal books, that is by repeating sections of varying lengths with new tone colouring. In *Perchè fuggi*, for example, almost every melodic phrase is repeated—not with a sterile one-voice-after-the-other method, but by using the second voice in the repetitions to add new counterpoints, enriching the harmony and timbre. As for the ornamentation, it is less 'monodic', or based on the expression of a single word or phrase, than an integral part of the melody—a dotted rhythm repeated again and again to balance the phrase, or a *portamento* which comes in each voice in turn to become a memorable fragment to shape the melody (as in *Ecco vicine, o bella tigre*). This is nearer the continuous application of ornament which was so common in the sixteenth century, though, it must be said, with the application of much more purpose and skill than the improvising singers can ever have achieved. Out of virtuosity has come a rhythmical melody which can truly be called tuneful.

All these duets are fine, and they show a very wide emotional range. The flirtatious *Tornate, o cari baci* with its refrain of kisses, the richly decorated *O come sei gentile* for two virtuoso ladies or the more serious kisses of *Perchè fuggi* form a splendid treasure which is every bit as deserving of revival as the early polyphonic madrigals. All are reward‚ing and only one of them can be mentioned as standing out from the rest—the set of variations on the *romanesca* theme, *Ohimè, dov'è il mio ben?* The idea is borrowed from the song‚books, for the duet is a set of strophic variations. There are four sections, each with the same stock bass, over which two tenors sing the lament, 'Where has my beloved gone, who has robbed me?' The words remind us of the *Lamento d'Arianna*, and so does the music. The first section, with its short, stabbing phrases intensified with dissonance between the voices, has the same bitter agony. If anything, the agony is greater, as the imita‚tions between the voices expand the scale and make pure declamation unnecessary by their overlapping rhythms. As in the earlier work, Monteverdi uses a refrain technique to make the music highly taut. The bass itself suggests this by a repeated cadential figure, but the repetitions in the melody are of greater length than those of the bass, and Monteverdi glories in the clashes which necessarily arise. Even more remarkable is the command of harmony which gives the piece its emotional variety. The final cadence in each successive verse expresses in turn despair, agony, the sweetness of hope and the finality of death:

It was another thirteen years before a new madrigal book of Monteverdi's appeared. They were years in which the nature of secular music changed completely. The serious monodic madrigals of the Florentine and Roman virtuosos went out of fashion, and a taste arose for the simpler, more obviously popular songs. Monteverdi's younger assistants at St Mark's were especially good at composing these. Berti and Grandi published some song-books in which tunefulness is all. Light rhythms, regular phrases, clear-cut diatonic harmonies became the order of the day. The verse was if anything even more trivial than the canzonet verse of the sixteenth century. In the more serious songs there are sometimes passages in the older declamatory style, but they often end with a gay triple-time section to provide easily memorable music (giving a division into recitative and aria, which became familiar later on). When more complicated music was required, it was usually given the form of the strophic variation, with the bass repeated in the manner of Caccini; or else an *ostinato* bass was employed. It is doubtful whether Monteverdi really cared very much for this frothy music, in which the academic theories of the earlier composers of monody had completely disappeared. Yet it was too important and popular for him to be able to ignore it. He contributed about half a dozen pieces to various Venetian anthologies; and the book of *Scherzi musicali* which came out in 1632 (significantly with a dedication by the publisher Magni, who clearly had gathered the collection together himself, a sign perhaps of Monteverdi's indifference) is in fact a book of arias in this new style.

The simplest of these songs are as near as Monteverdi ever went to writing in a purely conventional style. Catchy little tunes to insignificant verses, they have the charm of their *genre* but little individuality. The only way they can be said to differ from the works of many lesser composers is that Monteverdi can never resist the temptation to 'paint' the words, even if it breaks up the balance of phrases and the general mood of the song. A little chromatic passage to illustrate the word 'dying' or a succession of dissonances to express the cruelty of the lady intrude themselves. The strophic variation arias can accommodate these old-fashioned methods better, allowing for melodic variety in each verse, and Monteverdi usually adds a little *ritornello* for instruments in between, to give still more subtle emotional opportunities. *Et è pur dunque vero* is a good example of the style, the same bass allowing ample scope for melodic devices to express the weeping of the lover and the triumph and apparent indifference of the beloved, interspersed with a host of natural images such as the murmuring of the wind.

But as usual, Monteverdi's full inspiration is best found in *ensemble* music and especially in the duets, now clearly his favourite medium. The editor of one anthology, Anselmi, was very lucky to be given such a fine piece as *O come vaghi*. The poem is the conventional nonsense about Lydia and her eyes being wounding darts; but Monteverdi draws from it all its meaning and gives it a depth it scarcely deserves.

First there comes the rich sound of two tenors singing in thirds, and then as the lover is bewitched they split up, and in alert, lightly imitative phrases build up a climax. As the rays from Lydia's eyes become little arrows Monteverdi invents a motif which in pure sound, a dental consonant followed by a smooth vowel melisma, shoots out in a strikingly realistic way, multiplies in imitations between the voices and then, as the lover is wounded, is lost in dissonances. The harmonies become astringent as the pain increases:

Then quite suddenly the sweetness of love is felt, and with a motif reminiscent of the beginning of *O Mirtillo* a consonant and still section ends the duet, disturbed only by the cadential dissonance, as the 'dying' of the lover is mentioned in the poem. This is a subtle piece of erotic music, which, like some of the earlier madrigals from Book IV, is effortless in passing from flirtation to true love, from love's climax to perfect peace.

Of the other duets of this period, *Zefiro torna* is deservedly famous.
The poem is not the usual one by Petrarch, which Monteverdi had
set in Book VI. It is a sort of 'parody' (in the sixteenth-century sense)
of it by Rinuccini and, most important, keeps the same contrast
between joyful nature and the lover abandoned to his doleful thoughts.
Monteverdi sets this as a chaconne, using an *ostinato* bass pattern very
popular about this time:

The form is a difficult one. The shortness of the bass pattern (compared with others such as the *romanesca*) means short phrase lengths
which can become tiresome, and the harmonies are not easily varied
enough for an extended piece. Monteverdi conquers these problems
magnificently. His first paragraph lasts a dozen bars, as each voice
replies with a variant of the initial theme; and then the sweetness of
the breeze, slightly syncopated, is expressed by a succession of pure
consonances. There are gentle roulades for the murmuring waves,
pictorial motifs for the valleys and mountains (complete with the echo
device) in fact all the imagery of *Ecco mormorar l'onde* in the form of a
duet. Then, as the lover speaks of his plight, a piece of recitative with
dissonances is ushered in with a great chromatic change, brought to a
peaceful end as the lover sings praise of his lady's eyes in an ornamental,
sonorous passage with trills and scales in thirds. The technical mastery
of the piece is astonishing. Out of conventional features—the *ostinato*
bass, the by now customary division into speech-rhythm recitative and
dance-rhythm aria, echo music and so on—Monteverdi builds up a
vivid picture, and one which proves him to be a composer by no
means *semper dolens*.

The remainder of his secular music appeared in three collections, an
eighth book of madrigals (1638), the *Selva morale e spirituale* (1640)
and a posthumous collection put out by Vincenti in 1651. It is
impossible to date the individual numbers. All that can be certain is
that they were composed over a considerable space of time, probably

between about 1625 and 1635. Those of the trios which Vincenti put out in 1651 seem to belong in atmosphere to the lightest of the *Scherzi musicali*. They are gay dance songs with strong rhythms and tonalities typical of the trivia common in Venice around 1630. They are usually strophic songs, sometimes given a little variety by each of the three singers in turn having a little solo at the beginning of the verse, sometimes plainly repetitive. Most of them are either written completely or for a large part in triple time, although one or two divide into recitative and dance song as in so many arias of Berti, Merula and other minor composers of the time.

These works might make us believe that Monteverdi had sur-rendered the high ideals of music gained in the academies of his youth. He had certainly not followed blindly the ideas of the *camerata* composers and the 'advanced' madrigalists; but the old ideas were in his mind to the end. The eighth book of madrigals has a new title: *Madrigali guerrieri et amorosi*, not forgetting a preface which carefully explains the contents:

I have reflected that the principal passions or affections of our mind are three, namely, anger, moderation and humility or supplication; so the best philosophers declare, and the very nature of our voice indicates this in having high, low and middle registers. The art of music also points clearly to these three in its terms 'agitated', 'soft' and 'moderate' [*concitato, molle* and *temperato*]. In all the works of former composers I have indeed found examples of the 'soft' and the 'moderate', but never of the 'agitated', a genus nevertheless described by Plato in the third book of his *Rhetoric* [1] in these words: 'Take that harmony that would fittingly imitate the utter-ances and the accents of a brave man who is engaged in warfare.' And since I was aware that it is contraries which greatly move our mind, and that this is the purpose which all good music should have—as Boethius asserts, saying: 'Music is related to us and either ennobles or corrupts the character' —for this reason I have applied myself with no small diligence and toil to rediscover this genus.

After reflecting that according to all the best philosophers the fast pyrrhic measure was used for lively and warlike dances, and the slow spondaic

[1] Actually the *Republic*: the reference is 399*a*.

measure for their opposites, I considered the semibreve, and proposed that a single semibreve should correspond to one spondaic beat; when this was reduced to sixteen semiquavers struck one after the other and combined with words expressing anger and disdain, I recognized in this brief sample a resemblance to the passion which I sought, although the words did not follow metrically the rapidity of the instrument.

To obtain a better proof I took the divine Tasso as a poet who expresses with the greatest propriety and naturalness the qualities which he wishes to describe, and selected his description of the combat of Tancred and Clorinda as an opportunity of describing in music contrary passions, namely, warfare and entreaty and death. In the year 1624 I caused this composition to be performed in the noble house of my especial patron and indulgent protector the Most Illustrious and Excellent Signor Girolamo Mocenigo, an eminent dignitary in the service of the Most Serene Republic, and it was received by the best citizens of the noble city of Venice with much applause and praise. . . .

My rediscovery of this warlike genus has given me occasion to write certain madrigals which I have called *guerrieri*. And since the music played before great princes at their courts to please their delicate taste is of three kinds according to the method of performance—theatre music, chamber music and dance music—I have indicated these in my present work with the titles *guerriera, amorosa* and *rappresentativa*.[1]

If ever a madrigal book required some sort of explanation it is this one. It puzzles us today; it probably puzzled Monteverdi's contemporaries nearly as much. Instead of the usual chamber music for a few voices and instruments this one contains some big choral works and three dramatic ones (one, a ballet written thirty years earlier) as well as duets and trios. Then the arrangement into madrigals of war and those of love was unique. All madrigals (more or less) dealt with love: but what were warlike madrigals? No wonder the volume was never reprinted.

We might well dismiss the warlike part of the volume as speculative compositions to demonstrate a theory if it were not for two things.

[1] Translation taken from Strunk, *Source Readings in Music History* (London, 1952), pages 413–15.

One was that Monteverdi had always liked concrete imagery in the verse he set and managed to put it into realistic music. Then warlike music was not by any means new, although the audience of the 1620's and 1630's may not have remembered it. In the sixteenth century there had been a vogue of battle pieces, started by Jannequin's *La Bataille de Marignan*. By the second half of the century the vogue had reached Venice and two of the St Mark's musicians, Padovano and Andrea Gabrieli, wrote instrumental pieces called *arie della battaglia* for the Venetian wind band. Fanfares and military calls of various kinds were the stuff of this music, which was a form of elementary realism; and these pieces had an immense popularity in the 1590's. Monteverdi must have known them, but he would only use their methods after he had justified himself on theoretical grounds.

The works for a few voices from the 'warlike' part of the eighth book are the nearest to his normal style. One of them, *Armato il cor*, had been included by Magni in the *Scherzi musicali*, where it hardly seems out of place; and the other duet, *Se vittorie si belle*, also seems at first sight reasonably normal. Neither piece is a description of a battle. Both are settings of love poems with conventional warlike metaphors (as had been *Non più guerra* in Book IV); and both have the natural division between a fight and possible victory, and defeat and the wounds of death. There is no novelty in this, and seemingly not much in the music with its extended triple-time passages and contrasting, less rhythmic sections; and if there is some realistic musical imagery, this is, as we have seen, quite normal for Monteverdi.

Nevertheless there are differences. The warlike sections, built up from melodic fanfare arpeggios, are much simpler than anything we find in such duets as *Interrotte speranze* and *Tornate*. The harmonies are almost completely consonant and huge sections use two and three common chords, tonic and dominant predominating. Syncopations are rare, the rhythms being very straightforward and dance-like. The supposedly contrasting sections, where victory is in doubt and the poet is preoccupied with love's wounds, are equally unusual. Instead of the normal dissonances, Monteverdi maintains a remarkably pure harmony (again full of sequences and other devices which emphasize a diatonic key structure). *Se vittorie si belle* ends with a peaceful passage which completely ignores the implication of 'morir' (death):

è glo - ria il mo - rir per de - sio del - la vit - to - ria.

The result is curiously new. These works are completely Monteverdian, with all the old skills of creating a live, large-scale music which closely follows the sense of the words, but it is Monteverdi without the eroticism of his earlier works. In action or calmness, the works are extrovert, the images of the verse accepted at their face value rather than intensified as symbols of the lover's inner feelings.

Much the same may be said about the madrigals for six or more voices and instruments, although here the interest is often intensified by the splendid sonorities which are possible with a large group. *Ardo, avvampo*, for example, builds up a tremendous power in its first section, starting with two tenors, then adding two sopranos and finally four more voices and two violins. The first twenty-seven bars are simple repetitions of the G major chord, and the rest of this section is built from the simplest harmonic and melodic material. In *Altri canti d'amor* a similar effect is used in a big choral section, the fanfare material again well to the fore. These passages are thrilling, and yet the total effect of the madrigals is a little disappointing. They are too loosely organized, unlike Monteverdi's earlier *continuo* madrigals. It is customary to call them cantatas rather than madrigals, which means that they are sectional in construction. *Altri canti d'amor*, for example, has an overture, a trio, a central chorus, a bass solo accompanied by strings and a final chorus, all reasonably independent, though the final section grows out of the bass aria. The basic idea behind this kind of work came from the *concertato* motet, and like many of these it has too little sense of unity and climax for the form to be entirely satisfactory. The sections are not in themselves complete or well enough organized to stand as entities, but they seem to have distracted the composer from a satisfying overall construction. The problem is exactly the same one that Monteverdi had failed to solve completely in his first madrigal book. Clearly it took him a little time to gain the necessary experience with a new form.

The most successful piece in this style is one which approaches his earlier madrigals. *Hor che 'l ciel e la terra* is a setting of a poem by Petrarch, a sonnet which Monteverdi might have set at any time in his life. The lover cannot sleep, although heaven, earth and the wind are all silent. But his mind is at war within itself and only the thought of his beloved can bring peace. The image of war is only incidental to the theme, and so it appears in the music. The madrigal opens with a *parlando* section expressing the stillness of nature, very like those in the madrigals of Wert which had influenced Monteverdi in his youth. The colour of the voices—low in range—gives a magical, dark touch; and suddenly from this comes the dissonant, strident, curt lover's plaint, intensified in a duet for tenors. This is again very much in Monteverdi's older vein, and the only sign of the *stile concitato* comes in the passage actually setting the word 'guerra'. The passage is transient and gives way to a homophony expressive of the lover's peace while thinking about his lady. The madrigal which forms the second part of the setting is even more old-fashioned. For long passages the *basso continuo* could be removed and the harmony would remain complete. The eroticism is back, too, with chromatic scales imitated throughout the parts and declamatory sections repeated again and again to give the meaning to the words 'and thousands and thousands of times in a day I die and then am reborn'.

Hor che 'l ciel e la terra is successful because it really belongs to the *canti amorosi*, and in fact it is the second part of the eighth book that contains the most rewarding works. The madrigals for five or more voices are, as in the first part, less emotionally rich than the duets and trios, but they have a charm of their own. The two pieces marked *alla francese* are especially fresh, and *Dolcissimo uscignolo* is very effective, a charming melody given strength by the firm organization of alternating solo and *tutti* passages; and with some episodes tending towards the minor there is a touch of wistfulness which adds flavour to an otherwise contented and sweet-sounding piece. The same thing can be said of *Vago augelletto*, in which a small group of strings is added to the seven voices. The solo-tutti relationship is kept up and turned into a rondo form, and although there are some symbolic and more passionate bars for the words 'to pass the time in weeping', the same anacreontic spirit permeates the music.

The more intimate pieces—duets, trios and one quartet—are very different, and it is in these that Monteverdi's madrigalian art reaches its second climax. The trios are the lightest of the music—triple-time dance songs in the manner of a Venetian arietta but very deliberately handled and among the best of the *genre*. *Ninfa che scalza il piede* is a splendid example. One tenor first sings an arietta, with happy, regular rhythm organized into short repetitive motifs that remind us of *Tirsi e Clori*. A second tenor joins in for a new section as the lovers come together: and a touch of syncopation livens up the dance. Finally a bass is introduced and the dance continues, made more exciting by the gentle imitations in which the parts tumble one after another. And then, without interrupting the triple rhythm, a typically Monteverdian touch, the voices turn to the minor to exclaim, 'Ah, what a heart of stone', and with a dissonance here and there one voice or another anticipates the harmonies of the others.

The trios show one side of Monteverdi's musical character, the duets are equally typical of others. One of them, *Mentre vaga Angio-letta*, is a setting of a poem in praise of music and gives the composer every chance of showing off the clever external manner well known from *Zefiro torna*. 'Murmuring', 'alternating flights', 'broken accents' —one can imagine Monteverdi's delight in these opportunities for tone painting. He takes them all and gives the voices their opportunities in richly ornamented lines. The most deeply felt duets, on the other hand, are two which are shorter and in the erotic tradition. *Ardo* and *O sia tranquillo il mare* are such fine works that it is not surprising

that Vincenti printed them again in his volume of 1651. *Ardo* is in
the tradition of *O come vaghi* and *Interrotte speranze*. 'I burn', cries the
poet, 'but I burn more since I dare not tell of my passion.' Monteverdi
sets this with an expansive gesture, the harmonies remaining on the
chord of D minor as the voices rise to an immediate climax. They die
away in dissonance (as usual arrived at by separating the voices in an
imitative section) as courage fails:

The poet dares to call for help and the music surges to the upper
register of the voices. It is useless, for when he is with his lady he
would like to speak (a repeated fragment which breaks off suddenly)
and dare not. He only trembles, and as he starts to tell of his love the
words are broken on his lips:

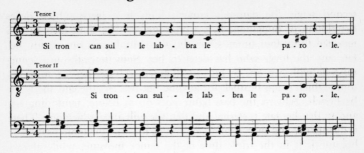

There is realism in this madrigal, but it is an inner psychological reality, an expansion of the verbal imagery made vivid especially by the sudden changes of vocal range, the growth and breaking off of the melody. *O sia tranquillo il mare* is cast in the same emotional mould, although its technique is different. The poet never leaves the cliff top, whether the sea is calm or troubled, as he laments the loss of his beloved; but Phyllis never returns, and his laments and prayers are carried away on the wind. Monteverdi, again following the Venetian aria composers, divides the piece into a recitative followed by a triple-time aria. The recitative (not perhaps a truly accurate description of it since it is always rhythmic; but it is declamatory) sets the scene: calm chords for the tranquil sea, dissonance for the lament, a cry of agony as he weeps; then the aria, not a gay dance as so often in these triple-time pieces, rather a lost bewailing in the words, 'You do not return, my Phyllis, oh, you do not return', which are repeated again and again—sometimes in a continuous flowing melody, sometimes broken short and left to suggest mere exhaustion.

These duets are masterpieces, and there is one more great work in the book. This is the *Lamento della ninfa*, written for a soprano and three male voices. Monteverdi calls it a work in the *stile rappresentativo* or theatre style, but it needs no acting, any more than did the madrigal comedies of earlier years. The men tell us the story. A nymph is lamenting outside her dwelling the loss of her lover. They are objective, though sympathetic, and their music is there only to prepare for the second stage, the nymph's lament. This is a piece which defies description or quotation. It is a chaconne with a short bass pattern repeated thirty-four times. Over this the nymph cries out against her fate and the lover who has deserted her. Sometimes the men commiserate with her, one by one, or all together. They never join in her song, which is too heartfelt for anyone but her. At the end she is left by herself. Always the bass figure goes on as before, reminding her and us that her fate is eternal and that she will always be alone. There is dissonance and marvellously expressive melody, the more passionate because it is in the triple time of the dance measure, while always avoiding the strong accents of the aria, and Monteverdi tells the singer to sing it not in strict time but 'according to the mood'. None of these devices is in itself remarkable but together they make the piece unforgettable; and when the epilogue is sung by the men in the same objective style as the prologue, the contrast is sharp, the lament being made almost unbearably intense.

The eighth book is a worthy end to the series. Like the other volumes, it is never purely fashionable, nor artificially difficult or experimental. It is impossible to discuss the madrigal as a single form, for Monteverdi managed to adapt it to a variety of purposes; and it is not very helpful to call these later works cantatas, as though they were quite different from the earlier music. It is equally unsatisfactory to assume that Monteverdi's development is in fact the development of all music over the half-century. There is one principle which informs all Monteverdi's madrigals. He would have called it 'imitation'. We may call it fidelity to the truth of the poetry. Taught him in the academies of Mantua, he never forgot it, even when his younger contemporaries bothered about it very little. It made him take the madrigal seriously to the end of his life, even in the lightest of canzonets and arias. In the madrigal there was freedom to choose the verse which music could enhance, to give an even greater variety than was possible in opera, much less in church music. For his madrigals Monteverdi deserves a proud title: a great humanist.

CHAPTER VI

THE DRAMATIC MUSIC

OPERA was very new in 1607. *Orfeo* was to be the sixth *dramma per musica* ever written. To Monteverdi the form was even newer. He may have seen one of the Florentine operas, or he may have studied one of the scores—that was all. But if opera was new, dramatic music was not; plays with music were extremely common, especially in the free courts of northern Italy. Mantua was famed for its players, Ferrara and Venice for their court entertainments. The fashionable plays at these courts by the early years of the seventeenth century were the pastorals. To the Englishman the pastoral idiom is best known through the lyric poetry of *Comus* and *Lycidas*; or in the dramatic form in *As You Like It*, where Shakespeare gently pokes fun at its conventions. The scene is always an idealized countryside, the characters are shepherds and shepherdesses. The main subject-matter is love, at first frustrated by circumstance but eventually brought to a happy ending. The shepherdess Sylvia refuses to love the shepherd Amyntas who loves her. At the climax of the play Sylvia will be reported dead, killed by a wolf, or in some other accident. Amyntas, given this news by a messenger, will despair and go away to commit suicide; whereupon Sylvia will reappear and realize on hearing of her lover's fate that she really loves him. Finally, Amyntas will come back, having failed to kill himself, and the pair will be happily united. Add to this a host of confidants, some gods and goddesses to speak a prologue and intervene at vital moments, and we have the recipe for the pastoral play.

Taken as drama the pastoral is usually far too slow and often preposterous. It is quite impossible to believe in these idealized shepherds who speak in beautiful lyrical verse and whose main interest is to convey hopeless passion at some length. When Shakespeare borrowed the pastoral idea he took care to insert some real yokels, who at least have some action in them. But such criticisms are rather beside the point. The pastorals were not considered purely as drama, and in reading them today we have only the bare bones of the entertainment. Its flesh was ornate scenery, machines and a great deal of elaborate music. The spectacle was especially important, and no expense was spared. Today it is difficult to imagine the splendour of the scene. How can we re-create in our minds the wonder and delight of the audience when they saw 'a vast and most lovely canvas painted with various animals hunted and taken in divers ways, which, upheld by a great cornice and concealing the prospect scene' took up the whole of one end of a great hall? Or their amazement at the perspective scenes in which the woods and fields seemed to stretch back to the distant horizon? Or the gorgeousness of the machines—clouds which opened to reveal gods and goddesses in the sky and which moved high across the stage?

The music for these pastorals was almost as splendid. We never possess it in its entirety, for full scores were unknown, but some of the numbers appeared in the madrigal books. The choruses, in which the voices were joined by instrumental *ensembles*, must have sounded magnificent. There were solo songs and some dances—as we know from one stage designer who insisted that the stage must be made solid enough to take the strain of the energetic *morescas*.[1] And as if this spectacle in the play were not enough, there were the intermezzos which came during the intervals and at the end of the play itself. The intermezzos had little dramatic action and their whole interest lay in the scenic designs and the machines. The gods here came into their own, and their cloud machines were ornate beyond belief. Infernal scenes where smoke and fire effects could be used were quite common. The allegorical figures of Hope and Fear and so on were carried on the stage in floats, splendidly decorated to illustrate the theme.

[1] For further descriptions see L. C. Campbell, *Scenes and Machines on the English Stage during the Renaissance* (Cambridge, 1923).

Speech was less important than songs, for there was no action to be made clear. The orchestra was often large—forty players were not uncommon—and it was used dramatically. Trombones for infernal scenes, recorders for the zephyrs, and similar effects, were the stock-in-trade of the composer. Here too there were large-scale choruses and elaborate dances. Such magnificence was bound to take up the energies of composers, not to mention the attention of the audience. 'Once', said one playwright ruefully, 'we used to have intermezzos to serve the plays. Now we have plays to serve as excuses for intermezzos.' Someone interested mainly in drama could have said much the same about the French court ballet at the time. Here again there was some dramatic action completely swamped by the interest in the spectacle. Naturally dances were of the first importance, but both drama and music had to be subordinated to the demands of the eye.

Monteverdi knew all these *genres* well; he was to write music for every one of them by the end of his life. But before his *Orfeo* came into existence there were the other five operas to make possible a drama set in continuous music. It is easy to see why the Florentine composers and theorists were dissatisfied with dramatic music in its conventional form. The plays with music mixed up with the intermezzos and the French court ballet were essentially distracted by spectacle from their principal aim—a truly dramatic action. It is also easy to see why they used recitative, for though it is true that they misinterpreted the ideas of the Greeks, their instinct was sound. If the full power of music was given only to the static moments of the play, interest would naturally concentrate there, and the conflict of action which is the basis of drama would inevitably be lost.

To regain a sense of drama in the new form the Florentines took to a process of simplification. In place of the complications of the pastoral play, with its sub-plots and large casts, they set the simple story of Orpheus and Eurydice to music. Admittedly they retained the pastoral idiom with a great deal of lyricism and the conventional happy ending. Orpheus finds his wife in Hades and thereafter there is no complication of losing her again. There is a prologue by an allegorical figure, Tragedy, which as we have seen was a common feature of the pastoral plays; and a messenger scene when the news of Eurydice's death is given is equally conventional. Some of the songs and choruses must also have seemed quite normal to the Florentine audience. Two features, on the other hand, are new. There is no sign of important orchestral music or the large number of instrumentalists assembled for the plays and intermezzos. Most important of all is the recitative in which the story is carried on.

The Florentine recitative has been much maligned. It has admittedly little variety of phrase length, since the composers nearly always stop at the end of each line of verse with a cadence. Even so, some of it is highly expressive and in the hands of intelligent singers and actors must have had an excellent effect. A juster criticism is that the composers seem to have had little conception of musical form on a broader scale. Believing that the drama must be left to do its own work they made no attempt to build up climaxes in musical terms. There can have been little in the music that the audience found really memorable, and none of the effects which can be brought about by organizing the music into the repetitive forms which give it its great emotional possibilities. In parts the audience may well have been deeply moved by the total effect of acting and music, but it is difficult to believe that it was continuously interested.

Given this background and Monteverdi's gift for intelligent borrowing, the form and manner of his new opera were almost predictable. Striggio, the librettist, must have known the poet Guarini, the most famous writer of pastorals, quite well, and the idiom of pastoral verse was second nature to him. In borrowing the idea of the Orpheus story in a pastoral version from the Florentines there may have been more than a small element of rivalry. What is interesting is that Striggio retained much more of the dramatic flavour in the story than Rinuccini had done.

First there is a prologue, sung by an allegorical figure, Music. The first act and a half are taken up with the rejoicing of shepherds and shepherdesses, including the hero and the heroine. This is purely in the pastoral lyrical tradition, and so is the first element of drama, the arrival of the messenger bearing the news of Eurydice's death.

Orpheus' reaction is again in terms of pastoral, a lyrical despair from which he emerges only slowly when he resolves to seek her in Hades. The beginning of Act III introduces another allegorical figure, Hope, who seems to have been brought in from an intermezzo, and Orpheus is led to the banks of the River Styx. There he is given an opportunity to persuade Charon to ferry him across to Hades. Charon eventually goes to sleep and Orpheus crosses the Styx. In the next act we see Orpheus in Hades. After a discussion between Pluto and Proserpina he is allowed to return to earth with his wife.

At this point Striggio, instead of surrendering the drama of the story as the Florentines had done, continues with it, in spite of the difficulty of ending it in the pastoral tradition. Orpheus must not look back on his journey; but 'though Pluto forbids it, Love commands it', sings Orpheus. He looks behind him at Eurydice and his beloved wife is claimed by death. The final act presented Striggio with a problem. A pastoral had a happy ending, the Greek story its inevitable, tragic one. Striggio instinctively preferred the strength of the original to the watered-down tragi-comedy dénouement. His first version (as we learn from the printed libretto of 1607) begins the fifth act with Orpheus in the fields of Thrace, singing a song which is echoed from a rock. This is again pure pastoral; Guarini has a splendid echo scene in *Il pastor fido*. After this, Striggio leaves the pastoral convention and becomes a purist. The Bacchants enter, and with solo and choruses bring the play to its macabre end. This, however, was too strong for Monteverdi.[1] Orpheus' echoed lament in the fields was just what he wanted. But after that he took the easier course and either wrote himself, or made Striggio write, a happy ending. The god Apollo takes pity on Orpheus and descending on a cloud takes him up to heaven, to the satisfaction of the chorus.

If this ending seems to us unsatisfactory we must remember that it

---

[1] What precisely happened between composer and librettist is unknown; but the situation is very reminiscent of that between Varesco and Mozart over *Idomeneo*. There the composer's emendations were sung, but the librettist's original verses were printed, so that the honour of both should be satisfied.

was no more preposterous than the ending of Tasso's pastoral *Aminta*, whose hero, having thrown himself over a cliff, has his fall most luckily broken half way down. Further, the last thing which the audience of a play usually saw was not the final act of the play itself, but the allegorical intermezzo which followed it. The new ending of *Orfeo* is clearly an intermezzo with the stage designer finding good use for his cloud machine. Indeed the whole opera libretto is a mixture of intermezzo and pastoral. The first two acts and the first half of the last one are completely pastoral. The prologue, the infernal scenes and the dénouement are intermezzos, all of them with splendid scenic opportunities. It is Striggio's achievement that the drama is still remarkably unified and in the third and fourth acts comes to a dramatic climax.

It is Monteverdi's achievement too, for he also welds the diverse musical elements which were suggested by Striggio's play into a unified structure. The first sign that he imagines opera in terms of the intermezzo and pastoral comes in the overture, a 'toccata' to be played on the complete orchestra. The orchestra is a large one, having fifteen string players, about a dozen brass and wind, and nine *continuo* instruments—harpsichords, a harp, lutes, organs, and a regal or reed organ. The strings are violins, violas and cellos (though there are bass viols and a contrabass viol as well), and two players have to be prepared to double on little violins (tuned an octave higher than those used today). The toccata must have sounded well, even though it is really a conventional flourish on a single chord.

When the curtain goes up to reveal the figure of Music (probably seated on some marvellously elaborate float) we hear Monteverdi's conception of monody. He uses not the pure recitative style of the Florentine operas but the *arioso* of the song-books such as Caccini's *Nuove Musiche*. Music's song is in fact an aria (in the monodist's sense), a set of strophic variations, the bass kept mainly the same for each verse while the voice varies the melody over it. The vocal melody is comparatively plain and gives its effects by different phrase-lengths and some 'affective' leaps which remind us of Monteverdi's madrigals. Intervening between each verse is a *ritornello*, a short instrumental piece rather like a pavane, to give a rondo form. There is nothing amorphous here. The music is as tightly organized as it can be, and could be played as a separate piece (it is very like *Tempro la cetra* in the seventh book of madrigals).

The prologue, on the other hand, is no test of the dramatic composer. The play itself is another matter. From the beginning of the first act we can see Monteverdi's strong desire for musical variety and form. A shepherd sets the scene with some recitative. His role is narrative and he cannot be allowed a full *continuo* madrigal. Nevertheless his recitative is well organized, and two phrases catch our attention with their brevity and isolation by rests:

When Monteverdi repeats his opening section to make a miniature *da capo* aria, it is these fragments that concentrate our attention on his formal pattern.

Then, broken only by short pieces of recitative, the shepherds' rejoicing is expressed in choruses. These are delightful. One could hardly have supposed Monteverdi capable of such charm and lightheartedness; for there is nothing like these lyrical dance songs in the madrigal-books. They are real canzonets, and are ornamental with a splendid lightness of touch which beats Gastoldi on his own ground.

Orpheus breaks into them with an *arioso*—a hymn to the sun. Again there is the same feeling of organization brought about, not this time by refrains, but by a balance of phrases, a similarity of rhythms and a large leap downwards to end each section. Then, to create the larger entity, Monteverdi repeats the choruses in the reverse order. As a coda he writes a chamber aria, setting three verses, one as a duet, the next as a trio and then a duet again, the bass each time kept roughly the same, with the melodies enriched by ornaments and a masterly variety of texture. And since the audience may not recognize the unity given by the bass, a *ritornello* again separates the verses to complete yet another rondo. The act ends with another chorus.

This act, lyrical in style and using established forms, must have been the easiest to write. The second act is much harder. The arrival of the messenger breaks the lyricism and demands a complete change of mood. The first part of it continues with the shepherds' rejoicing in the same manner as before; but it is clear that some climax must be brought about, if only to strengthen the contrast with the arrival of the tragic news. Monteverdi chooses an essentially modern means to bring it about—an aria. It is an aria in both the seventeenth-century and our modern sense of the word—a strophic song with a clear-cut melody, a strong rhythm and moving bass part to provide harmonic change. It is a *hemiolia* song, in much the same style as the *Scherzi musicali* of 1607, and like them provided with a *ritornello*. It has a splendid tune and could stand by itself as music; but, like all the best operatic music, it achieves its full significance only in its context. There is just time for a shepherd to praise the song and then the fateful messenger arrives.

Recitative is inevitable, for the messenger's news is narrative and must be understood; yet there is no loss of expressive power, rather the contrary. Monteverdi writes in a style quite different from that of the recitatives earlier in the opera. He reverts to the harmonic language of his madrigals and to the dissonance which seems to arise from a conflict between the movement of the upper part and the tardiness of the bass and its harmonies. Here his deliberate awkwardness of melody is at its finest:

The development of the scene follows the practice of Greek tragedy. The messenger at first tells the shepherds only of disaster, not of its nature. It is a shepherd who first asks her meaning. The messenger still tells only of sorrow. Orpheus himself asks her more sharply what she means. Only then in shorter and shorter phrases does she tell that Eurydice is dead. This is real musical dialogue, and the music with its curt sections and its changes of harmony as the messenger and Orpheus converse has the authentic accents of tragedy. The details of the messenger's story inevitably form a little of an anticlimax, for Monteverdi is preparing for Orpheus' own expression of grief. The description of Eurydice's death, crying 'Orfeo, Orfeo', makes one of the shepherds break out with the theme 'Ahi caso acerbo' with which the messenger had entered—a masterly touch. Orpheus' cry of despair comes in an *arioso* which ends with the helpless realization of his fate:

The dramatic action is now cast aside, and pastoral returns. The chorus of shepherds begin an elaborate *continuo* madrigal, in form like those of Book V, with duets and solos held together by a refrain for the full choir; and as a final stroke of genius, Monteverdi uses the messenger's entry theme as the bass of the refrain. Finally, the *ritornello* of the prologue returns to give the only hint that all may yet be saved.

This superb act is a remarkable achievement, the more so since so much of it had to be written in recitative and still had to avoid a lack of tension. The act which follows was so like an intermezzo in Striggio's libretto that Monteverdi probably found it more familiar. The figure of Hope leading Orpheus, the arrival at the Styx (with a boat to be pulled across) and the infernal chorus to end the scene, all offer the producer opportunities, so that such recitative as is necessary need not be so emotionally charged (though again it is well organized with refrains and never seems amorphous). The difficult moment must have been the song in which Orpheus used all the powers of music to persuade the boatman to ferry him across. Again Monteverdi uses a solo chamber aria with several verses held together by the same bass and separated from one another by instrumental interludes. With sure insight he starts his song with a virtuoso strophe, full of opulent ornamentation; and then finding the boatman still unyielding, tries even harder in a second and then a third verse, each richer in ornament than the last. This compels admiration, not pity; and as if realizing this, Orpheus sings a simpler and more natural melody, till his plea becomes a pathetic *arioso*. This in itself would be moving. The instrumental interludes make it more so. First violins, then cornetts, and then a *ritornello* from the harp reinforce the plea, until, in keeping with the general plan, the virtuosity of the soloist gives way to a small string *ensemble* which plays simple echoes of the voice.

The infernal scenes which take up the second part of this act and all the succeeding ones are musically less splendid, though with the smoke and fire of hell which the producer must have provided the total effect was probably impressive enough.[1] There is a lilting song for

[1] There is a close analogy between this scene and one of the intermezzos given during the celebrations of the wedding of the Prince of Tuscany

Orpheus to sing as he reclaims his beloved Eurydice and a very dramatic recitative when he fails to conquer his desire to see her again. The last act is less of a dramatic entity, but, as we have seen, an audience used to intermezzos would scarcely have noticed this. The first part is an echo song—a fashionable device of which scores were written in the years round 1600, but none the worse for that. Then, after Orpheus' *arioso* has reached its climax, a short instrumental piece allows Apollo to descend on a cloud machine, and the pair ascend to heaven singing an ornamental duet. A chorus and dancing (the inevitable *moresca*) end the evening's entertainment.

Orfeo has been called the first real opera, and with justice; for it was not an experimental work or the result of theorizing, as the Florentine operas had been. At the same time in using the term 'opera' there are dangers that we may expect the interests of later opera composers to be Monteverdi's also. He clearly made little attempt to produce a set of characters seen in the round, as Mozart did, or to provide vivid dramatic action. His interest was more in a series of moods, in setting poetry in a lyrical rather than a dramatic way and in preserving a basic unity of musical forms.

The score of his second opera, *Arianna*, is lost,[1] although the libretto and several versions of its greatest scene have been preserved. From Rinuccini's poem we can see the way opera was to change. He was still working in the medium of pastoral, and the prologue and the final scene, where Ariadne joins the gods as the wife of Dionysus, are pure intermezzo. Even so, there seems to be much more emphasis on the

---

described by Vasari (*Vite de' pittori*, page 340). Four horrible serpents came on the stage to the accompaniment of trombones and *violons* (double bass viols) and with smoke and fire which came from an opening in the ground. Cerberus with three heads and other monsters were seen, and finally Charon with his boat, into which the desperate Psyche entered together with Envy, Jealousy, Thought and Scorn. Similar examples can be found in other intermezzos, e.g. in the description of the marriage celebrations of Piriteo Malvezzi and Beatrice Orsina in Bologna in 1585.

[1] For a full synopsis of the plot see J. A. Westrup, 'Monteverdi's *Lamento d'Arianna*' in *Music Review*, i (1940), pages 146–7.

human beings, especially Ariadne herself. Her lament is one of Monteverdi's most moving compositions. Originally it was a solo interrupted by a chorus of fishermen, who moralize on the theme of her sadness, and again it seems likely to have been an offshoot of the *continuo* madrigals in the style of those in Book V. The recitative-arioso (which is all we have left) is clearly written in the style of the greatest moments of *Orfeo*, with strong dissonances arising between voice and harmony instruments, 'affective' intervals and refrains. Monteverdi had no compunction about repeating words, and right from the start he uses this to create balanced phrases and a natural development of the melody as melody (not just as declamation), which makes the first section of the lament, at least, unforgettable:

The loss of *Arianna* is irreparable, not merely for the historian but for music itself. The *Ballo delle ingrate* written at the same time is not consistently good, but its moments of beauty are intense enough to make us regret the loss of any music which Monteverdi wrote in this fecund time of 1608. It is an interesting work, the more so because it gives us some idea of the roots of *Orfeo*, since it is a ballet in the French style, a form known to Monteverdi perhaps since 1598. The scene, the jaws of hell, grimly lit with internal fire, is similar to that of Acts III and IV of *Orfeo*. The opening action of the ballet is a dialogue between Venus and Amor, in which Amor asks Venus to plead with Pluto to allow the *ingrate* (women who have preserved hard hearts against their lovers) to come up to earth. The resemblance to *Orfeo* becomes still more pronounced when Pluto eventually allows the *ingrate* to come to earth, to warn the ladies of the audience against a similar fate. The dialogue recitative during this part of the ballet is more interesting than moving, in spite of an attractive little *continuo* madrigal with *ritornellos* sung by Venus, and some very effective *arioso* using the deep register of Pluto's voice.

Then, quite suddenly, Monteverdi's inspiration returns. As the *ingrate* come from the fires of Hades, even Amor (whose reason for wishing to see them had been the malicious desire to gloat over them) is moved to pity, and in a short but moving duet Amor and Venus express their horror at the fate of these unloving ones. Dances in the French style ensue and at the end of them Pluto points the moral in a long *arioso* with a recurring instrumental interlude. Then, as he bids the *ingrate* return to Hades, one of the unfortunates sings a final lament, as pathetic and as powerful as Ariadne's. The ladies of the fashionable audience were moved to tears, and no wonder. For the 'cruel fate' which is so wonderfully expressed in Monteverdi's dissonant and broken *arioso* is given added point as he contrasts it with the consonance and smoothness and simplicity of the 'serene and pure air' which now the *ingrate* must leave behind for ever:

A - er   se - re - no e   pu - ro,   Ad - dio per sem - pre,   ad - di - o

This marvellous scene would probably have been lost with so much of Monteverdi's dramatic music if he had not in a mood of reminiscence included the whole *ballo* in his eighth madrigal book in 1638.

The next piece of music for the stage also survived in a madrigal book. This was the ballet *Tirsi e Clori*, written for Mantua in 1615. It is music for the stage—but hardly dramatic music, for it is purely dance song with the minimum of action. It begins with a dialogue, with Thyrsis trying to persuade Chloris to dance and Chloris resisting him. Thyrsis sings in a gay dance measure, his beloved replies in a less exuberant *arioso* and a chorus of shepherds combine with a small group of strings in a series of dances. It is a charming piece but not one of the first importance, significant mainly because it shows Monteverdi's lessening interest in recitative and his growing control of the light aria style which replaced the new music with still newer music in Venice.

In the succeeding ten years Monteverdi wrote a number of dramatic works, none of which exists today. In 1616 he was composing a *favola marittima*—in no way different from a pastoral except that it was to be performed on the water, perhaps on the Mincio at Mantua. The correspondence about this is fascinating. Monteverdi obviously believed when he received the libretto that it was to be an opera 'sung and represented in music as was *Arianna*'. From this point of view the poem was highly unsatisfactory, and in one striking passage we gain a good idea of his approach to the aesthetics of opera:

I have observed that the personages of the drama are winds, *amoretti*, *zeffiretti* and sirens, so that we shall need many sopranos: moreover that the winds—the west winds and the north winds—have to sing. How, dear sir, shall I be able to imitate the speech of the winds since they do not speak? And how shall I be able to move the passions by their means? Ariadne moved the audience because she was a woman, and equally Orpheus because he was a man and not a wind. [Musical] sounds can imitate sounds —the rushing of winds, the bleating of sheep, the neighing of horses and so on—only without using words; but they cannot imitate the speech of the winds which does not exist . . . This tale, taken all in all, does not move my feelings in the least, due perhaps to my no little ignorance, and I find it difficult to understand, nor does it inspire me to a moving climax. *Arianna* inspired in me a true lament and *Orfeo* a true supplication; but as for this libretto, I do not know what it will inspire in me.[1]

This serious view of opera is confirmed in subsequent letters, for when Monteverdi was told by Striggio that this 'maritime tale' was really a series of intermezzos he settled down to write it, and bothered only about severely practical details, though it is significant that he never finished it. But it is clear that for him opera involved certain

[1] Malipiero, op. cit., page 166.

principles. Intermezzos were much less important, for they did not involve characterization in the same way. And the demand for an inspired climax—some set piece which will act as a focal point—shows that he understood the nature of opera far better than most of his contemporaries.

The letters on the abortive *Andromeda* and the eclogue on Apollo reveal more about Monteverdi's character than about his thinking on opera; and the fragment of music for the sacred drama *La Maddalena* is also unimportant. The next work, however, we possess in its entirety, and although it is unique in form, neither opera nor intermezzo, it is of the utmost importance in his development. This is *Il combattimento di Tancredi e Clorinda* (the fight of Tancred and Clorinda), which was produced in Girolamo Mocenigo's palace in 1624 and published in the eighth book of madrigals. In the madrigal book Monteverdi tells us that it was intended to be performed during a musical evening after madrigals had been sung in the normal way, without any scenery or action to distract the eye. Clearly then, *Il combattimento* was not meant to be like any of the other music for the stage. It demands a small orchestra of strings and only three voices. The poem was not a specially written libretto, but part of Tasso's *Gerusalemme liberata*, a description of a fight between Clorinda, who disguised as a man assaults the Christian encampment, and Tancred, a crusader, with whom, finding herself cut off, she fights in single combat. Having mortally wounded her, Tancred unlooses her armour and finds that his adversary is a woman. He is stricken with grief as she dies.

The difficulty of making the piece a success as a dramatic scene lies largely in the inhibiting necessity for a narrator who is rather more important than the two characters. The attraction, on the other hand, was the great one of demonstrating the new *stile concitato*. The result is that the voice parts are comparatively inexpressive, except for the final part of the work where Clorinda dies and where the recitative blossoms forth in the way we expect from Monteverdi at moments of climax. Elsewhere the interest is in the realistic sounds of battle—fanfares, clashing of swords and Tancred's horse galloping on to the scene—rendered by all the tricks of the trade such as pizzicatos, tremolandi, sudden changes from loud to soft. For these tricks alone it is an interesting work; and for the biographer it is more so, as it reveals Monteverdi's tendency to realism which we have noticed in his letters about the *favola marittima* above (not an uncommon feature of opera composers). But in itself *Il combattimento* is not entirely a success, as the sympathy for its characters is rarely imparted to the audience. As a form, this kind of dramatic scene is a dead end—but Monteverdi, as so often, used the experience gained to good advantage in another context.

No music at all has survived of the various pageants for Mantua and Parma in which Monteverdi was engaged during the later 1620's. Our most important loss is undoubtedly the opera, *Licori finta pazza*; and since we have no trace even of Strozzi's libretto, it is difficult to know precisely the sort of problem which faced the composer. From his letters, however, we can see how his interests were developing. First, he was still trying out a theory of the affections and was trying to divide the human emotions in the way which we find in the eighth book of madrigals. Secondly, he was even more interested in characterization, and he wanted a principal figure who would be capable of several emotions within a brief space of time—hence his liking for a mad person who could simulate this in a natural way. This is an important step forward, and the results of such thinking are evident in his last operas.

After this Monteverdi had little opportunity for opera for over ten years, and by that time he was an old man of seventy. He would probably have never composed a big work again if the new opera companies of Venice had not been so successful. If the new audience was not socially very different from that to which Monteverdi was accustomed at Mantua, it was different in one significant way. It was not in the least interested in the old academic ideas. It was out for entertainment, and found it where it had always been found—in the spectacle. The scenery and the machines became even more important than before. *Orfeo* could have been produced with about five or six scenic changes. A score of them was not an uncommon number for a Venetian opera. As for the music, the audience had never heard of the discussion about the audibility of the words and the total impression of meaning and emotional sense which had resulted in the recitative style. The Venetian patricians were better acquainted with the arias in the song-books of the last two decades. As for the highly symbolical stories of the earliest operas, they were less interested in mythology and more concerned with human characters, at least in so far as the pastoral drama made them possible.

The two Venetian operas by Monteverdi which have come down to us both show the new style very well. The first of them, *Il ritorno d'Ulisse in patria* (the home-coming of Ulysses), has been held by some scholars to be a spurious work, so different is it from his earlier operas; and admittedly there are difficulties connected with it. The manuscript is now in the National Library in Vienna and no one knows when or how it came to be there. Then the libretto (in St Mark's Library in Venice) and the score are different in many particulars. Finally, it is held to be an inferior work (although this is surely flimsy evidence on which to come to any conclusion). In reply it must be said that stylistically the music is too like Monteverdi to be rejected on this evidence. There are passages in the *stile concitato*—very like the warlike madrigals of Book VIII—a plethora of duets in Monteverdi's style, the *arioso* laments and his general feeling for organization in writing recitative, and, above all, a sense of serious interest in the drama. If the work is not by Monteverdi himself, it is by someone who knew his music extremely well—not a very sensible conclusion to come to.

The story is taken from Homer. Ulysses has spent many years wandering over land and sea. His wife Penelope, though near to despair, is still waiting for him. But now he is near at hand, guided home to Ithaca by the goddess Minerva. Disguised as a beggar, he meets an old shepherd Eumetes, who helps him towards his home, although he does not as yet recognize the king. Ulysses' son, Telemachus, is also brought to meet Eumetes by Minerva, and Ulysses reveals himself. They plan to return to the court and rid Penelope of the unwanted attentions of her suitors, anxious to inherit the king's wealth. Telemachus is sent on ahead and warns Penelope that Ulysses is near. The suitors gather for a final attempt to persuade her to marry one of them, and Penelope suggests that whoever can bend Ulysses' bow shall be her husband. They try, and fail. And then Ulysses himself comes to try—as yet unrecognized by anyone at court. He kills them all with his arrows. Penelope at first cannot believe that the old man is Ulysses, in spite of the assurance of Eumetes and Telemachus; but eventually the opera ends with a triumphant recognition.

This has all the hallmarks of a Monteverdi libretto (and we know from his librettist that he moulded its shape himself in many particulars). There is the great dramatic climax of the trial scene, the situations of Penelope and of Ulysses himself which are so like that which inspired the lament in *Arianna*, a messenger scene when Telemachus arrives at court and a happy duet at the end (there is a similar one in *Poppea*). No less Monteverdian are the complicating features. The audience's need of the grand spectacle suggested to him the use of the old form of intermezzos. So we find a prologue with the allegorical figures of Human Frailty, Fortune and Love, who sing their rather irrelevant introduction in the form of a set of strophic variations (in exactly the same way that Music had introduced *Orfeo*). And at various points in the drama there are interpolations from the gods—especially from Neptune, who gives some excellent opportunities for spectacular sea machines (to make it almost a *favola marittima* like *Le nozze di Tetide*). As usual there had to be some link between gods and humans, and this is provided by Minerva, who carries out the wishes of the gods by turning from time to time into human form. In other words, the opera is again a story with intermezzos, as *Orfeo* had been. From the point of view of the stage manager, this form offers tremendous opportunities, and the score abounds with directions for machines and stage business of one kind and another. From the audience's point of view, it makes the basic progress of the opera a little too diffuse to be really satisfactory. This is a pity since it means that some of Monteverdi's most splendid music will rarely be heard in its proper surroundings.

The outstanding feature of *Orfeo* was the way Monteverdi crowded into it all the musical forms known in 1607, to express a totality of human emotion. *Il ritorno d'Ulisse* does exactly the same thing in terms of 1640. The Venetian ariettas, the older virtuoso *arioso*, the *madrigali*

guerrieri, the strophic variation songs, the chamber duets—all are used
to express the varied situations. There even seems to be a rather rough
but effective idea of characterization in music. The gods, for example,
usually maintain their dignity in the *arioso*-recitative of the older
operas and intermezzos. Neptune in fact is the natural successor of
Charon and Pluto (of *Il ballo delle ingrate*), a deep bass whose words are
ponderously painted in conventional musical images, with sudden
changes of register. All the gods have highly ornamented and virtuoso
parts and are deliberately denied the smoother aria rhythms which
would rob them of their superhumanity. Only Minerva is allowed to
sing pretty tunes, and only when she appears in human clothes.

Similarly Penelope, unhappy and beset with troubles until the very
last scene, is given her character in highly charged emotional recitative.
In the first scene we have a re-creation of the glories of Ariadne's
lament. Not so dissonant as the model, Penelope's plaint gains its
effects by changes in tempo, variations of phrase length and repetitions
of phrases. The first climax with its rising sequences of despair and
fall of a sixth reminds us so strongly of Monteverdi's earlier music that
it is difficult to believe it is by any other composer:

The whole scene is as tightly organized as ever, with the occasional
use of memorable fragments to make refrains and give musical power

to the recitative. Ulysses is introduced in a similar *scena*, and with recitative scarcely less poignant and powerful. But since in subsequent scenes he is led homewards by Minerva and therefore given hope and a purpose for living, he tends to interrupt the recitative with songs—rarely complete in themselves but expressive of his mood. His music is precisely what Monteverdi had planned in setting the libretto of *Licori*, full of sudden changes to express the detail of the words.

This shows the fine concern for the drama which had been Monteverdi's all his life; and it is confirmed in yet another way. The soliloquy is now less important than the dialogue. Every scene, even if it contains an important aria, manages to weave in an interplay of characters and gives them conversation which is significant dramatically. People talk to people, rather than as in *Orfeo* to the world in general; and this makes it an opera of *ensembles* (as all successful operas are). Not for nothing had Monteverdi written so many duet madrigals. *Il ritorno d'Ulisse* adds to their number. Perhaps the most beautiful of them is the one where Ulysses meets his son Telemachus. It begins in a passionate recitative style and gradually becomes *arioso*, full of the melting suspensions which Monteverdi uses in his most magical chamber duets:

Scarcely less beautiful are the duets between Eumetes and Ulysses in an earlier scene and the final love duet. Both are written mellifluously in triple time, and the first of these is a chaconne of impeccable technique:

Although these pieces and the arias could come straight out of the song-books of the 1630's, they never caused Monteverdi to lose sight of the larger formal patterns required in each scene, and he seeks out every opportunity to give large-scale organization to the music as he had done in *Orfeo*. The scene where the suitors plead with Penelope to marry them is a gift to the composer, who can repeat her refusals and punctuate their individual appeals with a thrice repeated *continuo* madrigal. In the scene where Penelope tests them with Ulysses' bow the relationship of aria and recitative is especially useful. In each case the suitor's aria comes first, to express his confidence. It is only when he tries and fails that the recitative comes—usually broken into short phrases to give the impression of breathlessness. Ulysses, on the other hand, starts in recitative and then breaks into aria as he succeeds; and a *sinfonia da guerra* as he deals with his foes is a particularly effective way of using the *stile concitato*.

Even now we have not mentioned half the beauties or the variety of character to be found in the opera—Penelope's maid, for example, who sings a lovely duet with her lover in the first act, using all the arts of the chamber duet; long-held notes on the voices while the harmonies go on underneath, quasi-recitative, *arioso* and triple-time aria, the last for a particularly seductive refrain; or Iro, the suitors' toady, who has to run away after Ulysses has returned to court and who parodies all the passionate tricks of the virtuoso singer in a scene which deliberately offsets the climax of the opera. Yet, in a way, this very variety is a weakness. The plot never develops steadily as *Orfeo* had done. It is too fussy, and lacks that overwhelming central point which Monteverdi had sought for in his earlier operas. Though it is always dangerous to condemn an opera which one has never seen on the grounds that its drama is not strong enough, it is not too much to say that if *Il ritorno d'Ulisse* is not produced today, the libretto is responsible more than the music.

There is no such excuse for neglecting Monteverdi's last opera, *L'incoronazione di Poppea*. Monteverdi and his librettist, Busenello, chose a historical subject—for the first time in the history of opera. This has some significance for the development of the *genre*; but it was not so important to Monteverdi, to whom Ariadne and Penelope were just as real as Poppaea. What is really significant is that in *L'incoronazione* the intermezzo elements have been considerably reduced. There is the customary allegorical prologue, and allegorical figures appear in the body of the opera. Yet they are interwoven into the progress of the play and never stand completely outside it as the gods do in *Il ritorno d'Ulisse*. Similarly, although there are many possibilities for scenic changes and a splendid production, the drama is developed in longer sections, scene leading into scene in a natural way. There is far less of the fussiness which mars the earlier work, and the dramatic unity is never abandoned merely for the glories of the producer. It is, in fact, a libretto which conforms to most of the criteria which we apply today, and in spite of a large cast there is never over-complication either of plot or character. Variety of human emotion was Monteverdi's principal aim in all his later operas, and in *L'incoronazione* he finds the most dramatic method for exploiting it. In this libretto the same situations affect different characters in different ways. There is a real conflict and hence a real opportunity for the

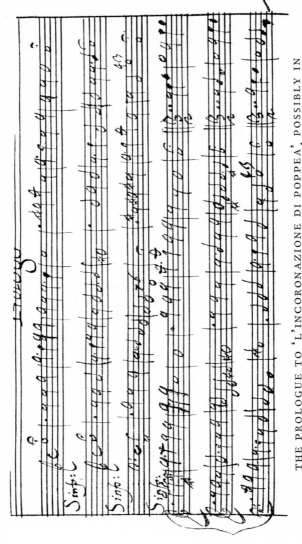

THE PROLOGUE TO 'L'INCORONAZIONE DI POPPEA', POSSIBLY IN
MONTEVERDI'S HANDWRITING

musician to build up characters in a consistent way. The story is taken from Tacitus and moulded into significant scenes, each carefully chosen for its musical possibilities.

Otho, returning from a journey of state, comes home to find soldiers guarding his house. He guesses what has happened. Nero is in love with his wife Poppaea and is visiting her. This is confirmed by the soldiers' conversation and, as the day dawns, by the appearance of Nero with Poppaea herself in the garden. Nero is loath to leave her, but dare not risk a scandal as yet. He declares that he will divorce his wife Octavia and then all will be well. Left alone, Poppaea becomes less the loving woman and shows her vicious ambition. 'Hope and fortune are on my side', she sings. Her nurse, Arnalta, who has joined her in the garden, warns her that these are not the best of allies. We now have a companion scene where Octavia, far from being confident and ambitious, regrets Nero's infidelities. She consults Seneca about her possible courses of action, but his counsel is merely to bear her burden stoically—little comfort indeed either to Octavia or to her page who is standing by her. These two depart, leaving Seneca alone; and suddenly the goddess Pallas Athene is heard (no doubt from some great cloud machine) telling Seneca that he will die that day. He is unmoved by this and looks forward to a better life.

At this point Nero enters (and we notice how Seneca acts as a focal point for several consecutive scenes). Nero tells Seneca that he has resolved to divorce Octavia and marry Poppaea. Seneca warns him that the people will be displeased. Nero becomes petulant and shouts that he cares nothing for the people or for anyone else. He tells Seneca sharply to go away. Poppaea enters (Nero acting as the link between scenes this time) and the two of them sing another love duet. Having put Nero in a good mood, Poppaea then whispers slanders against Seneca, who she fears is an obstacle to her ambitions. Nero orders a soldier to go to Seneca with the sentence of death. Nero departs and Otho enters to make a last attempt at reconciliation with Poppaea (now the linking personality in her turn). She will have nothing to do with him and Otho thinks darkly of murdering her. After his soliloquy Drusilla, one of the ladies of the court and in love with

Otho, comes in and manages to make him say that he loves her. But, 'Drusilla's name is on my lips, Poppaea's is in my heart', he sings. With this the first act ends.

Act II is in three main sections. The first is constructed around Seneca, who receives warning of his impending death from Mercury (the cloud machine again), and then the death sentence comes, borne by Nero's captain. Seneca's friends plead with him not to die, but he bids them prepare his bath, in which he will open his veins and bleed to death. Before the second section there is an intermezzo (in the modern sense)—a flirtation between the page-boy and the young girl; this is clearly to allow for the passage of time. Then we see Nero again with some friends, now celebrating Seneca's death with ribald glee. The third part of the act is taken up with Otho, now almost deter-mined upon the murder of his wife. His doubts are finally overcome by Octavia, who equally wants Poppaea out of the way. They plot to dress up Otho as a woman: in this disguise he is to gain entrance to Poppaea's room. They leave, and we next see Drusilla, happily confident in the love of Otho. He enters to borrow her clothes, which she gives him quite willingly. Now the moment of murder approaches. The scene is again Poppaea's garden, where she falls asleep while her nurse sings a lullaby. Then the god of love enters and sings yet another lullaby. The disguised Otho comes in and is just about to strike when the god (perhaps with an intricate movement of the cloud machine) stops him. Poppaea wakes up, and seeing the prospective murderer running away thinks it was Drusilla.

The final act begins with an aria by Drusilla. She is interrupted by Poppaea's nurse, who comes in with guards and identifies her as the attacker. Drusilla protests her innocence but Nero enters and threatens her with tortures if she does not tell the plot. She confesses to the crime to save her beloved Otho. Nero is ordering an exceptionally cruel death for her as Otho himself arrives, to confess his own guilt and Octavia's. Nero, realizing that it is Octavia who is ultimately to blame, banishes Otho, who departs with Drusilla. Nero announces his divorce and the banishment of Octavia. The final scene is the brilliant coronation of the new empress, Poppaea.

This detailed synopsis of the plot reveals some of the reasons why it is a masterpiece. The excellence of the libretto lies in the way it avoids unnecessary explanations and makes the reasons of the heart compelling. Nero, for example, acts in a predictable way in every situation and is seen in enough differing situations to appear as a complete man. He is amorous but sad on leaving Poppaea, petulant when Seneca disagrees with him, cruel with Drusilla, revoltingly gay with his friends and amorous and content at the end of the opera. Equally, Poppaea is flirtatious, ambitious and hard, triumphant and sensuously happy in turn. Monteverdi's power in expressing these differing emotions is beyond all praise. At the places where we expect him to be good he is magnificent—as in the love duets which derive from the madrigal books and yet outdo them in sensuousness. And it is the music which gives great variety to the love-making. The opening duet between Nero and Poppaea is full of longing, dissonances and minor harmonies predominating, and fragments of aria always being interrupted by recitative. The two voices never sing together, and their motif 'addio' is repeated time after time in harmonies which do not resolve, as they cannot break away from one another. Their final duet, on the contrary, is a smooth chaconne, the dissonances always resolving promptly and the melody continuous even when shared between the voices. The harmony has the usual richness of Monteverdi's duets, and as the bass repeats itself so their happy love seems endless.

Neither of these is like the duet between Nero and Lucan when, Seneca dead, the bachelor party thinks lustfully of Poppaea's charms. Again Monteverdi writes a triple-time chaconne, but this time while Lucan sings a *bel canto* melody, Nero can do no more than gasp, 'Ah what a destiny', in single notes or short phrases:

The love duet between the page and the girl which comes just before this in Act II is also completely different. This is light-hearted flirtation, the boy singing a song which might have come out of the *Scherzi musicali*, the girl taking it more seriously and more confidently in a smooth triple-time aria before they finally join rapturously together.

As always, there are laments, and very fine ones. Of the several set pieces the one sung by Octavia, leaving Rome for ever, inevitably reminds us of *Arianna*. Compounded of short pregnant phrases, it makes the same use of dissonance and has the same power of changing its mood rapidly, by changing from declamation to *arioso*. Drusilla's agony when falsely accused is shorter and part of a dialogue but is not less taut and gripping. Otho's opening scene is equally expressive. He starts in happy *arioso* as he asks Poppaea to open the door of the balcony, even breaking into a felicitous aria. Then he sees the soldiers. The recitative at once becomes agonized, broken and dissonant, and at its climax becomes obsessed with a tiny motif as the librettist piles up the appealing phrases: 'I am that Otho who followed you, who longed for you, who served you—that Otho who adored you.' These are offshoots of Monteverdi's earlier music. There are other moments which are quite unexpected. The use of the *stile concitato* is new, for it not only occurs to express the usual external images of war (as when the soldiers are talking in Act I) but also to conjure up the emotions of wrath and cruelty. Nero's anger when Seneca refuses to fall in with his wishes provokes an outburst which shows very clearly the imma‑turity of a monarch who has always had his own way:

A similarly pungent passage comes when Drusilla is interrogated in the last act.

The trio in Act II is also unusual for Venetian opera. Sung by Seneca's friends imploring him not to commit suicide, it is a most moving chromatic piece which culminates in a series of agonized cries: 'Non morir, non morir, Seneca, no!' The final surprise, perhaps, is the memorability of the melody. Not that Monteverdi had ever been untuneful, but in this opera he surrenders a number of times to the charms of the Venetian song‑books. Poppaea's aria after Nero has gone in Act I, Drusilla's song (a perfect *da capo* aria) as she awaits Otho, and the two lullabies in Act III are extremely attractive in themselves. These and the others are mainly in triple time, and because of their clear rhythm and lucid diatonic melody (although Monteverdi has a mannerism of juggling with alternate major and minor thirds), they stick effortlessly in the mind.

'Ariadne moved the audience because she was a woman, and

equally Orpheus because he was a man and not a wind.' This philosophy reaches its most practical realization in *L'incoronazione di Poppea*. Like Mozart and Verdi, Monteverdi saw that it was necessary to have a sufficiently large and contrasting cross-section of humanity with which to create the world of opera, and that all the resources of music would be needed to bring these characters to life. The only larger criticism which can be brought against the opera is that the strange morality of ancient Rome is too vividly drawn. The characters and situations are so alive that to end with the glorification of an evil couple at first sight seems rather revolting. And yet it is satisfying. As Wagner said of the ending of *Götterdämmerung*, when it was pointed out to him that with the gold returned to the Rhine-maidens there was no reason why the gods should perish, the emotional logic of art demands the destruction of Valhalla. Monteverdi also knew this kind of logic. *L'incoronazione di Poppea* is a great opera.

CHAPTER VII

THE CHURCH MUSIC

THE obsession of the last hundred and fifty years with the music of Palestrina and his followers has almost completely obscured the complexity of church music in the later sixteenth century. Counter-Reformation church music has the same complications as the Counter-Reformation itself. The Roman Church could have within its ranks evangelists with such differing methods as the Oratorians of St Philip Neri and the Jesuits. Its church musicians contain equally diverse figures. Palestrina, Victoria, the Gabrielis, Lassus and the host of cathedral musicians seem at times to have little in common with one another. To try to see them as part of a single movement is to despair of finding a general pattern. If there is a common denominator to be found, it is one of principle rather than of style or technique. The principle is a familiar one—that the words must fertilize the music and not act merely as its excuse. This was the demand of the Council of Trent no less than of the humanists who helped opera to come into being. But principle is one thing; its application is another. Just as the interpretations of the Greek theorists gave rise to a host of differing musical styles, so in church music we can find several interpretations of the basic idea, all of them valid and defensible.

There was, first of all, the demand that the words should be audible. The church had its own monody ready made in plainsong. Palestrina and one of his colleagues, Zoilo, were set to revise the missal and breviary. Then as now, plainsong was not always sung unaccompanied. The support of the organ was quite often needed, and this gave rise to yet another sort of music in which the words were heard clearly—the harmonized chanting known as *falso bordone*. Here the composer provided some simple chords and left the words to be chanted in speech rhythm, breaking into polyphony only at the end of each section of the text. This, at least, was the theory. In practice, singers found it far too elementary to satisfy their desires and they often added

ornaments to the chant in an ornate, not to say extravagant, manner.[1]
Falso bordone was the favoured medium in setting the psalms for
vespers. Its popularity probably rested on simplicity of performance,
and scores of books were published in the later years of the century.

Audibility was a prime consideration in the other popular outlet
for composition, the *missa brevis*. Here the composer admittedly
imposed a musical rhythm on the words, but in the *Gloria* and *Credo*
at least he followed the injunction 'to every syllable a note' (the phrase
is Archbishop Cranmer's, and it is interesting to see similar ideas
developing in the music of the liturgies of the Roman and Anglican
faiths). Elsewhere in the Mass the composer was allowed imitative
counterpoint and melismatic melody. Even so, the *missa brevis* shows
a strong tendency towards homophonic writing and therefore an
increased interest in harmonic devices. This is not to say that the
tradition of conventional polyphony disappeared, merely that it was not
alone. Yet it too shows some effect of counter-reform in the widening
gap between secular and religious music. Gone were the parody Masses
on secular songs. Thematic material was now taken from plainsong or
polyphonic motets. Palestrina's conscious attempts to produce consonant harmony from smoothly flowing melodic lines contrast powerfully with the growing dissonance and rugged melody of the madrigal.
The asceticism of the Jesuits has its counterpart in this music.

But the asceticism of the Jesuits was achieved through the sensuous
Spiritual exercises of St Ignatius Loyola. Nor were they averse to
using the sensuousness of art to impress and overwhelm the common
people. This too has its counterpart in the splendid church music
written for the ducal chapels of northern Italy. These had the resources
to give church music a glamour which, if it reflected the glory of the
prince or doge, was not unsuitable for praising an all-powerful God.
Castrati, a big choir and a large group of instrumentalists could
stimulate the church composer's imagination as well as that of an
opera composer or madrigalist. In St Mark's in Venice and St
Barbara in Mantua this was exploited to the full.

[1] The Sistine Chapel's singing of Allegri's *Miserere* in Holy Week is a
good example of how it was done.

Wert's church music, for example, shows that he made virtually no distinction between secular and religious music. When in his early life he was composing in a predominantly Netherlandish style, his church music was contrapuntal in the traditional way. But there is none of the asceticism of Palestrina about it. It is full of rhythmic life, with jaunty syncopations and cross-rhythms, and its harmony has that lively roughness which disappears from contrapuntal music only when the Roman school has become the chosen model. When Wert's madrigal style changes about 1580, his church music changes with it. The expression of the words becomes all important, and dissonance and chromaticism are as essential a part of his church music as of his madrigals, e.g. in the motet, *Vox in Rama*:

The large awkward leaps which we have seen in such madrigals as *Solo e pensoso* appear in the motets too, and for the same purpose. For joyful moments Wert's natural virility of rhythm turns almost to dance music, as rolling sequential phrases produce clear-cut strong accents, e.g. in *Amen, amen*:

In this later music of Wert and in the motets of the younger men, Pallavicino and Gastoldi, the Venetian style begins to predominate. This is based on the *cori spezzati*—choirs widely separated in the church and alternating with one another throughout a motet or

Mass. In the first place this means of expression, based as it was on ancient Jewish practice and simple in its homophonic declamation of the words (necessary to ensure *ensemble* at all), might well have been ordered by the reformers of Trent. By the 1580's, however, it had become rather debased. The Venetian love of orchestral colour saw that the emphasis was placed less on the words than on the grandeur of effect. Some of the 'choirs' now became groups of instruments with soloists placed among them. From these special effects were produced. Echo music was one favourite, even though it almost blasphemously turned 'clamor' to 'amor' and 'clamat' to 'amat'. Dialogue motets dramatizing the speeches of saints and apostles were also popular. As for the orchestra, it took its part in sumptuous canzonas and sonatas played during the Mass or vespers. There was, then, a tremendously varied choice before the composer of church music. In practice his style was conditioned as always by the resources to hand. At Cremona, for example, Ingegneri hardly needed to concern himself with the grand manner. He had instrumentalists for some of the greater festivals, but of necessity his music grew out of small resources. His music naturally follows the contrapuntal school, rather less austere than Palestrina's and more like the earlier church music of Wert. He is not averse to an occasional chromaticism, but expressiveness is not his main consideration.

Monteverdi's *Sacrae cantiunculae*, the work of a boy of fifteen, are an offshoot of such conservatism. They are *tricinia*, that is, motets for three voices; and this, coupled with the fact that the texts in question are for the most part unliturgical, suggests that they were probably meant for private devotions rather than for public performance. For domestic singing they are ideal. The melodic lines are always interesting—a thing not to be taken for granted at a time when composers were becoming more concerned with the total effect of vocal colour. Nor are they ever really difficult, for they remain largely diatonic and are constructed from the more familiar motifs and decorative figures. Monteverdi at this stage in his career was rather inconsistent in the way that he decorated unimportant words with melismas while often ignoring expressive ones; but this is something we might expect of a boy, for the manipulation of words is often no little embarrassment to a beginner whose main concern is making the counterpoint fit together. As for the counterpoint itself, it is very efficient indeed, with a pure consonant harmony and the skilfully overlapping phrases which maintain the contrapuntal flow. The *Sacrae cantiunculae* are not works of genius. It is enough that they are indistinguishable from countless other *tricinia* of the epoch.

At Mantua the choice became a real one. Everything was known there. We know from the descriptions of Duke Vincenzo's coronation that Wert commanded resources of Venetian sumptuousness. From the publications of Pallavicino and Gastoldi we learn that *falso bordone*, separated choirs and large contrapuntal music were used in St Barbara. Whether Monteverdi added to these works is not known. It seems probable that until Gastoldi left for Milan in 1609 his duties led him only to compose chamber music and opera. By the time that he did come to compose church music, the choice had widened even further, for the *basso continuo* altered church music just as much as it had changed the madrigal. Not that it altered the spirit of church music very much. Viadana's *Concerti* of 1602 are very like the older motets in their melodic writing and their harmonies. They spread the melodic writing among fewer voices and rid themselves of constant imitations. Apart from this they can have sounded very little different from some of the more harmonically conceived *a cappella* motets.

In the larger-scale works much the same thing happened. The Venetian composers now accompanied their soloists with the organ and added groups of soloists to the possible variety of groupings. By the ingenious positioning of these groups the soloists were not drowned by the *ripieno* voices and instruments, and sudden dramatic contrasts were obtained. The only novelty in technique was the increasing sectionalism which soloists engendered. One or two composers took advantage of the contrast between solo passages and *tutti* to insert duets and trios which were more or less complete in themselves and were punctuated by refrains sung by the choir. Finally, there was a continuation of the tradition of secularized church music and the sacred madrigal. Naturally enough the modern equivalent was to introduce monodic techniques into motets—declamatory lines, virtuoso ornaments, rich dissonant harmonies and the rest. This happened rather slowly, largely because the early composers of monody were courtiers and singers, while the church musicians were professional composers; but by about 1608 true sacred monodies were appearing, usually under titles like *Sacri affetti* or *Ghirlanda sacra*, deliberately non-committal about liturgical usage. The texts of these sacred songs come mainly from biblical sources rather than from the liturgy, and mirror the secular song in emotional richness. Like Monteverdi's *Sacrae cantiunculae* they were probably more often heard in the private chambers of the nobility and such members of the higher clergy who had virtuoso singers among their retinue.

The new never replaces the old suddenly, especially in church music, where traditions have always been treasured more than elsewhere. Even so, to find the profusion of styles and techniques that we have in Monteverdi's volume of 1610 is surprising. A Mass in the old polyphonic style, a set of vesper psalms in the grand manner, and a group of monodic *sacri affetti*—these are unusual bedfellows even for this period of change.[1] The explanation is not hard to seek. Trying to find a job outside Mantua he determined to show that he was competent in all fields and was fit for a post either in conservative Rome or scintillating Venice. It is no surprise that the collection was

---

[1] The contents are described as follows on the title-page:

> Missa senis vocibus
> ad ecclesiarum choros
> Ac Vespere pluribus decantandae
> cum nonnullis sacris concentibus
> ad Sacella sive Principum Cubicula accommodata.

That is to say: 'Mass for six voices suitable for church choirs, and vespers to be performed by larger forces (together with some motets) suitable for chapels or the apartments of princes.' In accordance with normal Latin usage *accommodata* goes with both *Missa* and *Vespere*.

never reprinted. Its size and contents suggest that it was a presentation volume, not meant for ordinary practical use.

That the Mass should be written in *a cappella* polyphony is not surprising in a book to please the Roman taste. The form the poly-phony takes is a little overwhelming. Monteverdi takes ten themes from a motet of Gombert (nothing recent or popular, we notice) and then works these out in the strictest possible way. There is none of Palestrina's rapturous delight in choral colour nor Wert's expressive-ness of the words—and no homophonic climax. The work is thick with imitative points. Voices are given rests only to emphasize new imitations, regardless of their breath capacity or proneness to be tired. The only sign of modern taste is in the regularity of the melody, in which the old modal system is replaced by the diatonic scales and sequences, and square rhythms appear quite often. The virility of Netherlandish rhythm and the bite of dissonance are both lacking, and since Monteverdi refuses to make clear even such contrasts as exist between 'Crucifixus' and 'Et resurrexit', the result is a curiously emasculated work. It was a work of great learning for Monteverdi to write, and it sounds like it. Only occasionally, as in the 'Hosanna', does it sound at all natural and alive.

The vespers music reveals Monteverdi's real inclination. This is indeed the work of a North Italian court musician. The big orchestra, the solo singers and the choir are all there, and the music reflects the worldly grandeur of prince and doge.[1] And whereas no one could find anything Monteverdian in the 'Gombert Mass', the vespers bear the imprint of his style, above all in the taste for compromise—the interest in putting old means to new uses. Separated choirs, *falso bordone*, the traditional Venetian canzona are the materials. Every one of them is given a new twist. The opening versicle and response, *Domine ad*

[1] The word 'big' is relative. If, as is probable, the vesper psalms were his test pieces for St Mark's, Venice, it is of interest to note that the account books show that he had an orchestra of six resident players and twenty specially hired for the occasion, and a choir of about twenty-five. Two extra organs had to be brought from St Mark's Seminary.

adiuvandum, for example, is really written in *falso bordone*. The choir chants on a single chord except at the very end. This is conventional enough. If the instruments had doubled them in some way it would have been completely conventional. But Monteverdi has given them music of their own to play—an adaptation of the toccata which had opened *Orfeo*. As an instrumental piece it is sonorous; with a choir adding sonority but not any thematic material to distract the ear from it, its splendour is increased.

The five psalm settings use an equally traditional technique, that of the *cantus firmus*. Each is founded on a psalm-tone, which is repeated several times, often altered very freely in rhythm. Super-imposed on this pattern is one of the common techniques of the early seventeenth century. In the first one, *Dixit Dominus*, the pre-dominant method is to mingle passages in *falso bordone* with duets and trios for solo voices. The organ bass over which these solos develop is the *cantus firmus*, giving the effect of strophic variation in the manner of the *continuo* madrigal. Each *falso bordone* section flowers into the traditional polyphony, which is expanded by instrumental repetition. These sections at first sight seem more revolutionary than they really are. One dance-like passage is in fact almost identical with Wert's motet *Amen, amen* quoted above (page 134); another is a common contrapuntal tag; yet another, highly ornamented, merely writes down what had been improvised by singers for many years, as a glance at the treatises on ornaments shows us. Even the solo sections are restrained—Viadana-like rather than secular in origin.

The first page of *Laudate pueri* looks quite conservative. It develops in the manner of a large contrapuntal piece by Andrea Gabrieli, announcing its plainsong theme with a jaunty rhythm and working it to a climax in polyphony. Only then does Monte-verdi start with the *concertato* technique which reminds us of the fifth book of madrigals. A series of trios ensues, one part singing the plainsong, the others decorating extravagantly. This is really secular in style; and after some double-choir interjections in triple time there is a voluptuous duet which is very like parts of *Ahi come a un vago sol*:

N.B. The right hand of the organ doubles the voices.

Laetatus sum uses a similar technique, except that here Monteverdi gives an added importance to the organ bass, which gives out a theme in crotchets and acts as an anchor in much the same way that the plainsong had done in *Dixit Dominus*. The actual chant is split up among the voices as the piece proceeds. Again Monteverdi draws clear contrasts, this time between the quasi-contrapuntal trios and quartets and sections in which *falso bordone* is left either as a simple chant or as the basis for voluptuous improvisation.

The other two psalms are more conventional. *Nisi Dominus* is a big double-choir setting in which the *cantus firmus* appears in long notes in the tenor part of each choir. Although the use of *cori spezzati* hardly ever fails to fascinate, the piece is constructed in too long sections, with a great deal of repetition, and lacks the cut and thrust of Gabrielian dialogue. The sonorities of the final climax are magnificent, but it is not consistently interesting. *Lauda Jerusalem*, on the other hand, is very exciting throughout. Though it uses contrasting groups from time to time, it is really a piece in the manner of Wert. The smooth unexciting rhythms of Palestrina are quite foreign to it, and the syncopations are given added force by a regularly changing harmony.

To match the grandeur of these psalms in the hymn *Ave maris stella* presented Monteverdi with a new problem. Hymns were normally sung in plainsong in Venice, and the only models to hand were the rather old-fashioned settings by Wert. Monteverdi's setting of the first verse is rather like these, with its eight independent lines following their own rhythms to give a complicated texture in which the rhythmicized plainsong in the *cantus* part is sometimes a little obscured. Then he has a brilliant new idea. He turns the plainsong, one of the most beautiful of hymn melodies, into a song in triple time, engagingly serene in its balanced, *hemiolia* accentuation. One choir sings a simple harmonization of it; the other repeats it; and then three soloists (the bass as usual being left out) sing in their turn, accompanied by the organ. In between these middle verses a *ritornello* in triple time is given to the instruments to provide a rest from the tune. The opening contrapuntal setting rounds off the piece in the final verse.

All this music is liturgical. The *Sonata sopra Sancta Maria* is only loosely so. The words 'Sancta Maria, ora pro nobis' come from the litany of the Blessed Virgin, but the idea of an orchestral piece around them is purely north Italian. Monteverdi borrowed it from a Ferrarese composer called Crotti. A fragment of plainsong is sung by a soloist eleven times. Around it the instruments play a *canzona francese* complete with the stereotyped rhythm and *da capo* form which are its hallmarks. These are the bare bones of the piece; but such a bald description does no justice to the tremendous invention that Monteverdi brings to it. Whereas Crotti's piece had been a small-scale chamber *canzona*, Monteverdi turns it into a splendid sonata in the Venetian manner—in fact, one of the largest orchestral pieces of its time. We have a swinging tune which turns into a triple-time variation in the way in which a pavane becomes a galliard, a series of *ensembles* in which each separate element of the orchestra is exploited to the full, virtuoso dotted rhythms and sequential phrases, and the initial *canzona* tune forming a climax by being played simultaneously with the plainsong *cantus firmus* at the end. Here is a magnificence which Crotti never knew.

Magnificence and splendour are recurring words in any account of this vespers music. They represent something quite new in Monteverdi's work. In the madrigals it is an intimate power which he commands, and grandeur is an extension of his range. The natural continuation of his earlier style is to be found in the *sacri affetti* (interspersed among the psalms) and the Magnificats which complete this volume of church music. The four motets for soloists were the first chamber music by Monteverdi in the style of the 'new music' to be published, and they show that the seventh book of madrigals of almost ten years later was given lengthy preparation.

The one solo motet, *Nigra sum*, is a setting of some voluptuous verses from the *Song of Songs*:[1] 'I am black, but comely, O ye daughters of Jerusalem. Therefore the king hath loved me and hath brought me in to his chambers and hath said to me: "Rise up, my love, and com eaway."' The relationship of the text to the words of Monteverdi's secular music needs no explanation. He puts on his finest *seconda prattica* manner and writes a monody which might well come from an opera. His capacity for inventing the memorable phrase, for fitting the music to the detail of the words, is displayed at its best. This can hardly be shown more completely than in the way Monteverdi isolates the king's words, 'Rise up, my love', with a preliminary rest, and then writes rapturously persuasive music for the constant repetition of the word 'surge', the shortening phrases melting into the continuous climactic phrase:

[1] A conflation of i. 4–5 and ii. 10.

As in the recitatives of *Orfeo*, the musical shape is always of primary importance. The motif set to the words 'Nigra sum' inevitably comes again, and the final section of the motet is repeated, even though there is no reason for it in the words.

The duet, *Pulchra es*, is another setting of verses from the *Song of Songs*. It is Monteverdi's first chamber duet and it needs little description here simply because it shows complete mastery of all the technical devices of the duets in the later madrigal books. The second voice amplifies the phrases, gives harmonic fullness and expands the scale of the music in just the same way. There is the same ability to organize the ornaments of the melody into satisfying patterns, and to change the mood abruptly with an alteration of harmony or a move from *arioso* to declamation. This is fine music and is capped only by a yet finer motet, *Duo Seraphim*. If it were not for its tenor clefs, this would look like a piece for the Ferrara ladies who so bored the ambassador Urbini. All the resources of ornamentation are deployed—sobbing trills, dotted notes and scale-wise melismas—and given to all the three voices they produce a marvellously rich effect. We are meant to admire the virtuosity, and we do. But true greatness is given to the piece by other things: the way the third voice, brought in to express the mystery of the Three (a triad) in One (a unison), is then retained for the repetition of the word 'Sanctus', making it still richer and more flowing; and the opening of the motet itself with its wonderful series of suspensions:

With *Audi, coelum* we come to the almost inevitable echo piece. But this does not remind us of the Venetian choral dialogues. It is a descendant of a piece by Peri for a Florentine intermezzo. The descending sixth in the melody, the passionate reiteration of the word 'Maria'

SELVA
MORALE E SPIRITVALE

DI CLAVDIO MONTEVERDE

Maeſtro Di Capella della Sereniſſima
Republica Di Venetia

DEDICATA

ALLA SACRA CESAREA MAESTA DELL' IMPERATRICE

ELEONORA

GONZAGA

Con Licenza de Superiori & Priuilegio.

SOPRANO   Primo

IN VENETIA MDCXXXX
Appreſſo Bartolomeo Magni

THE TITLE-PAGE OF THE 'SELVA MORALE E SPIRITUALE', THE LAST
PUBLICATION OF MONTEVERDI'S MUSIC DURING HIS LIFETIME

each time decorated anew and the careful declamation are the results of *seconda prattica* thinking. Nor are the echoes ever applied mechanically, for they are used to expand the phrases and add emphasis. Even when the full choral group is brought in at the end to express the words 'let us all therefore follow her', the solo and its echo maintain the sensuous mood as they sing the words 'miseris solamen' (the last word producing the echo 'amen', to lead music and words towards the ending).

Monteverdi provides two Magnificats, one for the large group of instrumentalists and voices needed for the psalm settings, the other simply for voices and organ. Both use the same techniques, and if we discuss the larger one it is because it is easier to see in this the union of the grand manner and the sacred monody. The Magnificat was traditionally a sectional work, with duets and trios interspersed between sections for the *tutti* of five or six voices. No doubt these contrasts were accentuated further when instruments took part. Where Monteverdi is original is in conceiving the work in such a way that instruments, solo and *ripieno* voices are each given something to do which only they can do well. He turns the Magnificat into twelve sections (ten verses and the doxology), and each of them is treated in a different way. The only common feature to them all is the plainsong *cantus firmus* which appears in long notes throughout. A choral setting of the first one gives way to a soprano, who sings the plainsong while the organ decorates. Two tenors weave their dotted notes and roulades round the alto in the next one, and then as a tenor sings out the plainsong, duets of instruments (flutes followed by trombones for the words 'the lowliness of his handmaiden', and recorders for the angelic 'call me blessed') enrich the texture. Violins with ornamental figuration are included in the next section. The fifth section returns to the voices alone, who sing a choral dialogue with contrasting upper and lower groups in the manner of a motet by Giovanni Gabrieli, *Beata es Virgo*.

After this first climax the humanity of the Virgin's song increasingly infects the music. The seventh section is in fact an operatic *scena*. The tenor sings of the abasement of the mighty; and cornetts and violins each in pairs, echo one another with the same magic that Orpheus used to bewitch Charon. After more duets and trios the two tenors sing another echo song, to the glory of the Father, Son and Holy Ghost. Their fine disregard for accurate declamation and their splendidly virtuoso phrases make this one of the most passionate moments in a passionate work:

Then, and only then, are the instruments allowed to double the voices to give a noble conclusion to the work.

Passion and magnificence—these two are inseparable words in

describing the volume, and a detailed analysis of it is necessary in any study of Monteverdi's music, since it shows the determined path for his later religious work. In Venice he developed passion in more *sacri affetti* and magnificence in the motets for festival days, not to mention the *a cappella* polyphony for ordinary use in St Mark's. The publishers sought the first of these, and sacred songs and duets by Monteverdi appeared in most of the anthologies of the time. He maintains in them a complete stylistic unity with his secular chamber music, never becoming deliberately conservative in any way. The four motets published in Simonetti's *Ghirlanda sacra* in 1625 are typical. Two of them, *Ecce sacrum paratum* and *Currite, populi*, are Venetian arias, both having extended triple-time passages interrupted by recitatives. The triple-time sections are completely diatonic, and the 'alleluia' refrain of *Currite, populi* is a lively tune which Berti or Grandi would have been pleased to write for their song-books:

This was an especially popular style, and Monteverdi wrote several of these lighter works, of which two solo motets, *Exulta, figlia*, and *Venite, videte*, are very attractive.[1]

[1] Not in the Collected Edition; reprinted in W. Osthoff, *12 composizioni vocali . . . (inedite)*, Milan, 1958.

The other two motets from the Simonetti *Ghirlanda sacra*, *O quam pulchra es* and *Salve Regina*, are among the most beautiful of solo madrigals. Both are *arioso* contemplations, and rapturous ones, of womanhood, settings of texts which were especially popular in Venice, where the Blessed Virgin was specially venerated. *O quam pulchra es* begins with Monteverdi's favourite downward sixth in the melody and then lavishes the extravagances of trill and melisma to express the beauty of the beloved. As usual, Monteverdi seizes on the chance to give his melody shape. The short phrases, 'Amica mea, colomba mea, formosa mea', suggest the repetition of a motif; and each time the opening words, 'O how beautiful you are', come round the *gorgia* returns. The climax comes as the lover 'languishes of love' with a chromatic bass pushing the belated melody down to form voluptuous dissonances.

Salve Regina is more serene, although it too has a touch of chromatic desire as the singer sends up 'our sighs, mourning and weeping' in his prayer to the Virgin. It is a piece of long phrases (not so usual for Monteverdi) organized at the beginning by a rhythm suggested by the repetition of the word 'salve' and given variety by sudden bursts of rhythmic energy—'ad te clamamus' or 'eja ergo, o advocata nostra'. Dissonance is reserved for the climax and the inevitable downward sixth comes in the very last phrase.

These motets are fine because they draw out the inner meaning of the words. But Monteverdi is not averse to painting the outer meaning any more than he was in the Tasso settings of his madrigal books. The motet, *Ab aeterno ordinata sum*, for bass, with its description of the creation of the world, is reminiscent of the recitatives of Charon and Pluto in its leaps to the depths for words such as 'abissos' and runs for 'aquis'. *Laudate Dominum*, published in the *Selva morale* of 1640, follows up the mood of *Zefiro torna* and *Armato il cor*. Some details are painted in the *stile concitato* (suggested by the warlike instruments mentioned in the psalm) and both the chaconne bass and the melody which develops over it—with *hemiolias*, held notes and descriptive melismas—are very like the secular duets. Even the sudden change from triple time to the quasi-recitative (not really justifiable in the psalm setting) brings *Zefiro torna* to our mind.

These works, then, are recognizably Monteverdian. This certainly cannot be said of the *prima prattica* Masses and psalms which we find in Vincenti's collected editions of Monteverdi's church music. Here he limits dissonance to suspensions and passing notes on the weak beats, and writes smooth melodic lines in the overlapping phrases which necessarily preclude any dynamic contrasts. These works are consciously archaic; but they are not self-consciously learned as the 'Gombert Mass' had been. Monteverdi composes in an idiom familiar to his age. Completely tonal melody, rhythms which are moulded by the bar-line, the harmonic language of the *missa brevis* rather than the exaggerated imitative counterpoint of 1610—all these give him plenty of scope for writing expressive music. The *Crucifixus* of the Mass published in 1650 uses suspensions most beautifully to express the words 'Passus et sepultus est', and there is genuine excitement in the triple-time 'Et resurrexit' and the sequential phrases of the 'Hosanna'.

The same is true of the psalms for double choir, which bear little relationship to the idiom of the Gabrielis. The dialogue interplay of the older Venetians is there, but the rhythms are rather square and the harmony is deliberately more consonant, more Roman than Venetian. The interest in sheer sonority is restricted to the effects which can be obtained from two equally balanced choirs which never use the extremes of the voice. Even so, the idiom is consistent and has a dignity of its own, though it remains impersonal. The true successors of the grand Venetian motets are to be found in the works written in the *stile concertato*. The grandeur, like Venice's own, becomes slightly diminished as the century proceeds. The huge variety of the Gabrielian orchestra is reduced in Monteverdi's work to a body of strings, sometimes with brass instruments, brought in to support the voices. At the same time he develops the idiomatic use of this orchestra in the way we have seen in the Magnificat of 1610. The instruments rarely double the voices, and then only at climaxes. They add material which is not really suitable for the voices, or else use the vocal material separately to contrast with the choral colour.

It is often said of these works that they are truly secular, and it is certainly true that they often use the same kind of material as Monte-verdi's later *continuo* madrigals. One setting of the psalm, *Beatus vir*, for example, uses *Chiome d'oro* from the seventh book of madrigals as its basic material. The warlike phrases of the eighth book appear a number of times in the church music—in the *Nisi Dominus* for six voices and, delightfully, to express the words 'He hath shown strength with his arm' in a Magnificat setting, to exactly the same figure that appears in the *Sinfonia da guerra* when Ulysses has equally shown the strength of his arm. Yet these works do not have the same inner spirit of Monteverdi's madrigals and they do not have the same power of expression. The reason is not, as has been suggested, a spiritual so much as a musical one. With the liturgical music which was needed for St Mark's there was no question of specially choosing or reorganiz-ing the words as in the madrigals. Many of the texts to be set were long, and as yet the new *basso continuo* motet had not evolved a form suited to making such settings continuously interesting. Some of the younger men were working on the right lines. Grandi divided his psalms into sections which were more or less complete in themselves; Tarquinio Merula was experimenting with sections bound together with *ostinato* figures. Monteverdi preferred rather conservatively to stick to the long duet and trio sections which Viadana had evolved. The result is that many of these works, while containing fertile ideas, do not hang together.

But where Monteverdi sees a real opportunity for large-scale organization, he writes church music that is both expressive of the words and worthily splendid in the Venetian tradition. Perhaps the most splendid of all his church music is to be found in the *Gloria* with trombones and strings which he composed in 1631 for the Mass in thanksgiving for the relief from the plague. The liturgical text suited him, for it was not unmanageably long and it had contrasting ideas to offset its general mood of rejoicing. The tenor intones with a lively rhythm, and then through a series of duets Monteverdi works up a motif into a tremendous climax:

[*continued on page 152*

'Peace on earth' suggests a homophonic passage for the full choir, using the lower register of all the voices, just as in the peaceful section of *Hor che 'l ciel e la terra*. Then there is a series of duets, two-bar phrases for tenors or sopranos being answered or echoed by a pair of violins. The words 'Gloria tua' suggest the opening motif again, and it is given to each of the voices in turn; but, very skilfully, it is not worked up to the massive climax of the first section and is deliberately broken off for more duet work. 'Qui tollis' is set in duet and trio texture held together with a *ritornello*. When Monteverdi comes to

'In gloria Dei Patris' he naturally brings back the beginning, and this time there is no interruption. The opening climax comes back with the increased force of complete thematic recapitulation after a broken development.

This form comes naturally out of the words. Elsewhere Monteverdi has to impose it on them. In the *Beatus vir*, in which he parodies *Chiome d'oro*, the *ostinato* bass of the madrigal comes to his aid; but even then he makes his opening vocal motif return from time to time to make a rondo, and a rondo which is the clearer because the memorable violin figure of the *Chiome d'oro ritornello* usually comes back with it.

The variations on the bass take the form of painting the image of the verse. 'Gloria' provides a sequential, lively, melismatic figure; 'irascetur' a semiquaver motif, and so on. Even so, the piece is slightly too long, not because a short song is difficult to develop into a long psalm (sixteenth-century composers had developed them into complete Mass settings), but because the interplay between the various pairs of voices often leads Monteverdi into short phrases which never grow into something longer and more significant.

He solved the problem in the third setting of *Laudate Dominum* which he included in the *Selva morale*. Here he wrote a duet for sopranos with a choir joining in from time to time to give the appear-ance of a rondo. In the duet section, the phrases have to develop—and very attractive they are:

The great climax comes when the sopranos' phrases are given to the full choir and extended with repetitions; thereafter Monteverdi is content to leave the doxology to the sopranos alone. Another solution was in his setting of *Confitebor tibi* in the French style. The piece resembles *Dolcissimo uscignolo* from the eighth book of madrigals, both in its rhythms (square two-bar phrases and a lack of dotted notes) and in the way the soprano soloist sings each section and then is greeted with a full harmonization of it by the choir. With its consonant harmony and easy-flowing melody it has the same charm as the secular piece. And then, as the word 'Gloria' comes, Monteverdi lets out an impassioned and triumphant cry from the soprano:

This, if proof is still needed, must convince us of the sincere and deep conviction which made Monteverdi turn to the priesthood at the end of his life.

CHAPTER VIII

REPUTATION AND INFLUENCE

'THE greatest fame which a man may have on earth.' With these words Follino coaxed Monteverdi back to Mantua to compose *Arianna*. Was the promise fulfilled? The question is of some impor-tance to a biographer, and the search for an answer has a twofold value. The reputation that a composer had in his lifetime reveals the manner of man which he appeared to be to his contemporaries. The reputation that his name has acquired in the years since his death throws light on our attitude towards him. To study both these things can therefore help us to avoid the more obvious errors of appraisal and prevent our reading into his life and work merely what we would like to find there. At the same time, it must be admitted that the evidence which we possess is insufficient to give us anything like a complete picture of the growth of Monteverdi's fame. Nor can it tell us how deeply his art affected other composers, for many things which today seem exclusively Monteverdian were in fact the common language of his day. We can, however, deduce certain attitudes, certain pre-ferences for and antipathies to his music which are revealing and significant.

Monteverdi came into prominence comparatively slowly. This is quite clear from the lack of reprints of his early music. The popular anthologies to which composers were invited to contribute by editors and publishers contain little of his music in his early years. While he was living at Cremona this was understandable enough. For his first years at Mantua it is significant. Living among Wert, Pallavicino and Gastoldi he must have had every opportunity to be brought in touch with the Venetian publishers. Apparently this was of no avail. Fewer than half a dozen pieces of his music appeared in his first seven or eight years there. The only reason for this lack of quick success can be that he was not considered a composer of light-weight or occasional music. He was essentially a serious composer who made few concessions to his audience. This is not contradicted by his sudden leap into fame after the production of *Orfeo*. His music then seemed to take on a new lease of life. A large number of editions of all his madrigal books, a large number of contributions to the anthologies display his widening audience—a large number, that is, until we look at the work of somebody like Marenzio, whose work appeared in anthology after anthology for over twenty years, and whose madrigal books rarely went through fewer than five or six reprints.

This sudden success appears to be due to the enthusiasm of connoisseurs. It lasted about six or seven years, during which the fourth and fifth books of madrigals found a special favour. Adriano Banchieri at this time could write in his *Conclusioni del suono dell' organo*; [1]

I must not omit the name of the most sweet composer of music in the modern style, Claudio Monteverdi, head of music to the Most Illustrious Sig. D. Vicenzo Gonzaga, Duke of Mantua (universally well known to the professional musician is his work), since his expression of the emotions, full of art, is truly worthy of complete commendation.

How rapidly things had changed. A few years earlier the same Bolognese writer and composer had acknowledged the receipt of Artusi's vicious attack on Monteverdi in these terms:

I have examined it all, and I say that the book is worthy of eternal praise, for rebutting the crudity of certain composers who destroy the good rules of Zarlino, Franchino, Guido and other intelligent writers, among whom, however, are not included the modern followers of the admirable Roman school, and in particular those who write church music, Sig. Gio. Pietro Pallestina [*sic*], and in chamber music Sig. Luca Marenzio. [2]

[1] 1608 ed., pages 57 f.
[2] *Lettere armoniche*, page 94.

This tide of popularity carried Monteverdi to Venice. After his arrival there the reprints of his old madrigal books gradually died away, and the new ones were never accompanied by the same demand from the public. The reason for this was surely that Monteverdi never bothered to follow the fashions. The song-books of his assistants, Grandi and Rovetta, were selling well. Monteverdi, on the other hand, made no concession to public taste until his second book of *Scherzi musicali* was published. By this time a writer could bewail the decline of conventional madrigal singing: 'Nowadays music is not much cultivated any more, for in Rome gentlemen do not indulge in it; nor do they sing with several voices from part-books as they used to in the past.' It is no wonder that Monteverdi's madrigal books, written for his Mantuan virtuosos, gradually faded into the past.

Oddly enough, in spite of this state of affairs in Italy, foreigners began to take to his music. The vogue for madrigals flowered in both Germany and England just late enough to give his works a new lease of life. The Germans had been interested in his work for some years, and the Nuremberg collector Kauffmann and the organist to the King of Denmark Borchgrevinck (a pupil of Giovanni Gabrieli) had both found opportunities to print Monteverdi's madrigals while he was still at Mantua. Then Phalèse, the enterprising publisher living in Antwerp, took them up, and from about 1615 found a market for the third, fourth and fifth books. He had no audience for the sixth book until 1639, and seems to have had no interest in the *continuo* madrigals.

England was slightly behind the times—when choosing Italian madrigals to copy or print it usually relied on the taste of Phalèse. Some Italophiles admittedly knew of Monteverdi's work. The younger Francis Tregian, copying his immense collection of vocal and instrumental music [1] to while away time in the Fleet Prison about

[1] British Museum, Egerton 3665. Several of Monteverdi's madrigals also occur in British Museum, Add. 31440. It has been suggested that this manuscript may be in the hand of the composer's English pupil, Walter Porter (see page 161); see Pamela J. Willetts, 'A neglected source of monody and madrigal', in *Music and Letters*, XLIII (1962), page 332.

1615, put a number of Monteverdi's madrigals into score, including virtually all of Book IV (why he missed out the first number, *Ah dolente partita*, remains a mystery), but he clearly had an abnormal source of supply in Italy. Another lover of things Italian was Henry Peacham, who published his book *The Compleat Gentleman* in 1622 and included a chapter on the art of music. After singling out Marenzio, Vecchi and Croce for high praise, he went on:

There are many other Authors very excellent, as *Boschetto*, and *Claudio de Monte Verde*, equall to any before named; *Giovannioni Ferretti*, *Stephano Felis*, *Giulio Rinaldi*, *Phillipo de Monte*, *Andrea Gabrieli*, *Cyprian de Rore*, *Pallaviceno* [*sic*], *Geminiano*, with others yet living.[1]

Monteverdi is in similar company in another context. One of the earliest biographers of Milton tells us that when Milton was returning home after a journey in Italy he arrived at Venice, whence

. . . when he had spent a Month's time in viewing of that Stately City, and Shipp'd up a Parcel of curious and rare Books which he had pick'd up in his Travels; particularly a Chest or two of choice Musick-books of the best Masters flourishing about that time in *Italy*, namely, *Luca Marenzio*, *Monte Verde*, *Horatio Vecchi*, *Cifa*, the Prince of *Venosa*, and several others,[2]

he returned to France and from there to England.

These were all men who had some special interest in Italian music; but there is no sign that Monteverdi was as popular as Marenzio or Croce with the ordinary madrigal singers. If the two books of *Musica Transalpina* came too early for his music, it is still significant that the manuscript part-books which have come down to us rarely include it either. This perhaps was due quite simply to the fact that the poetry which he set in his madrigals could hardly be translated with the exactness which would make the madrigals coherent and

[1] Op. cit. (1634 edition), page 102.
[2] H. Darbishire, *The Early Lives of Milton* (London, 1932), page 59.

acceptable. Even so, such a theory must remain unproven since we find some of the most literary madrigals of Books III and IV in still stranger surroundings. There are at least four manuscripts of viol music which contain these,[1] among fantasies and dances of such composers as Lupo, Ferrabosco and Wilbye. The anthologists who selected them had good taste and chose the best. What they made of them without the words is a matter for conjecture.

In Italy, meanwhile, it seems clear that it was the professional musicians and composers who were most appreciative of his work. One of the most distinguished composers of monodies, Claudio Saracini, dedicated to Monteverdi the first solo madrigal of his songbook called *Seconde musiche*. Whether or not he was an actual pupil of Monteverdi, the two composers were certainly musical kinsmen. Saracini was one of the composers who developed the passionate *arioso* and the striking harmonic clashes in Monteverdi's manner. Both composers were prone to academic arguments about the importance of monody in 'moving the affections'. More superficially influenced, perhaps, was Alessandro Grandi. He arrived in Venice a little too late to have his style completely founded on the master, and soon acquired an interest in the modern ariettas which were the favourites of the Venetians. In his church music, on the other hand, the change of style after his arrival to be Monteverdi's assistant was too marked for it to be purely a coincidence. From being a writer of conventional, though often beautiful, *concertato* motets he became one of the principal composers of the solo motet, written in the recitative-arioso style which Monteverdi had introduced in the solo music of the Vespers. Refrain techniques and the use of a rhythmic motif distinguished Grandi's work also and lead to the same sort of emotional richness. He even took up the *stile concitato*, and one of his psalm settings is full of the tremolando string passages which he must have learned from *Il combattimento di Tancredi e Clorinda*:

[1] British Museum, Add. 37402-6, Add. 29427; Christ Church, Oxford, 2, 21, 44; and manuscripts in Marsh's Library, Dublin, Z3, 4, 7–12.

Much the same can be said of Cavalli, who certainly borrowed various ideas from Monteverdi. The 'lament' appears in his operas to form a climax as in *Arianna*; and his solo motets have the same complete secularity which we have seen in Monteverdi's music. Even so, the detail of the Monteverdian style is left well behind in his work, which has none of the old-fashioned declamatory recitative or the virulent harmony of his great master.

At least two pupils came from abroad. One of them was an Englishman, Walter Porter, who, in publishing a book of motets in 1657, proudly pointed out that these were in the Italian style and were the result of his studies in Italy. In a manuscript note found in a copy of this book at Christ Church, Oxford, he tells us that his teacher was Monteverdi himself. What had Porter learned? Undoubtedly the technique of writing *continuo* madrigals and some of the tricks of the trade. In his book of *Madrigals and Ayres* (1632) he displays the ability to write declamatory melodic lines, the expressive use of dissonance and chromaticism, and the various ornaments which were the stock-in-trade of Italian composers. Further than this it is difficult, if not impossible, to find specifically Monteverdian traits. It is true that he occasionally uses that favourite downward leap of a sixth, but instead of expressing the meaning of some passionate poetic phrase, it is nearly always pictorial (to express the idea of 'falling', for example) in an older English tradition. And he is maladroit in his application of ornaments. The sobbing trill is just as likely to occur on the words 'and' or 'of' as on 'love' or 'grief'. The only closer connection with Monteverdi that we may notice is that his madrigals and airs are for the most part old-fashioned, at least for 1632, and follow the forms to be found in Monteverdi's seventh book. But in fact, Porter could have learned everything from even a minor Italian composer.

The other foreigner, Heinrich Schütz, is much more important. By the time of his visit to Monteverdi in Venice in 1628 he was a man of considerable attainments and over forty years old. It was not his first period of study in Italy, for he had come to Venice to work with Giovanni Gabrieli twenty years before. His style was by this time a unique mixture of Italian and German, completely personal in its adaptation of the Venetian church music technique into German usage. All the more remarkable then was his receptiveness in face of the work of Monteverdi. Whether he was a formal pupil of the Italian is not known and is unimportant; what is certain is that he studied Monteverdi's work with the greatest care. He did more than pick up a few tricks of style—though we can find Monteverdi's downward sixth, chromatic changes and astringent harmonies in Schütz's work too.

He studied the very basis of Monteverdi's 'academic philosophy', as we can see from a book by his own pupil, Christoph Bernhard, whose *Kompositionslehre* goes into the theory of the affections in some detail and with some insight. Most especially, since it was Monteverdi's latest invention, the *stile concitato* affected Schütz's attitude. It is no coincidence that a recently discovered German manuscript of the period [1] (probably the earliest German copy of a Monteverdi work) is a score of part of *Tancredi e Clorinda*, complete with a translation. Schütz may not have made this copy himself, but it must have been his interest that gave it its *raison d'être*. In his own music there are passages in this manner, and his motet *Es steh' Gott auf*, in the second part of the *Symphoniae sacrae* (1647), is largely an adaptation of two of Monteverdi's *continuo* madrigals, *Armato il cor* and *Zefiro torna*. Quite apart from details of the new recitative and *arioso* melody which are to be found all over the *concertato* motets which he published after this journey, we find a change of attitude in his religious music which is very Monteverdian. Such works as *Fili mi, Absalom* and *Saul, Saul, was verfolgst du mich?* are full of dramatic force and remind us of the description of Monteverdi's music for the memorial requiem of Cosimo II of Tuscany. Although we have lost Monteverdi's music for this occasion, Schütz's style helps us to fill in the gap.

In a way this influence on German music and especially on German theory was to be more important than the direct influence of Monteverdi's music on his immediate successors. He left no school of composers behind him. Cavalli, Cesti and the rest learned a great deal from the variety of forms in *Poppea* and *Ulisse*: they did not directly imitate them. Monteverdi was by this time a little too old-fashioned for forward-looking composers. He had 'too many scruples' (as Alfred Einstein puts it), that is, he was always a serious-minded composer with his roots in the old academic theories. His influence had passed into the life of music gradually over the years, by giving the ultimate power to technical means which for the most part had been discovered by other people. Hence in an age which had little

[1] Now in possession of the Musachino College of Music. There is a facsimile edition in 'Festschrift Helmut Osthoff' (Tutzing, 1961).

historical sense his progress in the art was taken for granted and soon
forgotten. When he died, however, he was revered as a great master.
Camberlotti's memoir [1] shows us that. So does Sansovino's guide-
book, which, describing the Chapel of the Lombardi in the Frari
Church, says that

in the Chapel, with a tomb by Milanesi is buried Claudio Monteverdi,
Maestro di Cappella in St Mark's, a great theorist of vocal and instrumental
music, famous for his valour and his compositions, of which many were
printed. [2]

It was to the learned men, the writers of treatises, that Monteverdi's
reputation was entrusted. Naturally their interests were in his theoretical writings, small in extent though they were. Even in his lifetime
one writer, Doni, was discussing his work from the academic point
of view. And he had one especially valuable thing to offer. Precisely
because he was unable to understand the Greek writers clearly, precisely because he was primarily a practical musician, he had tried to
realize what the Platonic theorists meant in terms of musical practice.
His promised treatise on the Second Practice was to be a very practical
book dealing with methods of representation, with details of harmony
and rhythm. To reinforce this, his *stile concitato* was an attempt to
apply theory to musical idiom in the most lucid way possible. This
was worth more than all the vague references to Platonic theory, all
the acoustics and arguments about temperament that had filled the
Renaissance treatises. It was a line which had a great deal to offer any
composer. First Doni, then Schütz's pupil Bernhard, then a number
of minor German writers began to speak of 'moving the affections' in
terms of specific musical figures. By the eighteenth century this had
flowered into a veritable philosophy of music, and Bach's contemporaries such as Scheibe and Mattheson developed a guide to
musical invention based on the various emotions of the verbal texts,

[1] Printed in Malipiero, op. cit., pages 50–62.
[2] *Venetia città nobilissima* (1663 ed.), page 195.

which, while certainly more complicated than anything envisaged by Monteverdi, none the less followed up his line of thought.

In this way Monteverdi's work passed into the main stream of musical tradition; and, as so often happens when a composer's ideas are developed rather than imitated by his followers, his music in itself had little interest for the musician and the public. By the early eighteenth century only an historian would have heard of it—and music historians were very few. When Padre Martini was gathering together his library at Bologna, he took care to collect all of Monteverdi's works that he could find, and he read the Artusi-Monteverdi polemic with some attention. Naturally his attention turned to the madrigals which had been criticized for their dissonance, and especially *Cruda Amarilli*. Although interested more in the style of Palestrina and the orthodox church composers of the sixteenth century, he was no dry-as-dust theorist. He saw Monteverdi's point quite clearly even though he thought it better for the young contrapuntist not to imitate him:

The young composer must reflect that the author [Monteverdi] does not use dissonances prohibited by the rules, except for the purposes of expressing the words, and then only in madrigals. And since by common agreement, as consonances are agreeable to the hearing, so dissonances are displeasing, thus it is that these must not be used unless they obey the rules by being suspensions or passing notes, so that they do not become horrible and displeasing. They are used in madrigals because, the parts composed being only sung, and without the accompaniment of any instrument, it was easier for them to be sung perfectly in tune by a few singers than in church music, in which a crowd of singers sings; for in the crowd, as experience teaches us, not all are capable of a just and perfect intonation.[1]

This is true enough, and Martini knew that Monteverdi could write orthodox counterpoint when he chose because he had scored part of the 'Gombert Mass'. But what is interesting is that he printed for the modern reader quotations from two extreme madrigals, full of the

[1] Quoted by H. F. Redlich, *Claudio Monteverdi*, I: *Das Madrigalwerk* (Berlin, 1932), page 104.

more progressive harmonies. This was equally true of Charles Burney in his *History of Music*. Burney had examined Monteverdi's music in Martini's library and naturally came to look at the novel passages (as they seemed to him). The legend of Monteverdi the revolutionary was now well established:

Monteverde was the first who used double discords, such as the $\frac{9}{4}$, $\frac{9}{7}$, and $\frac{7}{2}$, as well as the flat fifth and the seventh unprepared; and as he was possessed of more genius and science than the Prince of Venosa, his innovations were not merely praised, and then avoided, but abused, and adopted by other composers.[1]

Neither Burney nor Martini had, we may suspect, transcribed much of Monteverdi's music—the Burney transcripts now in the British Museum show a more complete coverage of many other madrigalists. Yet their authority was sufficient for this picture to persist into the nineteenth century, and Monteverdi's apparently revolutionary discoveries were made more prominent still by the appearance of music from the Vespers in Carl von Winterfeld's study of the music of Giovanni Gabrieli, published in 1834. A few personal documents which came to light about the same time did nothing to change this state of affairs. Verdi, thinking out a curriculum for the young composer to follow, recommended a thorough study of counterpoint, but took care to exclude Monteverdi on the grounds that his part-writing was bad.

As late as 1880 it was possible for a conscientious man such as W. S. Rockstro to write (of Monteverdi) in the first edition of Grove's *Dictionary of Music and Musicians*:

Well would it have been for Polyphonic Art, and for his own reputation, also, had he recognized [that his true vocation was dramatic music] sooner. Had he given his attention to Dramatic Music, from the first, the Mass and the Madrigal might, perhaps, have still been preserved in the purity bequeathed to them by Palestrina and Luca Marenzio. As it was, the utter

[1] *A General History of Music*, III (London, 1789), page 235.

demolition of the older School was effected, before the newer one was built upon its ruins: and Monteverde was as surely the destroyer of the first, as he was the founder of the second.

Rockstro certainly knew more than most people about Monteverdi, and had examined the score of *Orfeo* with care and admiration; but he relied on the same old sources—Artusi, Martini and Burney—for his knowledge of the madrigals. As by this time the music of the sixteenth century meant in fact the music of the Roman school, it is not to be wondered at that even scholars could accept this picture of Monteverdi heaving up the very roots of counterpoint and founding the new music single-handed.

Fortunately rescue was at hand. The Swiss historian Burckhardt, John Addington Symonds and a number of other believers in history as a study of culture rather than of politics were at work in the 1860's and 1870's. Painting and literature were their first subjects. Music followed a little later, being more difficult of access. Inspired by this new attitude a number of musicians and historians began researches into the music of the sixteenth and seventeenth centuries. Davari, in charge of the Gonzaga archives at Mantua, was the first to show an interest in Monteverdi. Working on the various papers over many years, he found the huge series of letters which form the principal material for a biographer, together with most of the minor documents which still exist there. Emil Vogel, a more professional music historian, made a wider search and wrote the first biography of any value, after examining documents at Cremona and Venice, as well as looking at and transcribing a great deal of the music.

By this time the music itself was coming back into view. Alongside the new histories and music journals, which the German revival of old music started with such great enthusiasm, were the new editions. *Orfeo* came out in 1881 in an edition by Robert Eitner, and from then until the beginning of the First World War the madrigals and operas were gradually made public again. By the 1920's Monteverdi's music was reasonably well known to scholars, and a number of these made the attempt to revive the various works. *Orfeo* and *L'incoronazione* were given a number of performances, and some years later the Vespers became almost a popular work in the edition of Hans Redlich. The resurgence of Italian nationalism between the wars bore one of its few pleasant fruits in a collected edition, and a number of excellent monographs have appeared in French, English, German and Italian.

Such activity may remind us of the Bach revival of the nineteenth century; yet the modern scholar must regret one thing. Even now the interest in Monteverdi remains on the whole an historical one. The monographs still echo, though more faintly, the opinions of Burney and Martini. The performances are often entrusted to semi-amateur resources or to professionals who treat the music as though it were a phenomenon rather than an experience. Our consolation must be that this once happened to Bach and Handel. Before long Monteverdi may join their company, not as the creator of modern music but simply as a genius.

APPENDICES

APPENDIX A

CALENDAR

(Figures in brackets denote the age at which the person mentioned died)

Year	Age	Life	Contemporary Musicians
1567		Claudio Zuan [Giovanni] Antonio Monteverdi born (baptized May 15) at Cremona, the son of a doctor, Baldassare Monteverdi.	Campian born, Feb. 12; Giacobbi born, Aug.; Vaet dies, Jan. 8. Anerio (F.) 7; Bull c. 5; Byrd 24; Caccini c. 22; Cavalieri c. 27; Corteccia 63; Croce c. 10; Dowland 4; Du Caurroy 18; Eccard 14; Ferrabosco (i) 24; Gabrieli (A.) c. 57; Gabrieli (G.) c. 10; Gesualdo c. 7; Guerrero 40; Handl 17; Hassler 3; Ingegneri c. 22; Lassus c. 35; Le Jeune 39; Luzzaschi c. 22; Marenzio 14; Mauduit 10; Merulo 34; de Monte 46; Morley 10; Palestrina c. 42; Peri 6; Porta (C.) c. 63; Ruffo c. 62; Sweelinck 5; Tallis c. 62; Tye c. 67; Vecchi (Orazio) 17; Victoria c. 19; Walther (J.) 77; de Wert 32.
1568	1		Banchieri born, Sept. 3; Rosseter born.
1569	2		
1570	3		Walther (J.) (c. 79) dies, March 25.

Year	*Age*	*Life*	*Contemporary Musicians*
1571	4	Maria Domitilla M. (sister) born (baptized May 16).	Corteccia (66) dies, June 7; Praetorius (M.) born, Feb. 15.
1572	5		Certon dies, Feb. 23; Goudimel (*c.* 58) dies, Aug. 27; Tomkins (T.) born.
1573	6	Giulio Cesare M. (brother) born (baptized Jan. 31).	Tye (*c.* 72) dies.
1574	7		White (R.) dies, Nov.; Wilbye born.
1575	8		
1576	9		
1577	10		
1578	11		Agazzari born, Dec. 2.
1579	12	Clara Massimilla M. (sister) born (baptized Jan. 8).	
1580	13		
1581	14	Luca M. (brother) born (baptized Feb. 2).	Farrant dies.
1582	15	*Sacrae cantiunculae* published. M. describes himself on title-page as a pupil of Ingegneri.	
1583	16	*Madrigali spirituali* published.	Frescobaldi born, Sept.; Gibbons born, Dec.
1584	17	*Canzonette* for three voices published.	
1585	18		Schütz born, Oct. 14; Tallis (*c.* 80) dies, Nov. 23.
1586	19		Gabrieli (A.) (*c.* 76) dies; Schein born, Jan. 20.
1587	20	1st book of madrigals published.	Ruffo (*c.* 82) dies, Feb. 9; Scheidt born, Nov.
1588	21		Ferrabosco (i) (45) dies, Aug. 12.
1589	22	M. visits Milan with a view to obtaining an appointment, but is unsuccessful.	
1590	23	2nd book of madrigals pub-	

Appendix A—Calendar

Year	Age	Life	Contemporary Musicians
		lished. M. appointed probably in this year to the household of Vincenzo I, Duke of Mantua, as a string-player (*suonatore di vivuola*).	
1591	24		Handl (40) dies, July 18.
1592	25	3rd book of madrigals published.	Ingegneri (*c.* 47) dies, July 1; Jenkins born.
1593	26		Agostini (P.) born.
1594	27		Lassus (62) dies, June 14; Palestrina (*c.* 68) dies, Feb. 2.
1595	28	M. accompanies the Duke of Mantua on an expedition to Hungary.	
1596	29		Lawes (H.) born, Jan. 5; de Wert (60) dies, May 6.
1597	30		
1598	31		Crüger born, April 9; Rossi (L.) born.
1599	32	M. marries the singer Claudia Cattaneo, daughter of the string-player Giacomo C., May 20. He accompanies the Duke of Mantua on a visit to Flanders, June.	Guerrero (72) dies, Nov. 8; Marenzio (46) dies, Aug. 22.
1600	33		
1601	34	Francesco M. (son) born (baptized Aug. 27) at Mantua.	Pallavicino dies, May 6; Porta (*c.* 96) dies, May 26.
1602	35	M. appointed *maestro della musica* to the Duke of Mantua, in succession to Pallavicino.	Cavalieri (*c.* 51) dies, March 11; Cavalli born, Feb. 14. Lawes (W.) born, April.
1603	36	Leonora M. (daughter), born (baptized Feb. 20) at Mantua. 4th book of madrigals published.	De Monte (82) dies, July 4; (?) Morley (46) dies.
1604	37	Massimiliano M. (son) born (baptized May 10) at Mantua.	Albert born, July 8; Merulo (71) dies, May 5.

Monteverdi

Year	Age	Life	Contemporary Musicians
1605	38	5th book of madrigals published.	Benevoli born, April 19; Carissimi born, April 18; Vecchi (Orazio) (54) dies, Feb. 19.
1606	39		
1607	40	Opera, *La favola d'Orfeo*, produced at the Accademia degl' Invaghiti, Mantua, Feb. (?) 22. M.'s wife dies, Sept. 10. *Scherzi musicali* (first set) published with an introductory essay by Giulio Cesare M., explaining the preface to the 5th book of madrigals.	Luzzaschi (*c.* 62) dies, Sept. 11.
1608	41	Opera, *L'Arianna*, produced at Mantua, May 28. *Il ballo dell' ingrate* performed there, June 4. Guarini's comedy *L'idropica* (with prologue set by M.) performed there, June 2.	
1609	42	Score of *Orfeo* published.	Croce (*c.* 52) dies, May 15; Du Caurroy (60) dies, Aug. 7.
1610	43	6-part Mass and *Vespers* published, with dedication to Pope Paul V.	
1611	44		Eccard (58) dies, autumn; Victoria (*c.* 63) dies, Aug. 27.
1612	45	Vincenzo I, Duke of Mantua dies, Feb. 18, M. dismissed by his successor, Francesco II, July 31. He returns to Cremona. In the autumn he visits Milan, where he conducts a performance of his music.	Hammerschmidt born; Hassler (47) dies, June 8. Gabrieli (G.) (58) dies, Aug. 12.
1613	46	M. appointed *maestro di cappella* at St Mark's, Venice, Aug. 19, in succession to Giulio Cesare Martinengo.	Gesualdo (*c.* 53) dies, Sept. 8.

Appendix A—Calendar

Year	Age	Life	Contemporary Musicians
1614	47	6th book of madrigals published.	Anerio (F.) (54) dies, Sept. 27; Tunder born.
1615	48		
1616	49	Ballet, *Tirsi e Clori,* performed at Mantua.	Froberger born, *c.* May 18.
1617	50	M. contributes music to Andreini's *sacra rappresentazione, La Maddalena.*	
1618	51	Francesco M. begins to study law at Bologna.	Caccini (*c.* 73) dies, Dec. 10.
1619	52	7th book of madrigals published.	
1620	53	Francesco M. becomes a Carmelite friar.	Campian (53) dies, March 1.
1621	54	Requiem Mass for Cosimo II de' Medici, Grand Duke of Tuscany, performed at Venice, May 25.	Praetorius (50) dies, Feb. 15; Sweelinck (59) dies, Oct. 16.
1622	55		Gastoldi dies.
1623	56	Francesco M. joins the choir of St Mark's, Venice, July 1. *Lamento d'Arianna* published.	Byrd (80) dies, July 4; Cesti born, Aug.; Reinken born, April 27; Rosseter (55) dies, May 5; Weelkes dies, Nov. 30.
1624	57	*Il combattimento di Tancredi e Clorinda* performed at Venice.	
1625	58		Gibbons (42) dies, June 5.
1626	59	Massimiliano M. graduates as a Doctor of Medicine at Bologna, March 16.	Dowland (63) dies, Jan. 21; Legrenzi born, Aug.
1627	60	Comic opera, *La finta pazza Licori,* composed. Massimiliano M. arrested by the Inquisition.	Mauduit (69) dies, Aug. 21.
1628	61	Massimiliano M. acquitted, summer. Intermezzo, *Gli amori di Diana e di Endimione*	Bull (*c.* 65) dies, March 13.

Year	Age	Life	Contemporary Musicians
		performed at Parma, Dec. 13. *Mercurio e Marte* (*torneo*) performed there, Dec. 21.	
1629	62		Agostini (P.) (36) dies, Oct. 3; Giacobbi (61) dies, Feb.
1630	63	Opera, *Proserpina rapita*, produced at Venice. Outbreak of plague in Venice.	Schein (44) dies, Nov. 19.
1631	64	Thanksgiving Mass for the cessation of the plague performed at St Mark's, Venice, Nov. 28.	
1632	65	M. now is a priest. *Scherzi musicali* (second set) published.	Lully born, Nov. 28.
1633	66		Peri (71) dies, Aug. 12.
1634	67		Banchieri (66) dies.
1635	68		D'Anglebert born.
1636	69		
1637	70		Buxtehude born.
1638	71	8th book of madrigals (*Madrigali guerrieri et amorosi*) published.	Pilkington dies; Wilbye (64) dies.
1639	72	*L'Arianna* revived at Venice for the opening of the Teatro di San Moisè, autumn.	
1640	73	*Selva morale e spirituale* published.	Agazzari (61) dies, April 10.
1641	74	Opera, *Le nozze d'Enea con Lavinia*, produced at Venice. Opera, *Il ritorno d'Ulisse in patria*, produced at Venice, Feb. Ballet, *La vittoria d'amore*, performed at Piacenza.	
1642	75	Opera, *L'incoronazione di Poppea*, produced at Venice, autumn.	Bononcini (G. M.) born, Sept.; Gagliano (c. 66) dies, Feb. 24.
1643	76	M. visits Cremona and Man-	Frescobaldi (59) dies, March

Appendix A—Calendar

tua, May. He returns to Venice and dies there, Nov. 29.

1. Albert 39; Benevoli 38; Bononcini (G. M.) 1; Buxtehude 6; Carissimi 38; Cavalli 41; Cesti 20; Crüger 45; D'Anglebert 8; Froberger 27; Hammerschmidt 32; Jenkins 51; Lawes (H.) 47; Lawes (W.) 41; Legrenzi 17; Lully 11; Reinken 40; Rossi (L.) 45; Scheidt 56; Schütz 58; Tomkins 71; Tunder 29.

APPENDIX B

The letter 'M', followed by Roman numerals, indicates the volume in Malipiero's collected edition. The spellings of titles have not been modernized.

(a) SECULAR

DRAMATIC WORKS

La favola d'Orfeo. Opera (Alessandro Striggio). Mantua, 1607. (M.XI.)

L'Arianna. Opera (Ottavio Rinuccini). Mantua, 1608. (Music lost except for the lament, for which see under *Miscellaneous Pieces*.)

Ballo delle ingrate. Ballet (Ottavio Rinuccini). Mantua, 1608. (M.VIII.)

Prologue to *L'idropica*. Comedy with music (Giovanni Battista Guarini). Mantua, 1608. (Music lost.)

Tirsi e Clori. Ballet (Alessandro Striggio). Mantua, 1616. (M.VII.)

Combattimento di Tancredi et Clorinda. Secular oratorio (Torquato Tasso). Venice, 1624. (M.VIII.)

La finta pazza Licori. Comic opera (Giulio Strozzi). 1627. (Music lost.)

Gli amori di Diana e di Endimione. Intermezzo (Ascanio Pio). Parma, 1628. (Music lost.)

Mercurio e Marte. Torneo (Claudio Achillini). Parma, 1628. (Music lost.)

Proserpina rapita. Opera (Giulio Strozzi). Venice, 1630. (Music lost.)

Volgendo il ciel. Ballet. Vienna (?), 1637. (M.VIII.)

Le nozze d'Enea con Lavinia. Opera (Giacomo Badoaro). Venice, 1641. (Music lost.)

Il ritorno d'Ulisse in patria (Giacomo Badoaro). Venice, 1641. (M.XII.)

La vittoria d'amore. Ballet. Piacenza, 1641. (Music lost.)

L'incoronazione di Poppea (Giovanni Francesco Busenello). Venice, 1642. (M. XIII.)

COLLECTIONS

Canzonette a tre voci (1584). (M.X):

Qual si può dir maggiore
Canzonette d'amore
La fiera vista
Raggi, dov'è il mio bene ?
Vita de l'alma mia
Io mio martir tengo
Son questi i crespi crini ?
Io mi vivea com'aquila
Su su, che'l giorno è fore
Quando sperai del mio servir mercede
Come farò, cuor mio ?

Corse a la morte il povero Narciso
Tu ridi sempre mai
Chi vuol veder d'inverno un dolce aprile
Già mi credev'un sol esser in cielo
Godi pur del bel sen felice
Giù li a quel petto giace
Si come crescon alla terra i fiori
Io son fenice e voi sete la fiamma
Chi vuol veder un bosco
Hor, care canzonette

Il primo libro de madrigali a cinque voci (1587). (M.I):

Ch'io ami la mia vita
Se per havervi oimè
A che tormi il ben mio ?
Amor per tua mercè vatene a quella
Baci soavi e cari (Guarini)
Se pur non mi consenti
Filli cara e amata
Poi che del mio dolore
{ Fumia la pastorella (1ª parte)
Almo divino raggio (2ª parte)
All'hora i pastor tutti (3ª parte)
   (Allegretti)
Se nel partir da voi, vita mia

Tra mille fiamme e tra mille cathene
Usciam, ninfe, homai fuor di questi
   boschi
Questa ordì il laccio (Strozzi)
La vaga pastorella sen va tra fiori
Amor, s'il tuo ferire
Donna, s'io miro voi, giaccio divengo
Ardo, sì, ma non t'amo (Guarini)
Ardi o gela a tua voglia (Risposta)
   (Tasso)
Arsi e alsi a mia voglia (Contra-
risposta) (Tasso)

Il secondo libro de madrigali a cinque voci (1590). (M.II):

{ Non si levav'ancor l'alba novella
   (1ª parte)
E dicea l'una sospirando (2ª parte)
   (Tasso)
Bevea Fillide mia (Casoni)
Dolcissimi legami di parole amorose
   (Tasso)

Non giacinti o narcisi (Casoni)
Intorno a due vermiglie e vaghe labra
Non sono in queste rive fiori così
   vermigli (Tasso)
Tutte le bocche belle in questo nero
   volto (Alberti)
Donna, nel mio ritorno (Tasso)

Quell'ombra esser vorrei (Casoni)
S'andasse amor a caccia (Tasso)
Mentre io miravo fiso de la mia donna
  gl'occh'ardenti e belli (Tasso)
Se tu mi lassi, perfida (Tasso)
Ecco mormorar l'onde (Tasso)
La bocc'onde l'asprissime parole solean
  uscir (Bentivoglio)
Dolcemente dormiva la mia Clori
  (Tasso)

Crudel, perchè mi fuggi? (Tasso)
Questo specchio ti dono, Rosa
Non m'è grave'l morire
Ti spontò l'ali amor, la donna mia
  (Alberti)
Cantai un tempo, e se fu dolc'il canto
  (Bembo)

Il terzo libro de madrigali a cinque voci (1592). (M.III):

La giovinetta pianta si fa più bell'al
  sole
O come è gran martire (Guarini)
Sovra tenere herbette e bianchi fiori
O dolce anima mia (Guarini)
Stracciami pur il core (Guarini)
O rossignol ch'in queste verdi fronde
  (Bembo)
Se per estremo ardore morir potesse
  un core (Guarini)
⎧ *Vattene pur, crudel, con quella pace*
⎪   (1ᵃ *parte*)
⎨ *Là tra'l sangu'e le morti* (2ᵃ *parte*)
⎪ *Poi ch'ella in sè tornò* (3ᵃ *parte*)
⎩   (Tasso)
O primavera, gioventù de l'anno
  (Guarini)

Perfidissimo volto (Guarini)
Ch'io non t'ami, cor mio (Guarini)
Occhi un tempo, mia vita, occhi di
  questo cor fido sostegno (Guarini)
⎧ *Vivrò fra i miei tormenti e le mie cure*
⎪   (1ᵃ *parte*)
⎨ *Ma dove, o lasso me, dove restaro?*
⎪   (2ᵃ *parte*)
⎩ *Io pur verrò là dove sete* (3ᵃ *parte*)
    (Tasso)
Lumi miei, cari lumi (Guarini)
⎧ *Rimanti in pace a la dolente e bella*
⎪   *Fillida* (1ᵃ *parte*)
⎨ *Ond'ei di morte la sua faccia impresa*
⎩   (2ᵃ *parte*) (Celiano)

Il quarto libro de madrigali a cinque voci (1603). (M.IV):

Ah dolente partita (Guarini)
Cor mio, mentre vi miro (Guarini)
Cor mio, non mori?
Sfogava con le stelle un inferno
  d'amore (Rinuccini)
Volgea l'anima mia soavemente
  (Guarini)

⎧ *Anima mia, perdona* (1ᵃ *parte*)
⎨ *Che se tu se'il cor mio* (2ᵃ
⎩   *parte*) (Guarini)
Luci serene e chiare, voi m'incendete
La piaga c'ho nel core
Voi pur da me partite, anima dura
  (Guarini)

A un giro sol de' bell'ochi lucenti
(Guarini)
Ohimè, se tanto amate di sentir dir
ohimè (Guarini)
Io mi son giovinetta (Boccaccio)
Quel augellin che canta si dolcemente
(Boccaccio)

Non più guerra, pietate (Guarini)
Sì ch'io vorrei morire
Anima dolorosa
Anima del cor mio
Longe da te, cor mio, struggomi di
dolore
Piagne e sospira

Il quinto libro de madrigali a cinque voci (1605). (M.V):

Cruda Amarilli (Guarini)
O Mirtillo, Mirtill'anima mia
(Guarini)
Era l'anima mia già presso a l'ultim'
hore (Guarini)
Ecco, Silvio, colei ch'in odio hai tanto
(1ᵃ parte)
Ma se con la pietà non è in te spenta
(2ᵃ parte)
Dorinda, ah dirò mia, se mia non sei
(3ᵃ parte)
Ecco piegando le ginocchie a terra
(4ᵃ parte)
Ferir quel petto, Silvio (5ᵃ parte)
(Guarini)

Ch'io t'ami e t'ami più de la mia vita
(1ᵃ parte)
Deh, bella e cara (2ᵃ parte)
Ma tu più che mai dura (3ᵃ parte)
(Guarini)
Che dar più vi poss'io?
M'è più dolce il penar per Amarilli
(Guarini)
Ahi, com'a un vago sol cortese giro
Troppo ben può questo tiranno amore
(Guarini)
Amor, se giusto sei
T'amo, mia vita (Guarini)
E così a poc'a poco torno farfalla (a
sei voci) (Guarini)
Questi vaghi concenti (a nove voci)

Scherzi musicali a tre voci . . . raccolti da Giulio Cesare Monteverde [1] (1607).
(M.X):

I bei legami (Chiabrera)
Amarilli onde m'assale (Chiabrera)
Fugge il verno dei dolori (Chiabrera)
Quando l'alba in oriente (Chiabrera)
Non così tosto io miro (Chiabrera)
Damigella tutta bella (Chiabrera)
La pastorella mia spietata (Sanna-
zaro)

O rosetta, che rosetta (Chiabrera)
Amorosa pupilletta
Vaghi rai di cigli ardenti (Chiabrera)
La violetta (Chiabrera)
Giovinetta ritrosetta
Dolci miei sospiri (Chiabrera)
Clori amorosa (Chiabrera)
Lidia, spina del mio core

[1] *Deh, chi tace il ben pensero* (Cebà) and *Dispiegate, guance amate* (Cebà),
included in this collection, are by Giulio Cesare Monteverdi. The composer of
the *balletto* which ends the collection, *De la bellezza le dovute lodi*, is uncertain.

Il sesto libro de madrigali a cinque voci, con uno Dialogo a Sette (1614). (M.VI):

Lamento d'Arianna [1] (Rinuccini):
  Lasciatemi morire (1ª parte)
  O Teseo, Teseo mio (2ª parte)
  Dove, dove è la fede (3ª parte)
  Ahi, ch'ei non pur risponde (4ª
    (parte
Zefiro torna e'l bel tempo rimena
  (Petrarch)
Una donna fra l'altre honesta e bello
  vidi (concertato nel clavicembalo)
A Dio, Florida bella (concertato)
  (Marini)
Batto qui pianse Ergasto (concertato
  nel clavicembalo) (Marini)
Presso un fiume tranquillo (dialogo a
  7, concertato) (Marini)

Sestina (Lagrime d'amante al sepolcro
  dell'amata) (Agnelli):
  Incenerite spoglie, avara tomba (1ª
    parte)
  Ditelo, o fiumi e voi ch'udiste (2ª
    parte)
  Darà la notte il sol (3ª parte)
  Ma te raccoglie, o ninfa (4ª parte)
  O chiome d'or, neve gentil del seno
    (5ª parte)
  Dunque amate reliquie (6ª parte)
Ohimè, il bel viso (Petrarch)
Qui rise Tirsi (concertato) (Marini)
Misero Alceo (concertato)

Concerto. Settimo libro de madrigali a 1. 2. 3. 4. & 6. voci, con altri generi de canti (1619). (M.VII):

Tempro la cetra (T., with *sinfonia* and
  ritornelli for 5-part str.) (Marini)
Non è di gentil core chi non arde (S.S.)
  (Degl'Atti)
A quest'olmo, a quest'ombre (a sei
  voci, concertato, with 2 vlns. & 2
  recorders or fl.) (Marini)
O come sei gentile, caro augellino
  (S.S.) (Guarini)
Io son pur vezzosetta pastorella
  (S.S.)

Dice la mia bellissima Licori (T.T.)
  (Guarini)
Ah, che non si conviene romper la
  fede? (T.T.)
Non vedrò mai le stelle (T.T.)
Ecco vicine, o bella tigre, l'hore (T.T.)
O viva fiamma, o miei sospiri ardenti
  (S.S.)
Vorrei baciarti, o Filli (A.A.)
  (Marini)

---

[1] Arranged by the composer from the only surviving fragment of the opera *L'Arianna* (see under *Miscellaneous Pieces*).

Perchè fuggi tra salci, ritrosetta? (T.T.) (Marini)

Tornate, o cari baci (T.T.) (Marini)

Soave libertate (T.T.) (Chiabrera)

S'el vostro cor, madonna (T.B.) (Guarini)

Interrotte speranze (T.T.) (Guarini)

Augellin, che la voce al canto spieghi (T.T.B.)

Vaga su spina ascosa (T.T.B.) (Chiabrera)

Eccomi pronta ai baci, Ergasto mio (T.T.B.) (Marini)

Parlo, miser, o taccio? (S.S.B.) (Guarini)

Tu dormi? Ah crudo core (S.A.T.B.)

Al lume delle stelle (S.S.T.B.)

Con che soavità, labbra odorate (*concertato a una voce* [S.] *e 9 istrumenti* [str., lutes, harpsichords, organ]) (Guarini)

Ohimè, dov'è il mio ben? (1ª *parte*)
Dunque ha potuto sol desio d'honore (2ª *parte*)
Dunque ha potuto in me più che'l mio amore (3ª *parte*)
Ahi sciocco mondo e cieco (4ª *parte*) (*Romanesca a 2* [S.S.]) (Bernardo Tasso)

Se i languidi miei sguardi (*Lettera amorosa a voce sola* [S.])

Se pur destina e vole il cielo (*Partenza amorosa a voce sola* [T.])

Chiome d'oro, bel thesoro (*Canzonetta a due voci* [S.S.] *concertata da duoi violini, chitarone o spineta*)

Amor che deggio far? (*Canzonetta a 4* [S.S.T.B.] *concertato come di sopra,* [2 vlns. & lute or harpsichord])

Tirsi e Clori (*Ballo*) (see *Dramatic Works*)

Scherzi musicali Cioè Arie, & *Madrigali in stil recitativo, con una Ciaccona a 1.* & *2. voci . . . Raccolti da Bartholomeo Magni* (1632). (M.X):

Maledetto sia l'aspetto (S.)

Quel sguardo sdegnosetto (S.)

Armatevi, pupille (S.)

Begli occhi, all'armi (S.)

Eri già tutta mia (S.)

Ecco di dolci raggi (T.)

Et è pur dunque vero (*a voce sola* [S.] *con sinfonie* [vln.?])

Io che armato sin hor (T.)

Zefiro torna (*Ciacona a 2* [T.T.]) (Rinuccini) (M.IX)

Armato il cor d'adamantina fede (T.T.) (M.IX)

Monteverdi

Madrigali guerrieri et amorosi con alcuni opuscoli in genere rappresentativo, che saranno per brevi Episodii frà i canti senza gesto. Libro ottavo (1638). (M.VIII):

Canti guerrieri

Altri canti d'amor (a 6 voci con quatro viole e duoi violini)

Hor che'l ciel e la terra e'l vento tace (1ᵃ parte)

Così sol d'una chiara fonte viva (2ᵃ parte)

(a 6 voci con duoi violini) (Petrarch)

Gira il nemico insidioso (1ᵃ parte)

Nol lasciamo accostar (2ᵃ parte)

Armi false non son (3ᵃ parte)

Vuol degl'occhi attaccar il baloardo (4ᵃ parte)

Non è più tempo, ohimè (5ᵃ parte)

Cor mio, non val fuggir (6ᵃ parte) (A.T.B.)

Se vittorie si belle (T.T.) (M.IX.)

Armato il cor d'adamantina fede (T.T.) (M.IX)

Ogni amante è guerrier (1ᵃ parte) (T.T.)

Io che nell'otio naqui e d'otio vissi (2ᵃ parte) (B.)

Ma per quel ampio Egeo spieghi le vele (3ᵃ parte) (T.)

Riedi ch'al nostr'ardir (4ᵃ parte) (T.T.B.)

Ardo, avvampo, mi struggo (a 8, con doi violini)

Combattimento di Tancredi et Clorinda (Tasso) (see *Dramatic Works*)

Volgendo il ciel (Ballo) (see *Dramatic Works*)

Canti amorosi

Altri canti di Marte (1ᵃ parte)

Due belli occhi fur l'armi (2ᵃ parte)

(a 6 voci et doi violini) (Marini)

Vago augelletto, che cantando vai (a 6 et 7 voci con doi violini e un contrabasso) (Petrarch)

Mentre vaga Angioletta ogn'anima gentil cantando alletta (T.T.) (Guarini)

Ardo, e scoprir, ahi lasso, io non ardisco (T.T.)

O sia tranquillo il mare (T.T.)

Ninfa che scalza il piede (1ᵃ parte) (T.)

Qui, deh, meco t'arresta (2ᵃ parte) (T.T.)

Dell'usate mie corde al suon (3ᵃ parte) (T.T.B.)

Dolcissimo uscignolo (a 5 voci, cantato a voce piena, alla francese) (Guarini)

Chi vol haver felice e lieto il core (a 5 voci, cantato a voce piena, alla francese) (Guarini)

Non havea Febo ancora (1ᵃ parte) (T.T.B.)

Amor, dicea (Lamento della ninfa) (2ᵃ parte) (S.T.T.B.)

Sì tra sdegnosi pianti (3ᵃ parte) (T.T.B.) (Rinuccini)

Perchè t'en fuggi, o Fillide? (A.T.B.)

Non partir, ritrosetta (A.A.B.)

Su su, pastorelli vezzosi (S.S.A.)

Ballo delle ingrate (in genere rappresentativo) (see *Dramatic Works*)

Appendix B—Catalogue of Works

Madrigali e canzonette a due e tre voci . . . Libro nono (1651). (M.IX):

Bel pastor dal cui bel guardo (S.T.)
(Rinuccini)
Zefiro torna (T.T.) (Rinuccini)[1]
Se vittorie si belle (T.T.)[2]
Armato il cor d'adamantina fede
(T.T.)[3]
Ardo, e scoprir, ahi lasso, io non
ardisco (T.T.)[2]
O sia tranquillo il mare (T.T.)[2]
Alcun non mi consigli (A.T.B.)
Di far sempre gioire amor speranza
dà (A.T.B.)

Quando dentro al tuo seno (T.T.B.)
Non voglio amare per non penare
(T.T.B.)
Come dolce hoggi l'auretta spira
(S.S.S.)
Alle danze, alle gioie (T.T.B.)
Perchè se m'odiavi (T.T.B.)
Si si ch'io v'amo, occhi vagi, occhi
belli (T.T.T.)
Su su, pastorelli vezzosi (T.T.B.)
O mio bene, o mia vita (T.T.B.)

MISCELLANEOUS PIECES

Lamento d'Arianna . . . Et con due Lettere Amorose in genere rappresentativo (1623):

Lasciatemi morire (S.) [4] (M.XI)
Se i languidi miei sguardi (S.) [5] (M.VII)
Se pur destina e vole il cielo (T.) [5] (M.VII)

In *Il primo libro delle Canzonette a tre voci, di Antonio Morsolino con alcune altre de diversi Eccellenti Musici (1594):*

Io ardo, sì, ma'l fuoco di tal sorte
(S.S.B.) [6]
Occhi miei, se mirar, più non debb'io
(S.S.B.) [6]

Quante son stelle in ciel (S.S.B.)
(Cerreto) [6]
Se non mi date aita (S.S.B.) [6]

---

[1] Previously published in *Scherzi musicali* (1632).

[2] Previously published in *Madrigali guerrieri et amorosi* (1638).

[3] Previously published in *Scherzi musicali* (1632) and *Madrigali guerrieri et amorosi* (1638).

[4] An extract from the lost opera *L'Arianna*. There are several manuscript copies. For the madrigal version see page 182, *Il sesto libro de madrigali*.

[5] Previously published in *Concerto. Settimo libro de madrigali* (1619).

[6] Printed in W. Osthoff, *12 composizioni vocali profane e sacre (inedite)* (1958).

In *I Nuovi Fioretti Musicali a tre voci d'Amante Franzoni Mantovano* . . .
Raccolti dall'illustrissimo Signor Fulvio Gonzaga marchese (1605):

> *Prima vedrò ch'in questi prati* (S.S.B.) [1]

In *Madrigali del Signor Cavaliere Anselmi* . . . *posti in musica da diversi eccellentissimi spiriti* (1624):

> *O come vaghi, o come cari* (T.T.) (M.IX)
> *Taci, Armelin, deh taci* (A.T.B.) (M.IX)

In *Quarto Scherzo delle ariose vaghezze, commode da cantarsi à voce sola* . . . *di
Carlo Milanuzzi* . . . *con una cantata, & altre arie del Signor Monteverde, e
del Sig. Francesco suo figliolo* (1624) [2]:

> *Ohimè ch'io cado, ohimè ch'inciampo* (M.IX)
> *La mia turca che d'amor* (M.IX)
> *Si dolce è'l tormento* (M.IX)

In *Arie de diversi raccolte da Alessandro Vincenti* (1634):

> *Più lieto il guardo* (S.) [3]
> *Perchè, se m'odiavi* (S.) [3]

Surviving in manuscript:

> *Ahi, che si partì il mio bel sol adorno* (S.S.T.) [4] (M.XVI)
> *Lamento d'Olimpia* (S.) [5]:
>> *Voglio morir: van'è'l conforto tuo* (1ᵃ *parte*)
>> *Anzi che non amarmi* (2ᵃ *parte*)
>> *Ma perchè, o ciel, invendicate lassi* (3ᵃ *parte*)
> *Voglio di vita uscir* (S.) [6]

---

[1] Printed in Osthoff, op. cit.

[2] The only known copy of this collection was formerly in the Hamburg
Staats- und Universitätsbibliothek.

[3] Printed in D. De' Paoli, *Claudio Monteverdi* (1945).

[4] Modena, Biblioteca Estense.

[5] British Museum, Add. 30491. Printed in Osthoff, op. cit.

[6] Naples, Archivio dei Filippini, S.M.-IV-2-23b. Printed in Osthoff,
op. cit.

Appendix B—Catalogue of Works

(b) SACRED

DRAMATIC WORKS

Prologue to *La Maddalena*. *Sacra rappresentazione* (Giovanni Battista Andreini). 1617. (See under *Miscellaneous Pieces*.)

COLLECTIONS

Sacrae cantiunculae tribus vocibus . . . Liber primus (1582). (M.XIV):

Lapidabant Stephanum	Hodie Christus natus est
Veni in hortum meum	{ O Domine Jesu Christe (1ᵃ pars)
Ego sum pastor bonus	{ O Domine Jesu Christe (2ᵃ pars)
Surge propera, amica mea	Pater, venit hora
Ubi duo vel tres congregati fuerint	In tua patientia
Quam pulchra es	Angelus ad pastores ait
Ave Maria, gratia plena	Salve, crux pretiosa
Domine Pater et Deus vitae meae	Quia vidisti me, Thoma, credidisti
{ Tu es pastor ovium (1ᵃ pars)	Lauda, Sion, Salvatorem
{ Tu es Petrus (2ᵃ pars)	O bone Jesu, illumina oculos meos
{ O magnum pietatis opus (1ᵃ pars)	Surgens Jesus, Dominus noster
{ 'Eli' clamans (2ᵃ pars)	Qui vult venire post me
O crux benedicta	Iusti tulerunt spolia impiorum

Madrigali spirituali a quattro voci (1583) [1] (M.XVI):

Sacrosanta di Dio verace imago	{ L'empio vestia di porpora (1ᵃ parte)
{ Laura del ciel sempre feconda (1ᵃ parte)	{ Ma quel medico (2ᵃ parte)
	{ L'human discorso (1ᵃ parte)
{ Poi che benigno il novo cant' attende (2ᵃ parte)	{ L'eterno Dio quel cor pudico scelse (2ᵃ parte)
{ Aventurosa notte (1ᵃ parte)	{ Dal sacro petto esce veloce dardo (1ᵃ parte)
{ Serpe crudel (2ᵃ parte)	
{ D'empi martiri (1ᵃ parte)	Scioglier m'addita (2ᵃ parte)
{ Ond'in ogni pensier (2ᵃ parte)	{ Afflitto e scalz'ove la sacra sponda (1ᵃ parte)
{ Mentre la stell'appar (1ᵃ parte)	
{ Tal contra Dio de la superbia il corno (2ᵃ parte)	Ecco, dicea (2ᵃ parte)
{ Le rose, gli amaranti e gigli (1ᵃ parte)	{ Dei miei giovenil anni (1ᵃ parte)
{ Ai piedi havendo (2ᵃ parte)	{ Tutt'esser vidi (2ᵃ parte)

---

[1] A single copy of the bass part only survives at Bologna, Biblioteca di Conservatorio.

Monteverdi

Sanctissimae Virgini Missa senis vocibus ad ecclesiarum choros Ac Vespere pluribus decantandae cum nonnullis sacris concentibus ad Sacella sive Principum Cubicula accommodata (1610). (M.XIV):

Missa de Cappella a sei voci, fatta sopra il motetto 'In illo tempore' del Gomberti :
  Kyrie eleison
  Et in terra pax
  Patrem omnipotentem
  Sanctus
  Agnus Dei
Vespro della Beata Vergine (da concerto, composto sopra canti fermi sex vocibus et sex instrumentis) :
  Domine ad adiuvandum (6 v., 2 cornetts, 3 tromb. & 6part str.)
  Dixit Dominus (sex vocibus et sex instrumentis)
  Nigra sum sed formosa (T.)
  Laudate, pueri, Dominum (a 8 voci sole nel organo)

Pulchra es, amica mea (S.S.)
Laetatus sum (a 6 voci)
Duo Seraphim clamabant (T.T.T.)
Nisi Dominus aedificaverit domum (a 10 voci)
Audi, coelum, verba mea (T. & chorus *a 6 voci*)
Lauda, Jerusalem, Dominum (a 7 voci)
Sonata sopra Sancta Maria, ora pro nobis (S. with 2 cornetts, 3 tromb., 2 vlns. & cello)
Ave maris stella (a 8, a 4, S.T., with 5part *ritornelli*)
Magnificat (7 v., 2 fl., 2 recorders, 3 cornetts, 2 tromb., 2 vlns. & cello)
Magnificat (a 6 voci, with organ)

Selva morale e spirituale (1640). (M.XV. 1 & 2):

O ciechi il tanto affaticar che giova (a 5 voci et doi violini)
Voi ch'ascoltate in rime sparse (id.)
È questa vita un lampo (a 5 voci)
Spuntava il dì (Canzonetta morale, A.T.B.)
Chi vol che m'innamori (A.T.B., with 3part str. *ritornello*)
Messa a 4 da Cappella :
  Kyrie eleison
  Et in terra pax
  Patrem omnipotentem

Sanctus
Agnus Dei
Gloria in excelsis Deo (a 7 voci concertata con due violini et quattro viole de brazzo overo 4 Tromboni)
Crucifixus (1ᵃ pars) (A.T.T.B., concertato con quattro Tromboni o viole da brazzo) [1]
Et resurrexit (2ᵃ pars) (S.S. or T.T., 2 vlns.) [1]
Et iterum venturus est (3ᵃ pars) (A.A.B.) [1]

---

[1] These three pieces are alternatives to the corresponding sections of the *Messa a 4 da Cappella.*

Ab aeterno ordinata sum (B.)

Dixit Dominus Domino meo (I) (*a 8 voci concertato con due violini et quattro viole o Tromboni*)

Dixit Dominus Domino meo (II) (id.)

Confitebor tibi, Domine (I) (*a 3 voci con 5 altre voci ne ripieni*)

Confitebor tibi, Domine (II) (S.T.B., 2 vlns.)

Confitebor tibi, Domine (III) (*alla francese, a 5 voci* or S. & 4-part str.)

Beatus vir (I) (*a 6 voci concertato con due violini et 3 viole da brazzo ovvero 3 Tromboni*)

Beatus vir (II) (*a 5 voci*)

Laudate, pueri, Dominum (I) (*a 5 concertato con due violini*)

Laudate, pueri, Dominum (II) (*a 5 voci*)

Laudate Dominum, omnes gentes (I) (*a 5 voci concertato con due violini et un choro a quattro voci . . . con quattro viole o Tromboni*)

Laudate Dominum, omnes gentes (II) (*a 8 voci et due violini*)

Laudate Dominum, omnes gentes (III) (*a 8 voci*)

Credidi propter quod locutus sum (*a 8 voci da Cappella*)

Memento, [Domine, David] et omnis mansuetudinis eius (id.)

Sanctorum meritis inclita gaudia (I) (S., 2 vlns.)

Sanctorum meritis inclita gaudia (II) (T., 2 vlns.) [1]

Deus tuorum militum sors et corona (id.) [1]

Iste confessor Domini sacratus (I) (id.) [1]

Iste confessor Domini sacratus (II) (S.S., 2 vlns.) [2]

Ut queant laxis resonare fibris (id.) [2]

Deus tuorum militum sors et corona (A.T.B., 2 vlns.)

Magnificat (I) (*a 8 voci et due violini et quattro viole overo quattro Tromboni*)

Magnificat (II) (*a quattro voci in genere da Capella*)

Salve Regina (I) (T.T. [echo], 2 vlns.)

Salve Regina (II) (T.T. or S.S.)

Salve Regina (III) (A.T. [or S.] B.)

Jubilet tota civitas (S.)

Laudate Dominum in sanctis eius (S. or T.)

Iam moriar, mi Fili (*Pianto della Madonna sopra il Lamento d'Arianna*) (S.) [3]

---

[1] These three pieces are set to the same music.

[2] These two pieces are set to the same music.

[3] An adaptation to sacred words of the solo *Lasciatemi morire* from the opera *L'Arianna*.

Messa a quattro voci, et Salmi A Una, Due, Tre, Quattro, Cinque, Sei, Sette, &
Otto Voci, Concertati, e Parte da Cappella, & con le Letanie della B.V.
(1650). (M.XVI):

Messa a 4 voci da Cappella :
  Kyrie eleison
  Et in terra pax
  Patrem omnipotentem
  Sanctus
  Agnus Dei
Dixit Dominus Domino meo (I)
  (8 v.)
Dixit [Dominus Domino meo] (II)
  (a 8 voci, alla breve)
Confitebor tibi, Domine (I) (S., 2
  vlns.)
Confitebor tibi, Domine (II) (S.T.,
  2 vlns.)
Beatus vir (a 7 voci con 2 violini)
Laudate, pueri, Dominum (a 5 voci
  da Cappella)

Laudate Dominum, O omnes gentes
  (B.)
Laetatus sum (I) (6 v., bassoon, 2
  tromb., 2 vlns.)
Laetatus sum (II) (a 5 voci)
Nisi Dominus aedificaverit domum (I)
  (S.T.B., 2 vlns.)
Nisi Dominus aedificaverit domum
  (II) (a 6 voci)
Lauda, Jerusalem, Dominum (I)
  (A.T.B.)
Lauda, Jerusalem, Dominum (II)
  (a 5 voci)
Laetaniae della Beata Vergine (a 6
  voci)

Miscellaneous Pieces

In *Parnassus musicus Ferdinandeus . . . a Joanne Baptista Bonometti . . . congestus*
(1615):

    Cantate Domino canticum novum (S.S. or T.T.) (M.XVI)

In *Musiche de alcuni eccellentissimi musici composte per la Maddalena sacra rappre-*
sentazione di Gio. Battista Andreini fiorentino (1617):

    Su le penne de' venti (T., with 5-part *ritornello*) (M.XI)

In *Symbolae diversorum musicorum . . . Ab admodum reverendo D. Laurentio*
Calvo . . . in lucem editae (1620):

    Fuge, anima mea, mundum (S.A., vln.) (M.XVI)
    O beatae viae, O felices gressus (S.S.) (M.XVI)

In *Libro primo de motetti . . . di Giulio Cesare Bianchi. Con un altro a cinque, e tre a sei del sig. Claudio Monteverde* (1620):

> *Cantate Domino canticum novum (a 6 voci)* (M.XVI)
> *Christe, adoramus te (a 5 voci)* (M.XVI)
> *Domine, ne in furore tuo arguas me (a 6 voci)* (M.XVI)
> *Adoramus te, Christe (a 6 voci)* (M.XVI)

In *Promptuarii musici concentus ecclesiasticos II. III. et IV. vocum . . . e diversis, iisque illustrissimis et musica laude praestantissimis hujus aetatis authoribus, collectos exhibentis. Pars prima . . . Collectore Joanne Donfrido* (1622):

> *O bone Jesu, O piissime Jesu* (S.S.) (M.XVI)

In *Seconda raccolta de' sacri canti . . . de diversi eccellentissimi autori fatta da Don Lorenzo Calvi* (1624):

> *Ego flos campi et lilium convallium* (A.) (M.XVI)
> *Venite siccientes ad aquas Domini* (S.S.) (M.XVI)
> *Salve, O Regina, O Mater* (T.) (M.XVI)

In *Sacri affetti con testi da diversi eccellentissimi autori raccolti da Francesco Sammaruco* (1625):

> *Ego dormio et cor meum vigilat* (S.B.) (M.XVI)

In *Ghirlanda sacra scielta da diversi eccellentissimi compositori de varii motetti à voce sola. Libro primo opera seconda per Leonardo Simonetti* (1625):

> *O quam pulchra es, amica mea* (T.) (M.XVI)
> *Currite, populi, psallite timpanis* (T.) (M.XVI)
> *Ecce sacrum paratum convivium* (T.) (M.XVI)
> *Salve Regina* (T.) (M.XVI)

In *Promptuarii musici concentus ecclesiasticos CCLXXXVI selectissimos, II. III. & IV. vocum . . . exhibens, pars tertia . . . Opera et studio Joannis Donfrid* (1627):

> *Sancta Maria, succurre miseris* (S.S.) (M.XVI)

In *Psalmi de Vespere a quattro voci del Cavalier D. Gio. Maria Sabino da Turi* (1627):

> *Confitebor tibi, Domine (a 4 voci)* [1]

---

[1] Printed in W. Osthoff, *12 composizioni vocali profane e sacre (inedite)* (1958).

In *Quarta raccolta de sacri canti . . . de diversi eccellentissimi autori, fatta da Don Lorenzo Calvi* (1629):

> *Exulta, filia Sion* (S.) [1]
> *Exultent caeli et gaudeant angeli* (*a 5 voci*) [1]

In *Motetti a voce sola da diversi eccellentissimi autori . . . Libro primo* (1645):

> *Venite, videte martyrem quam sit carus* (S.) [1]

In *Raccolta di motetti a 1, 2, 3 voci di Gasparo Casati et de diversi altri eccellentissimi autori* (1651):

> *En gratulemur hodie* (T., 2 vlns.) (M.XVI)

Surviving in manuscript:

> *Gloria in excelsis Deo* (*a 8 voci*) [2]

MADRIGALS ADAPTED TO SACRED TEXTS

(Figures in brackets refer to the number of the madrigal book in which the original occurs)

In *Musica tolta da i madrigali di Claudio Monteverde, e d'altri autori, a cinque, et a sei voci, e fatta spirituale da Aquilino Coppini* (1607):

Felle amaro	= *Cruda Amarilli* (5)
Gloria tua	= *T'amo, mia vita* (5)
Maria, quid ploras?	= *Dorinda, ah dirò mia* (5)
Pulchrae sunt	= *Ferir quel petto* (5)
Qui pependit	= *Ecco, Silvio* (5)
Sancta Maria	= *Deh, bella e cara* (5)
Spernit Deus	= *Ma tu più che mai dura* (5)
Stabat Virgo	= *Era l'anima mia* (5)
Te, Jesu Christe	= *Ecco piegando* (5)
Ure me	= *Troppo ben può* (5)
Vives in corde	= *Ahi, com'a un vago sol* (5)

---

[1] Printed in W. Osthoff, *12 composizioni vocali profane e sacre (inedite)* (1958).

[2] Naples, Archivio dei Filippini, S.M.-IV-2-23a. Printed in Osthoff, op. cit.

Appendix B—Catalogue of Works

In *Il secondo libro della musica di Claudio Monteverde e d'altri autori à 5 voci fatta spirituale da Aquilino Coppini* (1608):

Animas eruit	=	M'è più dolce il penar (5)
Florea serta	=	La giovinetta pianta (3)
O dies infelices	=	O come è gran martire (3)
O infelix recessus	=	Ah dolente partita (4)
O mi Fili	=	O Mirtillo (5)
Praecipitantur, Jesu Christe	=	O primavera (3)
Qui regnas	=	Che dar più vi poss'io ? (5)
Te sequar	=	Ch'io t'ami (5)

In *Il terzo libro della musica di Claudio Monteverde . . . fatta spirituale da Aquilino Coppini* (1609):

Amemus te	=	Amor, se giusto sei (5)
Anima miseranda	=	Anima dolorosa (4)
Anima quam dilexi	=	Anima del cor mio (4)
Ardebat igne	=	Volgea l'anima mea (4)
Cantemus	=	A un giro sol (4)
Domine Deus	=	Anima mia, perdona (4)
Jesu, dum te	=	Cor mio, mentre vi miro (4)
Jesu, tu obis	=	Cor mio, non mori ? (4)
Longe a te	=	Longe da te, cor mio (4)
O gloriose martyr	=	Che se tu se'il cor mio (4)
O Jesu, mea vita	=	Si ch'io vorrei morire (4)
O stellae	=	Sfogava con le stelle (4)
Plagas tuas	=	La piaga c'ho nel core (4)
Plorat amare	=	Piagn'e sospira (4)
Qui laudes	=	Quel augellin che canta (4)
Qui pietate	=	Ma se con la pietà (5)
Rutilante in nocte	=	Io mi son giovinetta (4)
Tu vis a me	=	Voi pur da me partite (4)
Una es [1]	=	Una donna fra l'altre (6)

In *Concerti sacri . . . libro secondo . . . del P. Pietro Lappi* (1623):

Ave regina mundi	=	Vaga su spina ascosa (7)

---

[1] Published five years before the original madrigal.

Monteverdi

In *Erster Theil geistlicher Concerten und Harmonien a* 1. 2. 3. 4. 5. 6. 7. &c.
*vocibus . . . ausz den berühmbsten italienischen und andern Autoribus . . . colligiret
. . . durch Ambrosium Profium* (1641):

Jesum viri senesque   = *Vaga su spina ascosa* (7)

In *Ander Theil geistlicher Concerten und Harmonien . . . colligiret . . . durch
Ambrosium Profium* (1641):

Ergo gaude, laetare	= *Due belli occhi* (8)
Lauda, anima mea	= *Due belli occhi* (8)
Pascha concelebranda	= *Altri canti di Marte* (8)

In *Dritter Theil geistlicher Concerten und Harmonien . . . colligiret . . . durch
Ambrosium Profium* (1642):

Haec dicit Deus	= *Voi ch'ascoltate in rime sparse* (*Selva morale e spirituale*, 1640)
Heus, bone vir	= *Armato il cor* (*Scherzi musicali*, 1632)
Spera in Domino	= *Io che armato sin hor* (ibid.)

In *Corollarium geistlicher collectaneorum, berühmter authorum . . . gewähret von
Ambrosio Profio* (1649):

Alleluja, kommet, jauchzet	= *Ardo, avvampo* (8)
Dein allein ist ja	= *Così sol d'una chiara fonte* (8)
Frewde, kommet, lasset uns gehen	= *Ardo, avvampo* (8)
Longe, mi Jesu	= *Parlo, miser, o taccio?* (7)
O Du mächtiger Herr	= *Hor che'l ciel e la terra* (8)
O Jesu, lindere meinen Schmertzen	= *Tu dormi?* (7)
O rex supreme	= *Al lume della stelle* (7)
Resurrexit de sepulcro	= *Vago augelletto* (8)
Veni, veni, soror mea	= *Vago augelletto* (8)

APPENDIX C

Achillini, Claudio (1574–1640), jurist and poet, sometime Professor of Civil Law at Bologna. Author of the text of *Mercurio e Marte*, a *torneo* set to music by Monteverdi and performed at Parma in 1628.

Amadino, Ricciardo (late 16th and early 17th cent.), publisher in Venice. He was in partnership with Giacomo Vincenzi from 1583 to 1586 and independent from 1586 to 1621. Monteverdi's *Canzonette* (1584) were published by Vincenzi & Amadino. Amadino alone published all Monteverdi's works from the 3rd book of madrigals (1592) to the 6th book (1614) inclusive.

Andreini, Giovanni Battista (1579–1654), actor, dramatist and poet. Director of a company of actors which had a particular success in Paris. Author of the *sacra rappresentazione, La Maddalena,* for which Monteverdi set the prologue.

Andreini, Virginia (1583–1630), wife of the foregoing, actress and singer, known as 'La Florinda'. She sang the title role in the first performance of Monteverdi's *L'Arianna* at Mantua in 1608.

Archilei, Vittoria (*née Concarini*) (1550–c. 1620), singer and lute-player, wife of the composer and singer Antonio A. She was for many years in the service of the Medici at Florence.

Artusi, Giovanni Maria (c. 1540–1613), theorist and composer, canon of S. Salvatore, Bologna. In his dialogue *Delle imperfettioni della moderna musica* (1600 and 1603) he criticized madrigals which were published in Monteverdi's 4th and 5th books (1603 and 1605).

Badoaro, Giacomo, Venetian nobleman, librettist of Monteverdi's *Le nozze d'Enea con Lavinia* (1641) and *Il ritorno d'Ulisse in patria* (1641) and of Cavalli's *Helena rapita da Teseo* (1653).

Banchieri, Adriano (1568–1634), composer, organist, theorist and poet. A Benedictine monk, he became abbot of the monastery of S. Michele in Bosco (near Bologna) in 1620. He founded the Accademia dei Floridi (later Accademia dei Filomusi) in Bologna in 1614.

Basile, Adriana (*c.* 1580–*c.* 1640), contralto, known as 'La bella Adriana'. Having made her reputation in Rome and Florence, she was in the service of the Mantuan court from 1610 to 1616 and again from 1623. She married Muzio Baroni. Her daughter Leonora, also a singer, won the admiration of Milton.

Berti, Giovanni Pietro (*d.* 1638), singer, organist and composer. Tenor at St Mark's, Venice, and second organist from 1624.

Busenello, Giovanni Francesco (1598–1659), lawyer and poet. After studying law at Padua he practised at Venice. Librettist of Monteverdi's *L'incoro-nazione di Poppea* (1642) and of Cavalli's *Gli amori d'Apollo e di Dafne* (1640), *Didone* (1641), *La prosperità infelice di Giulio Cesare dittatore* (1646) and *Statira, principessa di Persia* (1655).

Caccini, Giulio (*c.* 1550–1618), singer, lutenist and composer. For many years in the service of the Medici in Florence and a member of Count Bardi's *camerata*.

Cavalli, Pietro Francesco (1602–76), composer and organist. Originally named Caletti-Bruni, he took the name Cavalli from his patron, a Venetian nobleman. He held various posts, as singer, second organist, first organist and finally *maestro di cappella* (1668), at St Mark's, Venice. His first opera, *Le nozze di Teti e di Peleo*, was performed at Venice in 1639.

Chiabrera, Gabriello (1552–1638), lyric and epic poet. Although not attached to any court he enjoyed the favour of Ferdinand I of Tuscany, Carlo Emanuele I of Savoy and the Mantuan court.

Doni, Giovanni Battista (*c.* 1594–1647), theorist. Originally a student of law, he entered the service of Cardinal Barberini in 1622 and was secretary of the College of Cardinals in Rome from 1629 to 1640. Subsequently Professor of Rhetoric at Florence.

Gabrieli, Andrea (*c.* 1510–86), organist and composer. At St Mark's, Venice, as second organist (1564) and first organist (1585).

Gabrieli, Giovanni (1557–1613), nephew of the foregoing, organist and composer. In the service of the Duke of Bavaria at Munich, 1575–9. He was appointed second organist of St Mark's, Venice, in 1584, and succeeded his uncle as first organist in 1586.

Gagliano, Marco da (*c.* 1575–1642), composer. He became *maestro di cappella* of S. Lorenzo, Florence, in 1608 and was made canon in the following year. In 1611 he entered the service of the Medici as *maestro di cappella*. He founded the Accademia degl' Elevati in 1607.

Gardano, Angelo (1540–1611), head of a publishing firm in Venice. He published Monteverdi's *Sacrae cantiunculae* (1582) and 1st and 2nd books of madrigals (1587, 1590). After his death the firm was directed by his son-in-law, Bartolomeo Magni, who published Monteverdi's 7th book of madrigals (1619), *Scherzi musicali* (1632) and *Selva morale e spirituale* (1640).

Gastoldi, Giovanni Giacomo (*c.* 1550–1622), composer. *Maestro di cappella* of S. Barbara, Mantua, from 1582, and of Milan Cathedral from 1609.

Gesualdo, Carlo, Prince of Venosa (*c.* 1560–1613), composer. He was a member of one of the oldest families of the Neapolitan nobility.

Giacobbi, Girolamo (1567–1629), composer. He was successively choirboy (1581), singer (1584), *promagister* (1594) and *maestro di cappella* (1604) of S. Petronio, Bologna. His *Andromeda* (1610) was the first opera to be performed at Bologna.

Gombert, Nicolas (*d. c.* 1556), Flemish composer, a pupil of Josquin des Prés. For many years in the service of the Emperor Charles V and canon of Tournai.

Grandi, Alessandro (*d.* 1630), composer. *Maestro di cappella* of S. Spirito, Ferrara, from 1610 to 1617. Singer (1617) and vice-*maestro di cappella* (1620) at St Mark's, Venice. *Maestro di cappella* of S. Maria Maggiore, Bergamo, 1627.

Guarini, Battista (1538–1612), poet and political philosopher. Sometime Professor of Rhetoric and Poetry at Ferrara, and later employed as ambassador at Turin and on other diplomatic missions. His *Il pastor fido* (1580–2) was published in 1589 and first performed in 1595.

Ingegneri, Marc' Antonio (*c.* 1545–92), composer. *Maestro di cappella* of Cremona Cathedral from 1576. Monteverdi was his pupil.

Luzzaschi, Luzzasco (1545–1607), organist and composer. Pupil of Cipriano de Rore and master of Frescobaldi. Organist and *maestro di cappella* to the court of Ferrara.

Magni, Bartolomeo. See *Gardano.*

Marenzio, Luca (1553–99), composer. Successively in the service of several cardinals, of Sigismund III, King of Poland, and of Pope Clement VIII.

Marino, Giambattista (1569–1625), lyric and epic poet and prose writer. He enjoyed the patronage of the courts of Turin and Paris. Several times imprisoned for immorality and criticism of authority.

Martinelli, Caterina (1590–1608), soprano, a pupil of Monteverdi, whose *Lagrime d'amante al sepolcro dell'amata* (published in the 6th book of madrigals, 1614) was written in her memory. She sang in the first performance of Gagliano's *Dafne* (1608).

Martinengo, Giulio Cesare (d. 1613), composer. He followed Croce as *maestro di cappella* of St Mark's, Venice, in 1609 and was succeeded by Monteverdi.

Merula, Tarquinio (c. 1590–1665), composer and organist. *Maestro di cappella* of S. Maria Maggiore, Bergamo (1623 and 1639–52), court organist to Sigismund III of Poland (1624–6), *maestro di cappella* of Cremona Cathedral (1628–39 and from 1652).

Pallavicino, Benedetto (d. 1601), composer. In the service of the Mantuan court from 1582 as a singer. Succeeded de Wert as *maestro di cappella* in 1596 and was succeeded by Monteverdi.

Peri, Jacopo (1561–1633), composer and singer. In the service of the Medici at Florence and a member of Count Bardi's *camerata*. His *Euridice* (1600) is the oldest surviving opera.

Porter, Walter (c. 1595–1659), singer and composer. Tenor in the Chapel Royal under James I and Charles I from 1617, and master of the choristers at Westminster Abbey from 1639.

Raverii, Alessandro (late 16th and early 17th cent.), publisher in Venice, a cousin of Angelo Gardano (*q.v.*). He published reprints of Monteverdi's 1st and 2nd books of madrigals.

Rinuccini, Ottavio (1562–1621), poet, a member of Count Bardi's *camerata* in Florence and for a short time at the court of Henri IV at Paris (1601–3). Librettist of Peri's *Euridice* (1600), Gagliano's *Dafne* (1608; previously set by Peri, 1597) and Monteverdi's *L'Arianna* (1608).

Rovetta, Giovanni (d. 1668), singer and composer. Bass at St Mark's, Venice, from 1623, vice-*maestro di cappella* from 1627, and *maestro di cappella* from 1644.

Saracini, Claudio (b. 1586), composer, member of a noble Sienese family. He held no official appointment and seems to have spent a good deal of time travelling in Italy and elsewhere. A madrigal in his *Seconde musiche* (1620) was dedicated to Monteverdi.

Schütz, Heinrich (1585–1672), composer. He studied law at Marburg and Leipzig. *Kapellmeister* to the Elector of Saxony at Dresden from 1617 to

1639 and again from 1641. He visited Italy in 1609 to study with Giovanni Gabrieli and again in 1628.

Striggio, Alessandro (late 16th and early 17th cent.), poet and violinist, son of the composer Alessandro S. (*c.* 1535–87). Secretary to the court of Mantua, 1622–8. Librettist of Monteverdi's *Orfeo* (1607).

Strozzi, Giulio (1583–*c.* 1660), poet, member of a Florentine family. Librettist of Monteverdi's *Licori finta pazza* (1627) and *Proserpina rapita* (1630).

Tasso, Bernardo (1493–1569), poet. Secretary to Ferrante Sanseverino, Prince of Sorrento, 1536–*c.* 1551. Secretary for criminal affairs to Guglielmo, Duke of Mantua, from 1563.

Tasso, Torquato (1544–95), son of the foregoing, poet. At the court of Ferrara from 1565. In prison from 1579 to 1586. Subsequently in Mantua, Rome, Florence and Naples. Author of the epic poem *Gerusalemme liberata*.

Viadana, Lodovico (1564–1645), composer, so named from his birthplace (original name Grossi). *Maestro di cappella* of Mantua Cathedral, 1594–1609. He became a Franciscan in 1596 and was *maestro di cappella* in Fano from 1610 to 1612.

Vincenti, Alessandro (17th cent.), publisher in Venice. From 1619 to 1665 director of the firm founded by his father Giacomo V. (Vincenzi; see *Amadino*). He published Monteverdi's *Madrigali guerrieri et amorosi* (1638), *Messa a quattro voci et salmi* (1650) and *Madrigali e canzonette* (1651).

Wert, Giaches de (1535–96), composer of Flemish origin, who came to Italy as a boy. He was for many years in the service of the Mantuan court, first as a singer and later as *maestro di cappella* of S. Barbara.

APPENDIX D

BIBLIOGRAPHY

THIS bibliography is in no way complete. It includes only the most important sources for the present study, together with material accessible and of interest to the English reader.

Abert, A. A., 'Claudio Monteverdi und das musikalische Drama'. (Lippstadt, 1954.)

Arnold, D., 'Seconda Prattica, a Background to Monteverdi's Madrigals'. (*Music and Letters,* xxxviii [1957].)

Benvenuti, G., 'Introduction to facsimile edition of *L'incoronazione di Poppea*'. (Milan, 1938.)

Bertolotti, A., 'Musici alla Corte dei Gonzaga in Mantova dal secolo XV al XVIII'. (Milan, 1891.)

Bukofzer, M., 'Music in the Baroque Era'. (New York, 1947.)

Canal, P., 'Della Musica in Mantova, notizie tratte principalmente dall' archivio Gonzaga'. (Venice, 1881.)

Cesari, G., and *Pannain, G.,* 'La musica in Cremona'. (*Istituzioni e monumenti dell' arte musicale italiana,* vi [Milan, 1939].)

Davari, S., 'La Musica a Mantova'. (Mantua, 1884.)

—— 'Notizie biografiche del distinto maestro di musica Claudio Monteverdi'. (Mantua, 1884.)

Einstein, A., 'Abbot Angelo Grillo's Letters as a Source Material for Music History', in *Essays on Music.* (London, 1958.)

—— 'The Italian Madrigal'. (Princeton, 1949.)

Gallico, C., 'Newly Discovered Documents Concerning Monteverdi'. (*Musical Quarterly,* xlviii [1962].)

Goldschmidt, H., 'Studien zur Geschichte der italienischen Oper'. (Leipzig, 1901–4.)

Grout, D. J., 'A Short History of Opera'. (New York, 1947.)

Appendix D—Bibliography

Hughes, C. W., 'Porter, Pupil of Monteverdi'. (*Musical Quarterly*, xx [1934].)

Leichtentritt, H., 'Claudio Monteverdi als Madrigalkomponist'. (*Sammelbände der Internationalen Musikgesellschaft*, xi [1910].)

Malipiero, G. F., 'Claudio Monteverdi'. (Milan, 1930.)

Osthoff, W., 'Das dramatische Spätwerk Claudio Monteverdis'. (Tutzing, 1960.)
—— 'Monteverdi-Funde'. (*Archiv für Musikwissenschaft*, xiv [1957].)

De' Paoli, D., 'Claudio Monteverdi'. (Milan, 1945.)

Prunières, H., 'La Vie et l'œuvre de Claudio Monteverdi'. (Paris, 1924; English edition, London, 1926.)
—— 'Cavalli et l'opéra vénitien au XVIIᵉ siècle'. (Paris, 1931.)

Redlich, H. F., 'Claudio Monteverdi': Bd. I.: Das Madrigalwerk. (Berlin, 1932.)
—— 'Claudio Monteverdi: Life and Works'. (London, 1952.)

Sartori, C., 'Monteverdi'. (Brescia, 1953.)
—— 'Monteverdiana'. (*Musical Quarterly*, xxxviii [1952].)

Schneider, L., 'Claudio Monteverdi: l'homme et son temps'. (Paris, 1921.)

Schrade, L., 'Monteverdi: Creator of Modern Music'. (New York, 1950.)

Solerti, A., 'Gli albori del melodramma'. (Milan, 1905.)

Stevens, D., 'Ornamentation in Monteverdi's Shorter Dramatic Works'. (*Kongressbericht*, Cologne [1958].)

Vogel, E., 'Claudio Monteverdi' (*Vierteljahrsschrift für Musikwissenschaft*, iii [1887].)

Westrup, J. A., 'The Originality of Monteverdi'. (*Proceedings of the Musical Association*, 1934.)
—— 'Monteverdi and the Orchestra'. (*Music and Letters*, xxi [1941].)
—— 'Monteverdi's *Lamento d'Arianna*'. (*The Music Review*, i [1940].)
—— 'Monteverdi and the Madrigal'. (*The Score*, 1949.)
—— 'Two First Performances, Monteverdi's *Orfeo* and Mozart's *La clemenza di Tito*'. (*Music and Letters*, xxxix [1958].)

Worsthorne, S. T., 'Venetian Opera in the Seventeenth Century'. (Oxford, 1954.)

Zimmermann, F. B., 'Purcell and Monteverdi'. (*Musical Times*, July 1958.)

APPENDIX E

Venice, Archivio di Stato

1. *Procuratoria de Supra, Cassier Chiesa, vol. x*

   22 Agosto [1613] ꝑ spese diverse // a Cassa, ducati cinquanta, contardi a S. Claudio Monte verde, maestro di cappella ꝑ donaficio come nella sua conduta.

   [same day] alli facchini che portavano et riportavano duoi organi a S. Zorgi ꝑ il far della prova di S. Claudio Monteverde. mᵒ di Capella.

   2 [ducats] 6 [piccoli] 6 [grossi]

   10 Sett a XX sonatori ordinarij ꝑ haver sonato a S. Zorzi il far della prova della messa del nᵒ maestro di Capella, et il giorno di detta prova in chiesa di S. Marco.

   1 [lira] 2 [piccoli] 10 [grossi]

2. *Scuola di S. Rocco*

   (*a*) filza 166, cauzioni (1623–4).
   Polizza de spese fatte ꝑ la festa de S. Rocco [1623] ꝑ contadij al Sig. Maestro Monte Verde ꝑ la festa.

   (L 620.)

   (*b*) filza 168, cauzioni (1627–8).
   Nota dello spese fatte al giorno di Sant' Rocco [1628] contᵃ al S. Claudio, Maestro di Capella.

   (L 146.)

3. *Proc. de Supra, Reg. 193bis, fo. 64–64ᵛ. (Lettere 1594–1620)*

   A letter from the Procurators to the Venetian resident at Milan:

   Essendo venuto a morte il Rᵈᵒ Maestro di Capella della chiesa nostra di S. Marco, ne soño datti proposti diversi soggetti, tra quali il Sʳ Claudio Monteverde Maestro di Capella di S.A. Però la sarà contenta prender informatione del valor, et sufficienza sua, et darne raguaglio, et se le venisse raccordatto qualcħ altro soggetto, lo receveremo a favore esser particolarm*te* avisari delle cond*ni* loro, et si off*mo*

Ant° Landi   16 Luglio 1613

In margin: 'fu scritto a Roma, Pad*a*, Vicenza, Bressa, Berg°, Milā et Mant*a* alli Residenti.'

4. *Proc. de Supra, Reg. 194, fo. 40ᵛ. (Lettere 1620–36)*

A letter from the Procurators to Monteverdi:

Al maestro di Capella Claudio Monteverde
Molto Mag*co* S*r*
Habbiamo inteso da una sua quanto V.S. ci avisa, ma pche la sua absentia da q*ta* Capella p diversi rispetti nō si può più differire, sciamo necessitati à dirgli, cħ quante p*ma* si liberi, et ne venghi ad attendere alla sua carica, sapendo massime il termine delle sue obbligationi, et lei beniss° e quanto sij necessaria la sua psona et carm*te* la salutiamo.

Ven*a* li 27 9bre 1627.

5. *Ibid., fo. 50*

A letter from the Procurators to Monteverdi:

Al S. Claudio Monteverde, Parma.
Siamo alle santiss*e* feste di Natale, et p honor della Capella di S.M*co* et satisfat*e* n̄ra e necess*a* la v̄ra psona, vi habbiamo fatto scriver il med*mo* dal S. Rueta, tuttavia habbiamo voluto ancor noi stessi questo tanto farvi sape pcħ vi disponiate subito alla venuta, acciò giorni così solenni nō si celebrano senza la v̄ra assistenza, conforme alla v̄ra Carica, et vi aspettiamo cō desiderio, cō cħ vi salutiamo Caram*te*.

Ven*a* a 13 xbre 1628.

6. *Ibid., fo. 81ᵛ*

A letter from the Procurators to Monteverdi, written between August 14 and 18, 1632:

Al S*r* D. Claudio Monteverde m̄ro di Capella d̄lla Ser*mi*.
Sig*ri* di Ven.
Ill*m* et R*d* S*r*
Riceviamo la sua di 7 Ins*e*, che altra non nè habbiamo ricevuta et compatiamola sua indispos*ne* passata, et li disturbi delitti che ha tenuto

203

in q^{lle} parte, ma si ralegriamo però che si sij rihavuta, et che sij al fine^{mo}, et all'aggiustam^{te} delle sue contese, onde staremo quanto prime attendola a ciò possi ritornar al servitio della Chiesa, et al suo carico, conforme a quanto le permette, et e desiderio di cotesti S^i Ecc^{mi}, et n̄ro con che le gli racc^o.

INDEX

INDEX

Index

208

Index

Index

And Having Writ . . .

And Having Writ . . . .

A Science Fiction Novel

D. R. Bensen

The Bobbs-Merrill Company, Inc.

Indianapolis/New York

Published by The Bobbs-Merrill Company, Inc.
Indianapolis   New York

Designed by Rita Muncie
Manufactured in the United States of America

First printing

Library of Congress Cataloging in Publication Data

Bensen, Donald R., 1927–
    And having writ . . .

    I. Title
PZ4.B4739An   [PS3552.E54765]   813'.5'4   77-15442
ISBN 0-672-52078-8

And Having Writ . . .

For Nick

Through the rear viewport, I could see bits of *Wanderer,* glowing bright as a sun, flaking off and trailing behind us, almost lost in a flare of burning gases—we were making a tunnel of fire through this planet's atmosphere, feeding it with the ship's substance.

Dark, using all his strength, was wrenching and punching the levers and buttons that usually needed only a touch to make *Wanderer* respond smoothly, whether in deep space, paraspace, or any known or predictable atmosphere. Any atmosphere, that is, which it entered with due respect for the laws of physics. Some obscure malfunction had brought us in at the wrong angle and velocity, and the oxygen-rich stuff outside was eating the ship as we bored through it at meteor speed.

"Controls aren't responding!" Dark bellowed. "Fused—maybe burned off!" Those flaming bits had to be something, why not the external control surfaces and jet orifices? Very likely the hull itself would last long enough for us to impact with the surface and produce a really spectacular conversion of mass—ours and the ship's—to energy. But Dark either had not given up hope or, more probably, was doing his job as long as he could. You don't get to be pilot of an Explorer ship unless you're the kind that sticks to things.

The same is true of Recorders. With probably something under three hundred heartbeats left to me (taking into account an understandably accelerated pulse rate) before our violent encounter with this planet we had meant to investigate and catalogue, I was still observing, just as though I would be making a draft report and then a final version later on. At least I had something to do. Ari was simply sitting, looking peaceful or maybe switched off. Imminent vaporization or roasting is significant to a lot of people, but it provides very little material to interest a Metahistorian.

Valmis, in contrast, was noticeably jumpy, fingering a small black box he was holding on his lap. Now, if ever, would have been the time for him to Integrate with the Infinite, putting himself into a context in which the destruction of *Wanderer* and its crew was only an insignificant rearrangement of fluxes. Valmis's function in Exploration is to Perceive the whole mental and physical Pattern of a world, on all possible levels, from the particular to the gross structural. I understand that approach in theory, and it has been known to happen that an Integrator's work was the most fruitful result of a particular Exploration, but it is too arcane and tenuous for me to be comfortable with. I imagine my own specialty is too much involved with the finite for me to be much good at the Infinite.

"We're approaching the surface!" Dark called. "Any time now!" He seemed almost cheerful at being able to predict reasonably precisely the instant of our deaths.

Valmis scrabbled the box open and pulled out a peculiar luminous object. It was composed of some very odd shapes—I could make out a helix, but other pieces of it seemed to be all wrong in a way I couldn't quite grasp. Some sort of Integrator's amulet or meditative aid? A bit late for that, surely.

2

He took a deep breath and jabbed at it with one forefinger. I was curious to see what good it might do him, but just then there was a jolt that shook *Wanderer,* a kind of twitching that felt as if I had been turned inside out and then back again, and I knew we had impacted.

Then I realized that being able to have that thought meant it wasn't so—*Wanderer* was still up and moving.

"Controls responding now!" Dark yelled. "We're changing altitude and losing velocity!"

I looked out the viewport again. The glow behind us was dying, and there were no ominous flakes of *Wanderer*'s outside buffeting in our wake. It seemed we were not to blow a hole in the planet's crust—good luck for it, and us.

I checked the lower viewport. We were higher above the surface now, still moving desperately rapidly, but not enough to burn us. I could see nothing but vegetation, apparently large trees, flashing by beneath us.

"Do you plan to try to land here?" I asked Dark. "Looks very inhospitable."

"We land where *Wanderer* chooses," he said. "I've got some control back, not all—not enough to pick a spot. And no connection to the power plant or the antigravity—might have a last flick or so of thrust, but that's all. We're a ballistic problem now—moving on a trajectory and slowing. We'll hit the surface just about where the trajectory intersects it, with maybe a little adjustment at the last minute."

"How did you get control back at all?"

"No idea—I'd thought all the externals had ablated or fused, but there must have been something left, and maybe a servo cut in again for one last twitch. Anyhow, it's saved us."

I looked at the unending stretch of trees below us.

3

"Saved us from being vaporized in an instant so that we can experience the full sensation of being crushed inside *Wanderer* when it hits?"

Dark shrugged. "If the hull hasn't suffered too much, it might stand up to that. But there's water ahead—ocean-sized, that first orbital pass showed us. That's where we'll come down."

I turned back to the others. Ari still looked cool, only mildly interested in what was going on. Valmis, strangely, seemed more agitated than before, twisting his hands in front of him. I could see that the black box was empty, but did not see the strange object he had taken from it. His face looked haunted.

I sat next to him. "Well, it looks as though you may get to do some Integrating on this planet, after all," I said. "I wouldn't have thought it a while ago, but we do seem to have survived."

He looked at me wildly. "Did we? Did we, indeed? Yes and no, Recorder, yes and no. Record that, record that . . ."

"Tighten up, man," I said sharply. "You're saying everything twice."

He smiled in a way I didn't like at all, and said, "I didn't notice. But perhaps I have to."

I thought of asking what he meant, but decided not to. It was clear that he was in no state to make sense. Integrators are expected to be almost preternaturally stable and at the same time ultimately sensitive; they are bound to get off balance once in a while, and just barely avoiding being atomized is as likely as anything to do it.

There was nothing but gray water below us now. I went forward to Dark. "Are we any better off coming down out here than on land? There isn't much point in floating around until we sink.''

He shook his head. ''There's another land mass at the other side of this—I remember it from the orbital survey. Some evidence of population. I'll save up what power we have left and put us down as soon as we're in sight of it. That way we have some chance of help from the natives or of working out a way to get to shore ourselves.''

True—the prospect of being killed by this planet had for the moment made me forget what we had already learned about it: continental distribution, gravity, atmosphere and so on. I had had the information neatly filed in my mind right up to the point when we entered the atmosphere for descent and the deadly buffeting began. Lights on the night side, indications of industry—hydrocarbons in the atmospheric spectra— no sign of atomics or space-flight capability: probably somewhere on what the Explorers call Level Four of cultural development.

The natives ought to be able to handle the problem of getting us safely on land, provided they noticed us. But considering the shape *Wanderer* was in, it looked as though that was about as much help as we were going to get. A Level Four technology tends to be purely mechanical/chemical, and the ship, after its burning passage through the atmosphere, was certainly going to need some Level Seven refitting—involving advanced metallurgy and electronics, refined fissionables.

I looked again at the ocean slipping by beneath us. It was beginning to seem likely that this planet would be our permanent home, so I might as well start becoming familiar with it. But there is nothing particularly striking

5

about one stretch of water seen from above as against another.

Dark had been thinking along the same lines. "From what we saw, I doubt we'll find a shipyard that can handle *Wanderer*. But they do have industry of a sort, apparently. Just possible that they're far enough on so that we can give them the techniques and in a while they can develop far enough to let us get fixed up and out of here."

I was shaken. First our Integrator seemed to have fallen apart; now the Captain was proposing to violate one of the strictest tenets of the Explorers. "We can't possibly interfere with the planetary culture that much —it's the very first—"

"Not much point in Exploring," Dark said firmly, "if you don't get back to make your report. If we don't succeed in accelerating the locals so we can get away from here, the rules won't matter to us; if we do, we can handle the explanations—or take the penalties, if it comes to that—afterwards."

Valmis roused himself from his glassy-eyed lethargy and joined in. "Don't worry about that," he said bitterly. I waited for him to repeat it, but he seemed to have got past that habit. "We've already interfered with this world—and everything else. What have we done?"

"What's that mean?" Dark asked. "All I've been trying to do is keep this hulk from blowing a hole in the planet—now *that* would have been interference, if you like."

"Yes," Valmis said. "We were about to impact, weren't we? Just about to—there was *no way out of it*, right?"

"Well, we didn't." I gestured at the still-watery surface beneath us.

6

"We did, though," Valmis said.

"Are you maintaining that this is a sort of afterlife?" Dark said scornfully. "Seems pretty real to me."

"Not 'after'—*other*," Valmis said. We all three looked at him, Ari having evidently decided to switch on now that there was something to be argued about—though what it was I could not make out.

Valmis's explanation didn't help much. First there was something about the nature of Infinity, the idea being that it applies to possibilities as well as actualities—in an infinite universe, everything that can happen will happen. Otherwise it wouldn't be Infinity. But since every time something happens, something else doesn't—or many things don't—happen, Infinity is contradicted. Therefore it is necessary to assume that there are other parallel levels, planes, or what you will, of existence, in which all the things that don't happen in "reality" do take place. Whether these other levels are actual or only potential was still a matter of philosophical debate among Valmis and his fellow Integrators, who seemed to be the only people much occupied with this notion.

In any case, where there is a theory, instrumentation usually follows; and an Integrator with a fair grounding in paraphysics had come up with what he called a Probability Displacer, a device existing partly in "reality" and partly in some variant of paraspace that impinged on one of these alternate levels. Activated at a moment of high probability of an event's occurrence, it would displace the user to an alternate plane in which the highly probable event did not happen—theoretically the same in every respect as "reality" except for that one event.

This was obviously an effective shield against disaster—and Valmis had been intellectually curious enough about the Displacer to sneak it aboard and key it to *Wanderer*.

"Are you telling me," Dark said, "that it was your gadget that kept us from smashing up back there?" He looked as angry as you might expect a spaceship Captain who believes that his skill and nerve have prevented destruction would be at being told that it was all because of somebody's lucky charm.

"Yes and no," Valmis said, going back to his oracular manner. "It did and it didn't."

I could see that Dark was exasperated—so was I —over this yes-and-no business, but it seemed to interest Ari. "Fascinating," he said. "You mean that in the 'real' universe, *Wanderer* and we ourselves are now a dispersing cloud of random atoms, and that therefore we are in a different continuum in spite of having, in a sense, been destroyed?"

"Just so," Valmis answered, visibly relieved to have an understanding listener.

"But then," Ari went on, enjoying it, "there must have been a *Wanderer,* complete with Dark, Valmis, Ari and Raf, already in this continuum. Have we displaced them?"

Valmis tried to work it out that we *were* "them" as well as the luckless ones on the destroyed *Wanderer,* and he and Ari went at the logic of the situation in a fairly complex argument.

"It gets them after a while," Dark said quietly to me. "All that universal awareness. Valmis had set himself for being blown up, and finding he hasn't been has loosened his wits. We had some luck with the controls cutting back in, and we'll need some more to get down in one piece, but that's it."

I had to agree. This business of alternate planes was something well outside what a conscientious Recorder could deal with, and I suppose that, like most specialists, I rather tend not to believe in much outside my specialty. Meaningful reality is what I can observe: that's what I'm on an Explorer ship to do. Yet that odd twitch just as Valmis manipulated his gadget—I *had* observed that, but had put it down to the physical effect of the jolt when the control surfaces started to work again. . . .

"Valmis, where is this Displacer now?" I asked.

He showed me the empty black box beside him. "It vanished when we . . . changed," he said. "It existed in the actual reality and in the potential one at the same time—and when this potential reality became the actual one for us, the Displacer had to cease to exist, because the dynamic tension between the actual and the potential had vanished, so—"

I waved a hand impatiently. Left alone, he could go on forever about it. Just because a man is professionally involved with Infinity doesn't mean that he should talk at infinite length. "Well, it doesn't matter. If, as you say, this universe is like ours in every respect except that we're alive instead of dead, the thing to do is cope with it, whatever it is."

Valmis looked at me intently. "Raf—you're unmoved by the fact that we have wrenched the fabric of the universe, in a sense created a new one?"

"It was you that did that," Dark said. "If it was done at all," he added in a lower tone.

Ari spoke up. "As Raf said, the thing we have to think about is what we're going to do about being where or what we are."

"What I was saying when we got into all this talk,"

9

Dark said, "was that we've got to get the natives here, if we can, smartened up enough to do the repairs *Wanderer* is going to need. And never mind Rule Whatever-it-is about interfering with alien cultures."

I could understand a Captain having that attitude—his job is to get his ship to where it's going and back, and any rule that interferes with that can expect to be disregarded. But Recorders have the noninterference rule drummed into them from the beginning of their training—besides, if they were constitutional interferers, they wouldn't want to be Recorders in the first place. Integrators, though for different reasons, are just as strong on that rule; and I appealed to Valmis for backing.

He said, "Raf, I have already interfered with this world—with the universe—to an ultimate degree. I hadn't worked it out before; in panic, I used the Displacer, but this plane did not exist before then. *I* called it into being! So you will see that I am not very much concerned about any further interference with it or any part of it!"

There was no use arguing with Valmis—he was set on his notion that he had done something cosmic with his weird device, and that was it. I turned to Ari, "Surely you can see—"

"I must agree with Valmis and Dark," he said. "Whether or not Valmis's contention is correct, the clear truth is that we are in a position where we must choose between interfering with the natives of an obscure—and perhaps in a sense unreal—planet, on the one hand, and settling among them, on the other—and if I must believe in displaced probabilities and so on in order to be at ease about that interference, then that's what I'll believe."

10

I knew quite well what, aside from self-preservation, was in his mind. Metahistorians, studying the flow of history on a myriad of planets, with as close an approximation to the scientific method as possible, lack one thing: the experiment. They are good at making what has happened fit in with Metahistorical theory and at explaining what's going to happen in a way that can always be made to seem accurate later on, but they are barred from saying, "If you wish *this* effect under *these* conditions, then *that* action will produce it," and carrying the idea out. To do such a thing to prove a scientific (or quasi-scientific) point would be appallingly callous and would also, of course, be a direct violation of the Explorers' noninterference rule. But Ari now had a pressing motive to justify what he might do, and Valmis's bizarre talk eased his conscience enough to allow this.

"And I expect *you* intend to work out the best ways to interfere?" I said.

"I will certainly make available, when I have acquired it, my understanding of the trends and crisis points on this planet," Ari replied suavely. "It should give you some interesting material to Record."

"Trends or not," Dark said, "we'll have to get these fellows turned into competent metallurgists and technicians—and I have some plans for how to do that. Strap in, all of you—there's land ahead! If there's anything left in the control jets, I'll point her down and try to slow her so we'll be able to take the landing."

I could see a shoreline, backed by mountains, catching the light of the planet's sun, which was behind us. As we descended, I could see *Wanderer*'s shadow racing ahead of us—first smooth, then more and more distorted by the waves, now clearly recognizable as we

11

neared the surface. I also got a flash of what appeared to be vessels—far off, but obviously able to see us, if we could see them. Whatever our encounter with them was to be—rescue or attack—it would be happening soon.

Now we were racing in, the shore and vessels lost to sight, only the sky above and the sea, nearly surrounding us. *Wanderer* shuddered and white foam splashed past the viewports, then clear air again for an instant—we must have hit the crest of a wave—then a slam that flung us against our retaining straps, a rolling motion that left us leaning far to right, then to left, before we settled—if that is the word—into a helical swaying that I found remarkably unnerving.

"We're down," Dark said unnecessarily. "Gather what gear you want to have with you—then there's nothing to do but wait."

2

Our spectral data on the planet had shown the atmosphere to be breathable, but it was all the same a relief when Dark cracked the top hatch and we sniffed the air that flooded in—tangy, a little high in oxygen, but quite compatible to our systems and pleasant after *Wanderer*'s sterile, controlled atmosphere. We wouldn't have to worry about filters. Some planets which are technically hospitable to human life have really filthy air—it will keep you going, but you get into the habit of breathing shallowly and find it hard to respect the locals, who seem happy with the stuff.

An atmosphere of this sort strongly implied drinkable water. As for food, we would have to trust to luck after our store of concentrates ran out, though Explorer experience shows that a place where humans can breathe usually provides something they can eat. In any case, on joining the Service, we had all been surgically modified with a variety of implants so as to amplify the normal range of what we could safely and profitably eat—even wood in an emergency. But all of us made sure to load our coveralls with as many packets of concentrate as we could.

For me the most vital item of baggage was the Communicator, which after a short period of scanning any alien speech pattern, whether oral, gestural, or a combination, can give a skilled Recorder a reasonably good

13

command of the language and refine it to perfection in a little longer. My own contribution to the Communicator is one of which I am particularly proud: the mode controls. When a Recorder is sure of the general sense of a sequence of talk—that fear, inquiry, anger or whatever is being conveyed—he presses the proper mode stud, and the Communicator's internal computer, by restricting itself to expressions appropriate to that sense, is enabled to shorten the time necessary to arrive at an accurate and relevant vocabulary. All this assumes that you can find a native who isn't too frightened to sit down and talk for a while; nontechnological beings— Level Three and below—often get the impression that the Communicator is absorbing some of their vital essence, so the first topics you get a good grasp of are apprehension and distaste rather than anything useful.

Each Explorer has his stresses, of course, but I have always felt that the Recorder, though considered the least important crew member in Survey work, has to endure more than most, in effect having to turn himself into a native, learning to think as well as talk as they do. Many of us are really finished for Exploration after no more than a dozen trips; it is time to leave the Service when you find yourself less and less able to be sure who you are after having been so many other people. And the occasional, though rare, encounter with a non-humanoid intelligent race hastens the process. One Recorder I knew did a comparatively short tour on a planet inhabited by beings who communicated by graceful waves of a fringe of tentacles accompanied by a buzzing noise which served to indicate emotion, emphasis and, where relevant, social standing. Pleasant fellows when you got to know them, he insisted, but he was never very easy to talk to after that, being unable to suppress a tendency to drone and make his fingers writhe.

Once I had made sure of the Communicator, its power pack and its accessory kit, I stored up on food concentrate; then, as ready as I could be, I looked at the others.

Dark had his Captain's personal tool kit, containing medical supplies and instruments and gadgets useful for small repairs and adjustments. He was also in charge of the slim cylinder containing the equipment we preferred not to think of—the stasis devices. That is a Captain's responsibility, a fact for which all other Explorers are thankful.

Ari was cradling his Metahistorical microtapes, which contained analyses of the pasts and presents and futures of any number of worlds and solar systems, and the hand viewer he used to scan them. I knew that, as our senior member, he had with him also a supply of the age/stress counter-treatments the Service provided for the elderly.

Valmis carried nothing except food concentrates—Integrators' equipment is all in their minds (and in the minds and equipment of the Metahistorians and Recorders, whom they shamelessly exploit whenever they need something concrete to weave into their Patterns!). The one exception was his so-called Displacer, and that appeared to have blown itself up when he tried it. Well, if the rest of us ran short, Valmis could be considered as a walking supply of concentrates.

Dark had the only clear view of our surroundings, the pilot's seat being higher than the rest of the cabin, as well as forward; the other viewports were covered by water most of the time, with an occasional glimpse of sky and foam as a wave trough passed. He leaned down and said, "Visitors—close to."

He clambered amidships, pushed the top hatch fully open, and climbed out. We followed and gingerly balanced ourselves on *Wanderer*'s hull as it pitched in the waves.

Dark looked gloomily at the approaching native craft. "At least it's not using oars," he said.

It seemed to me that an oar-powered vessel would have had to be better designed than the one approaching us. Its makers had built it to float and to carry a propulsion plant, but apparently had not thought much further than that.

"Hydrocarbon-fueled," Dark said—unnecessarily, as the wind brought a cloud of black smoke hurrying ahead of the ship to engulf us momentarily, and the stink was unmistakable.

A shout came from the deck of the ungainly craft as it neared us; the figures lining it were reasonably humanoid in appearance, though on the short, squat side, as far as I could make out.

Very soon it was alongside, carrying its own stench—which I hoped reflected bad housekeeping rather than the inherent essence of the natives—and lines snaked down to us from the deck, now about a body length above our heads. Dark climbed up briskly, hand over hand, then leaned over the railing to give a boost to Ari, physically always the least adept member of the crew. Valmis went up next and I followed.

I could have wished for a more dramatic first encounter between two intelligent races than this. We usually try to make it an impressive business, with careful preparation and ceremony, conveying clearly

16

but tactfully that the Explorer team is both powerful and well-intentioned. A vital part of this is preliminary long-range work by the Recorder before actual contact, so that the first words spoken by the Explorers are in the native tongue, a tactic which has a powerful psychological effect.

As it was, there seemed no point in my saying anything; we stood in two groups, Explorers and natives, eyeing each other for a moment—my own concern being suddenly with the queasiness occasioned by the ship's motion, even more pronounced than *Wanderer*'s—before one of the natives spoke. His voice was loud and firm. I guessed what he said to be a ritual greeting, suitable for an encounter which must have struck him as uncanny, something along the lines of "Greeting and peace, O strangers. What are your intentions toward us?"—possibly with some flattering adjectives added to placate us.

I had started up the Communicator as soon as I boarded the vessel, and the native's words were instantly stored in its computer, but I knew there would have to be a considerable amount of steady, directed conversation before it could provide much of a grasp of what was being said.

"Greeting to you also," I said. "Our spaceship was damaged and we were obliged to land here; thank you for taking us aboard your craft." Not that there was any chance of his understanding me, but it is best under those circumstances to say what you would if communication *did* exist—at least the manner and tone are appropriate.

He turned to some of the other natives and asked them something. "Ha," Ari said. "The only question he can logically be asking is whether any of them understood us. From this we infer that some of these people have encountered visitors from another planet already, and learned their language—"

"It could also be," I said, "that they have no knowledge or concept that there is anywhere but this planet to be *from,* and consider us some sort of exotics from another part of it."

"And it could be," said Dark, who always inclined to a suspicious view of natives and their ways, "that he's asking if they ought to sacrifice us to the sea gods."

For two of the native sailors were advancing on us. We stiffened, but they brushed past us to the rail.

"Hey!" Dark yelled as they slid down the ropes to *Wanderer.* "Captain—nice of you to pick us up, but those fellows can't go down there!"

"Don't worry, Dark," I said. "A quick look around will convince them that we're from a culture very different from anything on this planet, and we can start off on a proper footing with them. It's not as if there were anything loose in there for them to steal."

Dark glared at me. "It's not stealing I'm worried about, but they might—"

A cloud of steam burst from the water behind *Wanderer*'s submerged stern jet; the ship lifted half its length above the surface, nose first, then slammed down with a smack like an explosion and raised a wave that heeled the native vessel so far over that for an instant I was looking down at the sea across the nearly vertical deck, as if I had been at the top of a wall. Then, of course, it rocked back nearly as far the other way. By the time we were certain the vessel would not capsize and I turned to look at *Wanderer,* there was nothing left of her but a boiling patch on the surface, as the last of her air was displaced by the alien sea.

"—meddle with the controls," Dark finished. "Just a whiff of power left, evidently. Blundering natives!" He subsided into an icy gloom.

The vessel's captain was roaring, and I fingered the *anger* mode stud on the Communicator. Two heads popped up in the agitated water, and the tone of the captain's roars changed; seamen hurried to throw lines to their shipmates, who were quickly hauled on board.

The dripping men talked excitedly to their captain, who glared at us and took them off to the crude cabin in the middle of the vessel. Evidently they had had a chance to take in some of the details of *Wanderer*'s interior that did not accord with the usual run of things on this planet.

The other crewmen drifted away uneasily, leaving us alone on the forward deck. The vessel turned and began plowing through the waves.

Valmis said, "This will be a strange but rich experience, unique in Exploration. We will be the first Explorer team to be really *part* of a world, investigating it with only its own resources and our human qualities to depend on—a whole new insight—"

"You need a whole new head," Dark said. "The experience is that *Wanderer*'s at the bottom of the sea and we're prisoners of a bunch of jumpy natives who aren't the least bit interested in being Explored."

I am by nature optimistic, but felt that Dark had summed the situation up all too accurately.

Soon a shoreline was visible, mountains running down almost to the sea. In a while we could make out buildings huddled densely, some tall and blocky, most low to the ground. Our vessel headed toward a tangle of ships, some larger than it was, but all of equally crude construction, and came alongside a wooden platform extending from the shore far out into the harbor.

The crewmen began fastening the vessel to the platform with lines, and the captain leaped onto it and walked to a shed at the shore end.

I had used the last part of our voyage for some planning. "The thing to do now," I said, "is to find some person of consequence who will at least understand that we are out of the ordinary and be interested enough to be willing to communicate with us. Once I have a command of the language, we can explain our predicament and our mission and set about enlisting the natives' aid."

"It might be as well to do so quickly," Ari said, nodding toward the remaining sailors. These—especially the two who had so disastrously boarded *Wanderer,* whom I was able to distinguish from their fellows by their still-sodden condition—were looking at us in what I felt sure was a menacing fashion. I got their expressions on the Communicator's visual scanner, keyed to the appropriate mode; this may have been a mistake, as pointing the device at them seemed to increase their anger.

"Thank you for your help," I said. "We are grateful for the rescue, but we must leave now to see to some business." Again I was relying on the principle of speaking normally so as to get the proper tone.

We moved to the edge of the craft and prepared to step down, and the natives immediately surrounded us. They did not actually seize us, but made it impossible to get past them without violence, which it would have been imprudent as well as discourteous to offer.

"I don't recall that any of them is likely to have said anything like 'Let us go' since we've been here," Ari said thoughtfully. "There wasn't any situation that called for that. If there had been, I suppose you could find the spot on your speech record and play it back to them."

So I could have, but Ari was right: nothing that had been said by any of the natives would have applied to our situation. However . . . I ran the recorder back to the captain's angry roaring when *Wanderer* had made its last leap and gone down, apparently drowning two of his seamen, and pressed the *play* stud.

At the sound of their chief's voice, the natives fell back; as I had thought, they were conditioned to respect his wrath. They stood indecisively for a moment, and we jumped over the side and onto the platform.

We walked briskly down it toward the shore, moving especially quickly past the shed where the captain, his back to us, was talking with another native, presumably telling him of his strange catch at sea.

We did not take time to observe the curious features of the city we found ourselves in, but hurried down first one street and then another, taking right and left turns at random, until we were fairly sure we were not being followed by the captain.

I suppose we were not—at least he was not visible in the crowd we found about us as soon as we stopped. They seemed to have sprung out of the ground, and were jabbering and pointing. I had hoped that we might not be so unlike the natives so as to attract undue attention, but this was clearly not to be. There were at least thirty individuals surrounding us; and, while of a variety of sizes, shapes and modes of dress, they obviously had far more in common with one another than with us.

They continued to gesticulate and talk as their numbers increased, but did not approach us closely or attempt to touch us.

Having assumed the leadership of *Wanderer*'s crew for the moment, I felt it was up to me to take some productive action, but I could not think of any.

"Tell them to take us to their leader," Dark suggested.

"How? I don't have the native words for anything yet, except what a sea captain says when he sees two of his crewmen dragged to the bottom by a metal sea monster!"

"We could mime it," Valmis said. To my irritation, largely because I should have thought of it first, I must admit, my colleagues immediately agreed, and we fell to working up a short bit of pantomime that would convey our wishes.

After quick consultation, we gathered around Dark, who stood at first with his arms folded, frowning, then made brusque gestures of command—move, kneel, turn, and so forth—which we obeyed with exaggerated respect. Valmis, Ari and I then pointed at Dark, holding the gesture for a moment. If the natives could not understand from this that he was our leader, it would really be hopeless to expect anything of them.

Once we were sure this idea had been gotten across if it was ever going to be, we all turned to point at the crowd, made a gesture as though drawing or fetching something toward us, then pointed back at Dark. If that didn't say, "Take us to your leader," or at least, "Bring your leader here"—there could be confusion on that point—I don't know what it did say.

To the crowd, though, it did not seem to be that clear. They laughed, waved, jumped, but did nothing that looked as if it would result in a leader turning up.

Then I saw one of them throw something; it clinked as it hit near me and rolled a bit before toppling on its side: a metal disc. Others began to do the same, and I feared we were under some sort of attack, though an inefficient one, as none of the discs came near hitting us or was thrown with any force.

Ari picked up a couple of them and said, "Probably tokens of small units of credit—characteristic of Levels Two to Six. See—several are identical, hence mass produced; probably a government monopoly."

"Could they not be amulets?" Valmis said. "That would be a more appropriate offering to strangers from another world—the images of their deities seem to be stamped on them."

"Ha!" Dark said. "Your charade has got us taken for wandering clowns—these natives have the impudence to toss us payment for entertaining them! Though I must say you fellows looked funny, kneeling and bobbing like that. You'd better pick those things up; we don't have anything else anybody on this world seems to want."

At this point a native pushed through the crowd,

23

parting it with peremptory cries and a jab now and then from a stick he carried. He was dressed differently from any of them and, by the deference they showed in giving way, was certainly someone of authority.

This would not be the leader we were looking for, but he ought to be able to put us in touch with him or someone else of standing.

He stood looking at us severely—I was becoming more familiar with the natives' facial expressions, and his had many points of resemblance to the sea captain's—and said something in their incomprehensible language.

Now I had to make one of those judgments sometimes forced on Recorders—to make an intuitive leap toward communication with an alien race. The first sequence on my Communicator was the captain's opening words as we boarded his vessel—almost certainly, I had sensed at the time, a carefully polite greeting and query about our intentions. That being so, it should serve at least roughly for a salutation to this official. I slid back to that portion of the recording and depressed the *play* stud.

The captain's words boomed out, with instant, though varied, effect. Some of the crowd laughed, some opened their mouths and widened their eyes, some—females at a guess, from certain differences in costume and apparent structure—turned and left that place. The man with the stick grimaced—looking very like the captain now—and menaced me with it. He then called out, and others appeared, dressed like him and also carrying sticks. He spoke to them loudly, and they surrounded us and hustled us off.

"Whatever did you do, Raf?" Ari asked as we were trotted down the street. I explained.

"Well, at least," Dark said with a noticeable bite in his voice, "we have learned that ritual politeness to strangers is not a constant rule in this culture. Useful knowledge, Recorder, if hard won."

"What was it the captain actually said, do you suppose, Raf?" Valmis asked.

Dark answered, "Probably 'Where did you drop from, you ugly-looking freaks, and what do you think you're playing at?' Plus whatever they use for insulting expletives here. Those sailors looked like a crude lot."

I suspected that Dark's interpretation was based on what his own reactions might have been—he was never a very patient man—but had to admit that the effect of my playback made it probable. My own guess, I felt, had been the logical one, but it appeared that these natives' habits did not necessarily conform to logic.

We soon arrived at a large, substantially constructed building, and after what appeared to be official formalities—including, to our dismay, the removal of my Communicator and Dark's and Ari's equipment—we were thrust into a small room with bars at the door and window. It was dimly lit, and we did not at first notice a native already in the room; he was stretched out on a shelf against the wall, apparently asleep.

"Fascinating," Ari said. "Absolutely fits in with Level Four and lower. Special facilities for storing undesirable or dangerous individuals. It's really rather elegantly simple and efficient; they combine keeping people where they can't do whatever it is that got them disliked, with sufficient unpleasantness to deter others who might be inclined that way. Ingenious, for a primitive culture."

"What *sort* of unpleasantness?" Dark said, looking around the chamber with distaste. The native on the shelf was now sitting up, looking at us with an expression which was new to me, but which, if I could still trust logic, was very likely fear. In the gloom of the place, our one-piece coveralls had their characteristic glow, and that, combined with our small but distinct difference in height and proportion from the natives and our easy conversation in a tongue unknown to them, must have produced a powerful impression on his unsophisticated mind.

Ari shrugged. "It varies. Sometimes nothing special—one is just kept there. In other cultures, there may be punishment or torture administered"—we glanced quickly around for anything that might be used for such a purpose, but saw nothing— "or such a place may merely be for temporary detention until something definite is decided. Ah!" He brightened. "There was a most interesting report from *Drifter,* several Explorations back. Much the same arrangement as this, with the function of keeping assembled those individuals chosen to contribute to the food supply."

None of us seemed to want this made any clearer, but I felt I should ask. "You mean slave labor for farming?"

"No, no," Ari said good-humoredly. "A *direct* contribution. Such persons were confined, fed well, kept in good health, and then, um, processed as foodstuffs. Given a society unstable enough to produce conflicts and intolerable behavior, it is really an economical way of handling things."

"Elegantly simple, you might say," Dark said heavily.

"Precisely."

"Would you say," Dark asked after he had looked at Ari for a moment with silent loathing, "that there is much chance of that being what *we* are in for?"

26

"Oh, no, no, no." Ari was amused. "That was a Level Two culture! Very far behind this one. Among human races, at least, you hardly ever get cannibalism much past midway through Three. Once they're into Four to any extent, the primitive community spirit required for ritual cannibalism is lost."

"What a pity." For once, Dark and I spoke at the same time and said the same thing.

The native who shared the room with us now seemed to have lost his fear. He pointed and laughed at us. He said some things in what I took to be a friendly tone, and I decided to pass the time with some practical "freehand" communicating.

It must not be thought that we Recorders are totally dependent on the Communicator; before being allowed to use it, we are trained in establishing contact with no aids whatever, thus getting the most solid grounding in basic principles. I had done especially well in training, and I rather looked forward to the opportunity of reawakening my old skill and of demonstrating to my colleagues the difference between my own expert approach and their amateurish efforts on the street, in which I had participated only out of momentary lack of another idea.

I pointed at myself and said, "Raf." He nodded his head up and down—I registered this as some sort of affirmative gesture—then pointed at me and said, "Raf," then at each of the others, saying "Raf, Raf, Raf."

At this point Dark shouldered me aside and confronted the native, who said, "Raf!" to him. He seemed to find the sound amusing.

"What are you doing?" I asked.

"I want to find out what's in store for us!" Dark

snapped. "If there's any prospect of us being eaten, I don't want it to come as a surprise!"

"That is just the sort of thing I should think one would prefer to be surprised by," Ari said. "That way, one is spared thinking about it, which is probably as bad as having it happen. Or, if not as bad, it lasts longer."

Dark ignored him and pointed vigorously at himself and the rest of us, then at his mouth, which he opened and shut as if chewing something. The native looked at him, then nodded his head up and down, smiled broadly, and, lifting his hands in front of him, palms inward, brought them almost together.

"What's that supposed to mean?" Dark asked uneasily, very much as if he were hoping he had not understood.

"Our native has done a very capable job of signing 'yes' and 'soon,' " I said.

"They're going to eat us!" Dark howled. "And I suppose that means this fellow gets spared for a while because of us—that's why he's so cheerful about it!" He glowered at the native, who backed away from him.

"It is a curious idea," Valmis said. "By ingesting the substance of individuals, they expect to take on some of their qualities; in a limited way, a striking recognition of the unity of all existence."

"I would be inclined to consider it more in the light of a political and economic manifestation," Ari said with the bright interest that always came to him when he had the chance of a good theoretical argument. "Though it is, of course, remarkable to find it in a Level Four culture. I am afraid I was rather dogmatic on that point a moment ago!" He chuckled ruefully, as at a good joke on himself. Dark's hand twitched, giving the impression that it wished, independently of its owner, to strike Ari.

28

"Consider: they hardly know enough about us to decide whether they would want to share our qualities, so we must dismiss Valmis's suggestion. The little we have seen of these people and their works inclines me to the view that they are mechanistic pragmatists—note for example the complete absence of awe at our mysterious appearance; the lack of ritual greeting formulas (as Raf's ill-advised experiment demonstrates!); their crass perception of us as street entertainers. I would say it is a matter of a combination of limited food supply, perhaps with a growing population, which can be expected, no matter what the cultural level, to produce aberrant—I might even say brutal—behavior."

"It's nice to know that you think it's aberrant of them to eat us," Dark said. "I don't think I could bear to feel you approved of it."

"No," Ari said seriously. "While it is my task to understand the dynamics of any culture and their relationship to the fundamentals of Metahistory, I admit that I cannot be objective in considering *every* manifestation of such a culture. Though dispassionate in observation, I *would* feel obliged to add my own opinion in a final report—"

Dark slammed his fist against the stone wall of the room. "Final report! *Your* final report'll be a hearty belch from some savage while he's picking fragments of you out of his teeth!"

Ari bridled, and I intervened. "The problem, Dark, may be one of communication. The native apparently understood the concepts of 'eat' and 'us' as you conveyed them, and rather neatly gave you his 'yes—soon' answer, but the whole thing was very sketchy around the operants. You really ought to leave that sort of thing to me; I am trained for it."

29

Dark ground his teeth. I continued, looking past him through the barred door to the corridor beyond to verify my conclusion. "For instance, may he not have understood you to mean 'Do we eat?' rather than 'Are we to be eaten?' If so, the reply 'soon,' together with an expression of cheerfulness, becomes logical and friendly rather than a piece of heartless barbarity."

"A bit far-fetched," said Ari, clearly reluctant to abandon his unique discovery of industrialized cannibals.

"I think not. If you will look into the corridor, you will see one of the attendants bringing along dishes of something and placing them in the rooms—if not food, what?"

"Fattening us for the slaughter, then," Dark grumbled, though he did seem relieved.

In a moment the native was at our door, opened it, and slid in five bowls heaped with an unfamiliar but pungent-smelling substance, and closed the door again in a practiced series of motions.

"Our" native took one of the bowls, lifted a utensil inserted in the stuff, and began to eat it, after waving at us and the remaining bowls.

Dark, Ari, Valmis and I picked them up, fished out the utensils, and sampled the food. After a mouthful, by common consent we laid the bowls down and opened and ate a unit of food concentrate each. I signed to the native that he might have our bowls, but he seemed to find his own fairly hard going after the first pangs of hunger were stayed, and did not take the offer.

"Well," Dark said thoughtfully, "I suppose we're safe from being eaten. Whatever that stuff is, it can't be meant to fatten anything up!"

We were now well if not enjoyably fed, and as we could see through the small window that we were now well into the planet's night cycle, there seemed little to do but compose ourselves for sleep on the shelves along the walls. Ari wished to discuss our plight and what to do about it, but the events of the day had left us all exhausted.

"I have the feeling we'll have plenty of time to figure things out while we're here," Dark said. "I somehow don't see a delegation of local dignitaries coming to fetch us in the morning and wanting to know what they can do for us." He nodded at the native, who, after eating his meal, had yawned, wrapped himself in some pieces of cloth, and fallen asleep. "That chap looks as if he's not expecting anything to happen for quite a while." Dark looked almost savagely gloomy, and I could sense that he, most of all, wanted to be finally done with the day that had seen the loss of his beloved *Wanderer*.

As Valmis settled onto his shelf, he muttered, "This would be quite uncomfortable, if it were real." Dark and I exchanged glances. It would be too bad if Valmis suffered a breakdown at a time when our only hope lay in functioning as effectively as any Explorer team had ever done. I fell asleep resolving that first thing in the morning I at least would set about my own duty, Communication, in spite of the absence of my equipment.

Nobody in the cell was at all cheerful when we awoke. We four Explorers each experienced the dreadful moment of coming back to consciousness with the realization that we were marooned on an alien world, after a comforting split-second of thinking ourselves in our quarters on *Wanderer;* the native, sitting bolt upright on his shelf, looked at us with alarm and incredulity, as if he had not seen us before. He shook his head several times, then finally shrugged.

Mindful of my decision of the previous night, I approached him; while he pressed himself against the wall, he did not actually flee from me. I considered asking the others to help me establish Communication with him, but recalled the less than satisfactory results of our performance on the street the day before, and decided to handle it on my own.

It seemed to me that the most important thing was to get across to him the idea that we did not come from his planet. Anything we might wish to accomplish with any of the natives had to start from that fact. I also hoped to determine from his reaction whether our reception as off-worlders would be more likely to be respectful or hostile.

I squatted on the dusty floor in front of him and sketched a circle with my forefinger, to represent his planet. I then pointed at him and rapidly sketched in a stick figure standing on the border of the circle: *you* belong to *this* world. He looked at it blankly, then at me. I studied the lines in the dust and had to admit that they appeared to form the picture of a man balancing himself on a ball, like an acrobatic performer.

I brushed it away and moved to a clear space. This time I drew a larger circle and, inside it, an irregular line resembling what I could remember of the nearby coastline as seen from the air; I had not paid all that much attention to it, but there were some distinctive inlets and promontories that I was able to dredge from my memory, which apparently registered with the native, who narrowed his eyes and nodded slowly. At about the position of the port, I made a smudge with my thumb, pointed once again at the native, and sketched a diminutive figure near the smudge. He nodded vigorously.

I moved some distance away across the floor and drew another circle, then pointed at myself, Ari, Dark and Valmis, and drew four rudimentary figures on the border of that circle: *we* belong to *that* world.

The native looked at the farther circle and at us, nodded once again, and muttered something aloud.

Moving with some difficulty, he levered himself up off his shelf and walked to the circle representing our home world. He bent over, placed his hand on the sketched figures representing us, then raised it, walked over to the drawing of his planet, and laid it down with an explosive noise: you have traveled from your world to mine and impacted on it?

I nodded, and he sat back on his shelf, looking at us thoughtfully. I was anticipating the next information I would try to get across to him—the need for us to meet with someone of importance—when, to my surprise, he jumped up, ran for the door, and began yelling urgently.

In a moment, one of the uniformed natives appeared, and, after an exchange of shouts, our fellow tenant was marched away and out of sight.

"What was that all about?" Dark asked.

"As soon as I managed to convey to the native that we were from another world, he started raising that fuss," I said uneasily. I could not see why he had done

33

so, but it was an unexpected and therefore disturbing reaction.

"Level Four cultures are rarely geared to deal comfortably with alien contact," Ari said. "Industrialization promotes a world view that places great reliance on mechanics and simple physics, hence denies the unfamiliar as a matter of principle, and the idea of voyagers through space is bound to be the most unfamiliar one possible. Some such cultures retain Level Three (and lower, of course) characteristics of superstition, and begin by treating alien visitors as supernatural beings, which often has amusing results."

Dark started. "Amusing? I'll bet that fellow has gone off to denounce us as demons and suggest that we be burned or something!"

"That would probably be only fair," Valmis said.

I forestalled Dark's violent response by saying, "Look, Valmis, I know you're brooding over that business of switching universes about, or whatever you think you did, and I'm sorry if it's weighing on you. But it's done, and we're here, and I don't think it matters whether this universe *is* an alternate that you've somehow called into being, or the real one. It seems to work the same way the one we were in yesterday did, and we are in just as bad a spot as if it were real—we've got to do everything we can, use all of our abilities to the utmost, to get out of it! So leave off that stuff about wrenching the cosmos, and act like an Explorer!"

I think that Valmis was as much impressed by Dark's and Ari's respectful response to my brief harangue as by the words themselves; none of them were used to my being at all forceful, since Recorders usually look upon themselves as being, however vital to the success of any mission, rather passive instruments, or machines in human form, with the decision and action left to the

34

others. However, this was a new and, so far as we knew, unprecedented situation, even aside from Valmis's notions, and a new approach seemed called for.

"Well, then," said Dark, "let's get to it. What sort of plan had you in mind?"

Unhappily, even my un-Recorderlike behavior did not seem to affect our situation, which was that we were locked up.

We discussed several possible approaches, with even Valmis shedding his philosophical gloom and guilt and joining in, but none of them seemed at all productive. Without an improved attitude on the part of the natives or, at the very least, access to my Communicator so that we might make a beginning at explaining ourselves, there seemed no place to start. I own that I felt a certain pride at my fellow Explorers' clear acknowledgment that my specialty was the necessary starting point for any of them to employ theirs, but this gratification was considerably diminished by the fact that I wasn't able to do anything at all in my line under these conditions, and what I had done in making our origins evident to the native who had shared our chamber appeared to be of distinctly two-edged significance.

We had pretty well exhausted our fund of ideas when a crowd of natives boiled into our corridor, and one of them unlocked and opened the door. Our former companion was among them, though he did not now seem to be in the custody of any one of them, and made urgent beckoning gestures to us. We were surrounded and hustled down the corridor to the room where our equipment had been taken away from us, and to my surprise it was handed back to us. Our native friend, now seeming, for reasons I could not understand, to exercise some authority, superintended its return.

A great wash of relief and, I confess, comfort flooded

me as I felt once again the familiar shape and bulk of my Communicator. And I daresay Ari and Dark felt the same way about their own equipment. A specialist can accomplish much by relying solely on his training, but it is undeniable that the machinery we use amplifies our abilities enormously.

Our native, unaccompanied, I was relieved to see, by the others, led us outside the building and into a vehicle, which started off with a roaring noise as soon as we were inside. I did not take much note of its nature, my interest not being in that direction, and in any case I was absorbed with the Communicator. Dark and Ari were exclaiming at the curious spectacle of the city we were passing through; Valmis was looking at the view with a detached expression; and the native, who now seemed to be effectively in charge of us, was regarding us with an air of speculation.

I fingered the *Inquiry/information* mode controls and gestured, first at the passing panorama, then at the Communicator, while looking meaningfully at the native. He appeared to understand something of its function, for he leaned toward the mechanism and spoke, more loudly and slowly, I noticed, than had been his habit.

I then pressed the *replay* stud, and his words were repeated; he nodded as though to show he understood. Either sound reproduction was known in this culture or he was willing to assume that visitors from another world would be likely to have some such device. This was a relief to me, as the responses of the ship's crew and the crowd in the street had left me uncertain about whether this particular bit of technology might not be looked on here as witchcraft, a notion that Ari's earlier comments had made appear all too plausible.

36

"Are you explaining things to him, Raf?" Dark asked. "Any prospects that we can get help in refitting *Wanderer?*"

"It'll be a while before I can do that, I'm afraid. First we have to store an immense amount of language information, then let the computer sort it out and—"

"But you fellows are supposed to be able to start chattering the local lingo as soon as you run up against the natives. That's your job, isn't it?"

"If," I said with some asperity, "things go properly and we have a decent period of surveillance, as laid down in regulations, there is no problem. With enough to go on, the Communicator can build up a decent vocabulary by encounter time and achieve perfect fluency as soon as we've been able to do some directed work with the indigenes. I'm not blaming anybody, you understand, Dark, but if we're dumped in the middle of an alien culture by what I'm sure was unavoidable mechanical failure, you can't expect the same results as if it had all gone as it was supposed to."

I was really rather irritated, not so much by Dark's criticism as by the fact that our exchange was taking up time that I would rather have used in gathering information from our native host.

"I don't know if you can find out about it now," Valmis observed, "but it would be worthwhile looking into what's happened to this city lately. The Pattern is all off: there are bare spaces and new buildings right alongside old ones in a way that doesn't make sense. When you can, you might try to find out it they've had a war here recently, or some other kind of disaster."

I didn't appreciate Valmis's attempt to load more work on me at a time when it was impossible to do as he asked, but I did feel somewhat cheered that he was emerging from his gloom enough to take a practical interest in his work. A capable Integrator can be tremendously useful in Exploration, in spite of the mystical bent of most of them, in spotting anomalies the other specialists might overlook. "I'll look into it when I can," I said, "though once I've got the language stored and interpreted, any of you will be able to put your own questions."

Our vehicle stopped at that moment in front of an imposing building of several stories, and our native guide hustled us inside and up a flight of stairs, pausing in the large room at the entrance to secure the services of another, smaller native, one of a throng standing about, who trotted ahead and opened a door for us. The room into which we were ushered was luxuriously furnished and was evidently a living apartment.

"Ten to one this is a sort of inn he's putting us up at," Dark said, looking around with satisfaction. "Seems as though our little friend is prepared to do handsomely by us. Now all you've got to do, Raf, is get to work with your machine and educate him enough to understand us."

I sighed; would it ever be possible to make an Explorer pilot understand the nature of a Recorder's work? "It's the other way around," I said patiently. "The Communicator makes it possible for *us* to learn *their* language. What you suggest wouldn't be reasonable; they're at an earlier stage in cultural development and wouldn't have the ability to frame enough concepts in our language to make it useful. The fact that *we're* the ones making the first contact shows the difference readily enough."

In the course of the ensuing planetary days, the native who had taken us in charge saw that our wants in

38

the way of food were attended to, though it was made clear that we were not allowed to leave our quarters. He brought to view us a number of his fellows, whom I at length divined to be scientists of varying sorts. To these I conveyed what I had to our host concerning our origin on a planet other than theirs, though I was dismayed when they set about poking, prodding, probing and scraping me in an evident effort to determine what physical characteristics might verify our difference from their race. This they also did to the others, which at least relieved my companions' boredom.

After some time, it was clear that they were satisfied on this point, and they departed. Some of their conversation had been added to my Communicator's memory banks, though not enough to advance my understanding of the local language to any useful extent, at least not to the point of being able to use it. I could pretty well understand some of what was said to me, however, and thus could relay it to my companions.

On the fifth day I was able to give them some news that brightened their moods, which were somewhat dampened by our enforced seclusion: another native was to join us and prepare us for wider contact with the people of this world.

"Now we're getting somewhere!" Dark exclaimed. "What are they giving us? One of their technicians? Maybe we can start finding out what sort of help they can give us with *Wanderer*."

"I should think that whatever the local analogue is for a Metahistorian would be more fruitful," Ari observed.

"Well . . . " I said. "It isn't either of those."

"Another scientist? What sort?" Ari asked.

"Not a scientist, either. It's a . . . a composer of fictions."

They looked at me in amazement for a moment. "I

don't suppose," Dark asked heavily, "that your Communicator gadget might have got a crossed circuit in it someplace?"

"The sealed unit is completely—"

"Ah, never mind. It's of a piece with the rest of this idiotic place—*I* can't make out what any of it means, and this is no odder than the rest of what we've gone through. D'you suppose this planet's a dumping ground for the feeble-minded from some other worlds? That would explain—"

A chuckle from Valmis interrupted him. "It may be that these folk have an intuitive sense of Patterns, that they *know,* don't you see, that we're fictions now and so are they . . ."

"Stow that!" Dark said hotly. "Or we'll see if a fictional fist can raise a bruise on your fictional hide!"

Valmis looked at him calmly. "I expect you're right, Dark. Whether this universe was here before I used the Displacer or not, it's what we're in, after all. What's done is done. But I wonder," he added after a pause, "if all this is real *now* . . . is anything more real than that? Are all the Probabilities no more than the sum of our agreements to Perceive them?"

I never knew an Integrator who could say something simply, without raising unanswerable and irrelevant questions. It is probably unkind to think that this is how they maintain the idea that they're necessary.

5

Bizarre though the notion was as our friend explained it,
I was able to see the sense in this plan of having a
romancer deal with us. It seemed that he had actually
composed fictions which had brought the theme of flight
through space to public attention and that these had
gained wide popularity. Therefore, when the news of
our existence was made known to the public, it would
be helpful to have the authority of this person employed
to this end, as the generality of people were unclear as
to the distinction between fact and fiction in any case.

Though still badly hampered by not being able to
make myself understood, and beginning to be apprehensive on this account, as the Communicator
should by now have been able to instill in me a perfectly
adequate fluency in this tongue, I was able to gather
from our native much information to clear up some
matters that had puzzled us.

It appeared that he was an employee of an infor-
mation-gathering organization, or, more accurately,
once more so occupied. At the time we met him, he had
been confined by the authorities for offenses committed
while celebrating his dismissal from his position, but,
upon noting in his cell the uncanniness of our nature, he
had communicated with his former chief and arranged
his and our release.

It was his chief's anticipation that his organization

would benefit greatly from controlling the dissemination of information concerning us, and to this end he had agreed to undertake the expenses of our maintenance and the verification of our nature, as well as to rehire our friend and put him in charge of the operation. I noted that our agreement to this arrangement had not been sought, but could not see that we had any choice. At least something was happening, which appeared to be all that we could expect at this point.

We had to wait a few more days for the romancer to join us, as he had been summoned, at considerable cost, from another region of the planet. When he arrived, he proved to be a physically unimpressive specimen, but ebullient and inquiring of manner and most frustrated by my inability to provide him with any detailed information. Fortunately, the operation of the Communicator, even though it was not completely fulfilling its purpose, fascinated and diverted him.

Now that our party was completed to our guide's employer's satisfaction, events moved quickly, and we and our possessions were soon conveyed to a string of narrow wagons which removed us from the seaport at a great rate of speed.

"Evidently the fellow our friend works for carries a lot of weight," I told my companions. "He's set it up for us to meet with the native political chief."

"Of the planet? That is good news," said Ari.

"Not quite. They do that by sections here, I gather —one chief here, one there, dozens of them for the planet. The romancer himself is from another of these sections."

"Another Level Four characteristic, is it?" Dark said with some asperity. "If this chief fellow ran the whole world, it'd do some good to speak to him about helping us, but if he's only in charge of one potty little patch of land inhabited by savages, what's the point?''

Dark's estimate of the size of the native ruler's realm was undergenerous. It took us six local days to cross it, the chief's steading being on the other side of it from where we had come ashore; and at that we made a fair rate of speed for land transportation. I did not bother myself with the details of our conveyance, but they delighted Ari, who claimed that the whole method could clearly be seen to derive from an earlier age, Levels Three and Two most probably, in which the motive power had been draft animals.

"You must perfect yourself in this language, Raf,'' he said to me on the second day, ''and pass it on to us. I can't wait to start finding out all about this place. It looks perfectly fascinating, a textbook example of cultural progression, with fossil remnants of the past embedded in it according to the best principles of Metahistory. Just look at that!''

He pointed to the landscape which rolled by us, and I could see a cluster of huts made of some sort of fabric huddled in the desolate landscape. "Just at the border between Levels One and Two, I'd say, and here we are passing them in a high-grade Level Four device. Theory predicts that, but I don't know when I've seen it so clearly embodied.''

Valmis spoke up, something he did rarely. "Raf, once you do have the language, I've been wondering, what are we to tell them about ourselves?''

"How do you mean?'' Dark said.

"Well, if we're set on interfering with them so as to

get their science and all that in the shape we want, I wonder how they're going to like being told that? Not very much, I'd say.''

This was a thought that had not struck me, or any of the others, it developed. It soon became apparent that it would not be much good explaining to the natives that we were Explorers, either, since without *Wanderer* we should not be able to do any worthwhile Exploring or Survey work, and so would have no visible function; from the little we had seen of this planet, it did not look like a place very hospitable to those considered of no use.

It was Dark who hit on the idea that we ought to present ourselves as an embassy from the Galactic Empire.

"But there isn't a Galactic Empire," Ari said. "It wouldn't work—the galaxy's too big. Only the smallest solar systems have empires, and they're pretty rickety."

"The natives aren't to know that, though, are they?" Dark said. "The thing to do is give them an impressive story, the more puffed up the better, to make sure they'll treat us right."

We agreed on this, and I began polishing the details of the imposture against the day when the Communicator might function well enough to allow me to use it.

This had not happened by the time we were making our approach to the meeting with the native chief. We were proceeding in open wagons toward his headquarters, having left the conveyance which had been our home for six days, and I was once more trying to persuade the Communicator to give me instantaneous access to the native vocabulary stored within it that it was meant to provide. Dark watched me for a moment and asked, "What seems to be wrong with it, anyhow?"

"*I* don't know. It just doesn't seem to be doing what it ought to."

"Well, have you . . . here, let me have a look." After he had examined its interior for a moment, he looked up at me. "How well," he said in a gentle tone, "do you expect a piece of machinery to work if one of its two power leads is loose?"

"Ah . . . not very?"

"*Just* so. Now, give it a try."

I adjusted the control and placed the earpiece in position, then pressed the *activating* stud.

I experienced with a joyous excitement the familiar avalanche of sensations, in itself not at all pleasant, but overwhelmingly welcome under the circumstances, of an entire alien language being impressed upon my mind. In a moment it was all there: I could place names to all I saw, converse with anyone, and in general feel like a civilized being again.

"Thank you, Dark," I said in our own tongue. "It's worked, finally. That was a bit of luck. I'll adjust it to see to you fellows when we've done talking to this chief, for I see we're almost to what must be his place."

This was an ornate edifice of wood in a fenced-off open space in the midst of the town through which we had been driven. We were ushered into it, and into a room where an imposing native stood ready to greet us.

He was an impressive figure, well fleshed and exuding an air of fitness—belied, I was surprised to see, by a pair of lenses perched on his nose; it was certainly odd, even for a Level Four culture, for a ruler to be chosen who required artificial aids for his sight! Even if medical

45

correction of such a condition were expensive, it seemed to me that so powerful a chief as this man was supposed to be ought to have had it as a matter of right.

However, he did not seem to be daunted by his infirmity, and he bared his teeth in what I had come to understand as a sign of welcome, the gesture somewhat obscured by a substantial growth of hair beneath the nose, a local fashion I still found somewhat unnerving.

I gave a prideful glance at my companions, both Explorers and natives—what a surprise it would be for them to hear me flawlessly deliver a greeting in the native tongue, rather than leaving it all to our guide!

"We, the representatives of the Galactic Empire, thank you for your graciousness in receiving us," I said. "And, in turn, we ourselves bring you greetings from beyond the stars, President Roosevelt."

The effect of my statement, handsomely phrased though it was, was electric. My companions, except for Dark, the only one aware that the Communicator had finally done its job, looked startled to hear me use the native tongue; the two natives who had accompanied us jumped as if bitten. Only the President seemed composed, and said, "Nice of you to say so."

"What's all this about a Galatic Empire? And, say, how do you come to talk English all of a sudden?" our native mentor asked. "Are you trying to pull a fast one?"

"No, Mr. Oxford," I said—I was pleased at last to be able to use his name, Ted Oxford—"it's just that my Communicator is working at last, and I acquired a full command of your language just as we were approaching the White House."

"Well, you might have let me and Wells know," Oxford grumbled. "Lord, that was a worse shock than waking up in the clink and seeing you fellows for the first time. Sorry, Mr. President—I didn't mean to spring any surprises on you like that."

"Willie Hearst didn't say anything about a Galactic Empire when he called me from California," the President said. "Just that these were definitely people from another planet, and I ought to see them before he broke the news. Looks as though he's got a bigger story than

47

he bargained on. Are you sure this isn't one of your yarns, Wells? I read that story about the Martians, and it was bully stuff, but I don't care for being fed fairy tales in my own office.''

I reassured myself with the knowledge that, though he had stated the situation with essential accuracy, the President had no way of actually knowing this, and I launched into a presentation of the wonders of the Empire, its benevolence and advanced civilization. I contrived to make it seem as though it were Imperial policy, when a new planet was come across, to drop an embassy on it, which would then inspect it with a view to establishing favorable relations. Our own had suffered a misfortune in landing, I explained, leading to the loss of our ship, but we were untroubled by that, as, within a period of time I did not specify, our masters would inquire after us and ascertain our opinion of Earth. The Empire, I made a point of explaining, considered hospitality to strangers one of the marks of a world worth dealing generously with.

When I had done, the President whistled. "This is going to raise an almighty fuss, no mistake," he said. "Half the people in the country won't believe it or will hope it isn't so. Good Lord, Bryan'll go out of his mind—he'll probably spend the campaign preaching against you, saying you're devils or something, as there's nothing about you in the Bible. *What* a mess it'll be!''

"Well, Mr. President," Oxford said, "that'll be Taft's problem, won't it?''

Roosevelt looked at the far wall. "So it will. I hope he's up to it. If I hadn't promised not to run again . . . By George, I'd cut my hand off to *here*"—he pointed at his right wrist—"if I could only not have said that!''

It was agreed that we should return the next day to continue our conversation after the President had had a chance to consult his advisors and to talk to Oxford's employer, Mr. Hearst, on the telephone—this in order to make sure that there was no release of any news concerning us until government policy was fully set— and I had had a chance to employ the Communicator on my companions so that they might make whatever contributions they were capable of.

We spent the evening at an inn, talking at great length to Wells and Oxford, keeping firmly in mind the fiction of our ambassadorial status and our nonexistent Empire. We were able to mingle fact and fiction quite nicely, drawing on many of our Exploration experiences in painting word pictures of the far-flung realm we supposedly represented.

I in turn asked for some enlightenment on matters that had puzzled me, notably Mr. Roosevelt's wish to part with his right hand.

"Well, in ought-four, he put his foot in his mouth"— I nearly asked what that odd performance had to do with his hand, but refrained; this language was evidently rich in poetic images which it would be profitless to analyze each time they came up—"when he promised not to run again this year." This, as far as I could understand, came from the superstition that no President should hold office for more than two fixed periods, and that four years previously Mr. Roosevelt had considered a partial term he had served to count as a full one. The explanation for the abbreviated term was even odder than the superstition: the previous President had been killed while in office, apparently not as a ritual sacrifice, although two earlier Presidents had, at roughly twenty-year intervals, abandoned their office in the same manner, a fact which I am sure Ari would have found significant.

The more usual method of changing the head of government was to allow the two chief factions in the country to put up candidates and allow the populace to choose between them. Mr. Roosevelt had persuaded his group to champion his friend Taft, a large and amiable man, while the opposition had put up one Bryan, a noted orator, who had twice unsuccessfully entered earlier contests.

"If he lost twice, why would they want to use him again?" I asked. "Wouldn't they do better with someone who might win?"

Oxford explained to me that the emblem of this party was an animal known for stubbornness and lack of sense, and that loyalty obliged them to display these qualities in all their proceedings.

In any case, Mr. Roosevelt, having come to enjoy the presidency mightily, now regretted his earlier statement, but felt he could not disavow it, hence the wistful comment about cutting off his hand. It seemed rather a lot of information to have to get in order to answer such a simple question, but I supposed it might in the long run prove useful, if I could keep it clearly enough in mind to convey it to Ari; it was really more in his line than mine.

"Teddy's a lame duck now, d'you see?" Oxford explained. "So already people are paying more attention to Taft than to him, and it gets under his hide."

I suppressed a sigh. The Communicator had acquainted me with the language, but apparently there were aspects of it even that instrument could not convey.

50

When we arrived next morning at the White House, Mr. Roosevelt did not yet seem at all clear on what his plans might be. Accepting me as spokesman for our party, he directed the establishment's steward, a Mr. Hoover, to show Wells and the others around the premises, and led Oxford and me to his office. I was startled when we entered to find it already occupied—it seemed to me, for an instant, filled—by the bulkiest native I had yet seen. He wore a moustache larger than the President's, and his broad face expressed a basic geniality overlaid with worry.

"Will, this is the . . . visitor I told you about. And Mr. Oxford, Hearst's man. He's been in on this from the start and has as big a stake as anyone in keeping mum until the right time. Gentlemen, Mr. Taft."

Roosevelt cut short our greetings and went on, "Now, Will, we've got to get things on a proper footing right off. I think I'll have Loeb draft whatever documents are called for now. Loeb!" he shouted.

When his secretary entered, Mr. Roosevelt gave him the required instructions and sent him off once more, then turned to Taft.

"This will be a deucedly hot potato during the campaign, Will. How do you propose to handle it?"

Taft stroked his luxuriant moustache for a moment before he replied. "I suppose," he said hopefully, "that I *could* talk about the Philippines. The job I did there's my strong suit, and I could point out that it qualifies me to deal with—"

Roosevelt snorted. "Will, you've got to realize that . . ." He stopped, and his shoulders slumped. He looked at his right hand and gave a grimace.

"Look here," he said. "Bryan's going to jump on this with both feet and stir up a lot of feeling. Right now he's a sure loser, but this could turn the whole thing around. You've *got* to have some sort of policy!''

Taft ruminated once again. ''Couldn't we delay the announcement until after the election?'' he asked. ''Then, once I was in, I could handle it pretty easily, I suppose.''

Roosevelt sighed. ''If that's the best you can—''

''Mr. President,'' Oxford said, rather loudly. ''Excuse me, but I don't think Mr. Hearst is going to be overjoyed about sitting on this story for four months.''

Roosevelt smiled, though with little mirth in the expression. ''If Willie Hearst wants to try conclusions with the government of the United States, he'd better be prepared to—what *is* it, Loeb?''

The secretary had entered the room and now crossed to the President's desk. ''Two visitors, Mr. President, on urgent business.''

''Well, I've got something pretty urgent here! You can just tell 'em, whoever they are, to wait 'til I'm ready to see them.''

''Mr. President,'' Loeb said firmly, ''you have asked me to do a number of pretty tough things in this job, and I haven't minded. But I just don't see myself telling J. P. Morgan and Thomas Edison to cool their heels for an hour or so!''

Roosevelt sprang from his chair and slammed a fist onto his desk; Taft manifested almost equivalent agitation by lifting himself some inches from his chair, then sinking back again. Next to me, Oxford whistled softly.

''That's torn it,'' the President said. ''Those fellows wouldn't barge in like that unless . . . Well, it *might* be something else, though I can't imagine what. Bring 'em in, Loeb.''

''Morgan's the biggest money man in the country,'' Oxford whispered to me. ''Banks, steel-making, finance.

Even passes the plate in church on Sunday—can't get out of the habit of collecting money. Edison's invented just about everything since the wheel, from the electric light to the electric chair.''

I looked on with interest as Loeb ushered these two notables into the office. Morgan was a tall, imposing man, with piercing eyes and a remarkable nose, bulbous and bright red in hue; it seemed to me odd that a man so wealthy would not have had something done about it. Perhaps, though, it played some role in his business; it might be useful for him to be identifiable at a considerable distance.

Edison was a shorter, stocky man with a thatch of white hair and a constantly darting glance; he appeared to be taking mental note of everything he saw.

"Mr. Morgan, Mr. Edison," the President said.

"A council of war, Roosevelt?" Morgan asked, looking first at Taft, then at Oxford and me.

"Now, what are you fellows—" Roosevelt began.

"Mr. President," Morgan said, "if you don't know why we're here, you're a lot less sharp than you used to be. I didn't get where I am by letting myself be surprised, and I make it my business to have ways of finding out what's going on. And when I hear both from San Francisco and Washington that creatures from another world are among us, it seems to me that it's time to sit up and take notice. Once the news gets out, the market will go wild, and there could be a panic worse than last year's unless the banking community *and* the Treasury take steps to control it.''

He looked at Oxford and me. "Are these they? They look ordinary enough.''

"That one of 'em?" Edison asked, as though he had not heard Morgan. He pointed at me. "Been sorting

53

through faces I've seen, and I don't know as I recollect one just like it. Something about the set of the eyes."

"Mr. Edison, that is in fact Ambassador—" the President began.

"Hey?" Edison said. "You from another planet?"

I was taken aback at the inventor's rudeness to his chief of state and at the President's apparent acquiescence to the interruption. Edison studied my face intently as I replied that I was, indeed, not from Earth.

"Edison!" Morgan fairly shouted. "You can talk to him later! Right now, let's get some things settled with the President!"

"Right, Mr. Edison!" Roosevelt yelled. "Now that you're here, it's clear that we can't keep this quiet much longer!"

Oxford saw my bewilderment at this sudden alteration in the mode of speech, and explained to me that Edison was what he called stone-deaf.

I considered this—while Morgan, Edison and the President boomed at one another—then asked, "But doesn't that make it hard to talk to him? Why doesn't he have something done about it?"

Oxford looked at me curiously. "Isn't anything *can* be done. Lord knows, Edison's tried. Didn't get anywhere, except, of course, inventing the phonograph."

I thought for a moment, then whispered to Oxford, "I'll be right back," and slipped out of the room unnoticed by the shouting President, Morgan and Edison. In the anteroom, I fetched out the Communicator and its accessory kit from the pocket of the native costume with which I had been provided and rummaged through it. There was a modification device which had been standard equipment ever since the discovery of a race of beings which used sound, but at such a high volume that ordinary Exploration devices could not cope with it, and the team Exploring that planet had come back suffering from extreme hoarseness owing to having had to scream constantly to get anything across. No such people had been encountered since, but each accessory kit now came equipped with a small self-powered amplifier which could be attached to the Communicator's speech element, magnifying its output substantially. I fished mine out; as I had recalled, it was a small, light, metallic wafer, threaded to fit into the Communicator. I breathed into one side of it, and Loeb, seated at his desk, jumped and looked at me sharply as a loud rasping noise echoed through the room.

I found a stiff piece of wire in the kit, bent it into a loop at one end to hold the amplifier, and shaped the rest to fit the curve of the human head. I then reentered the President's office, went to Mr. Edison, and slipped the device onto his head, positioning the amplifier just above an ear.

He started back in his chair, protesting, "What are you up to—*say!*"

"What is it, Edison?" called Roosevelt.

The inventor clapped his hands to his ears. "Don't need to *shout,*" he said peevishly. He dropped his hands and looked about the room. "Don't . . . need . . . to . . . Hell's fire, gentlemen, I can hear! How'd you manage that, young fellow?"

"A spare part I happened to have," I said.

"Spare part for *what?* Ah, never mind that—how does it work?"

I shrugged. "I don't know much about that sort of thing. Our Captain might have some idea."

Edison touched the amplifier. "Believe I'll have a talk with him sometime. Now, gentlemen"—he turned to the others—"what do we propose to do?"

With Edison brought effectively into participation without the need to shout, the discussion went on in a brisker yet more relaxed fashion.

"There's no chance of keeping the secret of these . . . these . . ." Morgan flapped one hand toward me as he searched for a suitable term.

"Wells coined a word," Oxford said. "Figured if the fellows who sailed in the *Argo* with Jason in that legend were called 'argonauts,' it'd do to call Raf and his friends 'astronauts'—sailors among the stars, d'you see?"

Morgan considered this. "Not quite a parallel. To be exact, you ought to use the name of their ship as a prefix—"

"In your language, that would be *Wanderer*," I said.

"—but on the whole, it'll do. Anyhow, Mr. President, Mr. Taft, you must see that if *I've* got onto this, it'll get around within days or weeks. The question is, how do we handle it?"

"I've been trying to think of a precedent for any of this," Taft said from the corner where he sat—his first contribution—"but there isn't any I know of."

Roosevelt grimaced, and Oxford whispered to me, "Bet he's wishing he'd made Big Bill Chief Justice instead of running him for President. Bet Taft wishes that, too."

"Hell, there ain't no rules for this kind of thing," Edison said. "We're just trying to get some'p'n done here."

I was fascinated to note that his voice, high-pitched and comparatively uninflected earlier, was a tone deeper and notably more expressive. He must, I reflected, have a remarkably quick and vigorous intellect to adjust so quickly to the restoration of his hearing.

"Now, Morgan," he said, "this is going to break any time, and, from what you've told me, Randolph Hearst's got a lock on it, so it'll get a huge play in all his papers. Is he likely to turn it into a big scare— 'Remember the What's-it' and so on?"

"If I can intrude, sir," Oxford said, "I can say that Mr. Hearst doesn't want to do that. He figures there'll be enough excitement over the facts to sell—to make journalistic history. And with Mr. H. G. Wells and me having the inside track with the, uh, astronauts, the rest of the papers'll have to make do with the crumbs from our table, so W.R. doesn't have to pull any funny stuff to keep out in front on this."

After more discussion, it was decided that Hearst would be placed under pressure to hold off his release of the news for two more days, during which time we would be sequestered in a hotel in a city called New York. This would allow Morgan, Edison and others they chose to notify confidentially to make the commercial dispositions necessary to cushion whatever shock this might occasion. Immediately after the announcement, our party would be sent on a tour around the nation, the custom with foreign dignitaries. It was felt that this adherence to habit would make us appear more ordinary and therefore more acceptable—and also not particularly interesting—to the populace, so that this course might, with luck, allow us to remain comparatively obscure until after the elections, some four months in the future.

"After that it'll be in your lap, Will," Roosevelt said.

"Not much room there," Taft observed genially, patting the swell of his stomach—I estimated his mass at about twice that of an ordinarily sturdy man—but Edison, Morgan and the President did not seem amused at his jest.

My consent to the plan was asked. It was clearly a matter of form, as three of the most powerful men in the country had determined on it, but in any case it suited me well enough. It would afford us time to study this strange world and its ways and would allow Ari to perfect his plans for turning those ways to our advantage.

The others, when we conferred in a corridor of the White House, agreed. "That's the way to do your Exploring," Dark said. "Let the natives make all the arrangements and stand the expense."

I was a little nettled to be reminded of the fact that we were Explorers, in view of the gross violation of Exploration rules our own plans entailed, but I let the remark pass; Dark was a complete pragmatist, interested only in whether things worked and not in the grand design behind them or in the laws under which both beings and devices operated. In this it seemed to me that he resembled Edison, and I recalled the inventor's remark that he proposed to have a long talk with Dark sometime. I imagined it should be quite an interesting conversation.

7

The two days we spent in New York before the announcement was made were instructive but largely uneventful. Wells and Oxford showed us some of the city; Ari pronounced himself pleased with the many typical Level Four characteristics it displayed, such as the simultaneous presence of opulence and misery; Dark was fascinated by the many modes of transportation—powered by steam, electricity, hydrocarbons, draft animals, and even, in the case of certain mobile shops, natives; Valmis claimed that there were Patterns there, but that he could not as yet Perceive them.

During the sightseeing on the second day before the announcement was to be made, we alighted from an electric vehicle near a tall, wedge-shaped building, which Dark wished to sketch, as he had never seen anything like it on any world; it was called after a utensil used to smooth clothes, I suppose because such items were manufactured or sold there. He pulled out the sheaf of molecule-thick metal sheets which Captains affect as notebooks and made his drawing.

We were at this time standing on a pavement beneath the building, and were frequently jostled by hurrying natives. That at least one had been motivated by more than thoughtlessness became evident shortly after Oxford suggested we repair to a place of refreshment across Fifth Avenue from where we stood, called the

Hoffman House. This establishment boasted a long counter at which a number of natives stood and consumed a variety of liquids.

"Ha!" Dark said enthusiastically after his first draught of what Oxford had recommended as suitable for a hot day, a substance called Würzburger. "This is the right idea! Here, let me pay for this round."

The gesture was less generous than it might seem, as the local currency we possessed had been provided by Mr. Hearst through the instrumentality of Oxford, who had presented us with well-filled flexible money containers and instructions on their use. It was also pointless, as Dark, reaching for his container, suddenly began patting his costume and glaring about.

"Hey, it's gone! That wallet thing, with the mazuma in it!" I wished that Dark, having been effortlessly granted the gift of communication in this tongue, had not evidenced quite so much fondness for the undignified cant terms in which it abounded.

"Welcome to Gotham," Oxford said equably. "Baghdad-on-the-Subway, home of some of the lightest fingers in the world."

"Come, now," Wells objected. "London's pickpockets are the deftest known. Look at Oliver Twist and Fagin. It's well known that social conditions—"

"It doesn't matter," Oxford said. "We've got the white card from W.R., and there's no problem about drawing some more cash and even springing for another wallet. Maybe a card of safety pins'd be a good idea, too."

"Well," Dark said uneasily, "that's all very well about the money and so on. But the chap got away with my notepad and, uh . . . " He searched for the word, but there was no equivalent in this language. "What I use to write with, you know. Among other things."

Oxford set his glass down. "Write with?" he said. "Among other things? What other things?"

"Well . . . " Dark took a sip of his liquid. "It's a tool we have, d'you see? You can set it to write on metal, or for small cutting and welding jobs, or for melting, or drilling, or punching holes. It's a matter of controlled, um, energy."

"Holes," Oxford said thoughtfully. "What *size* holes?"

"Oh, pretty much what you choose. It's a matter of focus."

Oxford emptied his glass and demanded that it be refilled. When this had been done, he took a long drink from it. "What does this jim-dandy little tool *look* like?" he asked softly.

"Well, like a . . . like what it is. About *so* long, and a bit thinner than my finger. Comes to a point at the end."

"Something like this?" Oxford said heavily, reaching inside his coat and bringing out an object.

"Fairly. Only it's metal, of course, not wood. What's that thing?"

"We call it a pencil. Only all it does is write. It doesn't cut, melt, weld or punch *holes* in things. Damn it, man, do you realize—"

At this moment there arose a hubbub just outside the room—shouts of amazement, alarm and rage, and the sound of running feet.

Oxford turned and ran from the counter. We followed, heedless of the attendant's cries for payment for what we had consumed.

In the anteroom, a large area paved with decorative

stone and adorned with trees in containers, we observed a slightly built native struggling in the clutches of three others. A cloud of smoke was rising from a large glass case containing a number of boxes and piles of elongated brown cylinders. The top of the case was marred by an irregular hole with a melted edge, and feeble flames flickered among the case's contents, producing the smoke, which was highly aromatic.

"Say, what d' hell is dis?" The native behind the case called out in agitation. "Dis bloke comes in an' asks fer a hot tip on a horse, so I'm a pal an' give him one, an' he goes to write it down, and next thing you know, dere's a hole in me case an' eight dollars' wort' of Perfecto Perfectos are goin' up in smoke all by demselves!"

"It wasn't me!" the captive native squealed. "Somebody must of set off a bomb in—"

"I'll handle this," Oxford said, stepping forward. He pulled his wallet from his pocket, flapped it briefly in front of the men holding the struggling native, so quickly that I doubt they could have had time to see anything displayed to them, and said, "Inspector Callahan, Anarchist Squad. We've had our eyes on this fellow for a long time, and now we've caught ye in the act, ye dim spalpeen! All right"—he gestured at us, grimacing ferociously, from which I deduced that he wished us to aid him in this sudden impersonation—"Sullivan, Dougherty, O'Brien, Levinsky, Napolitano, secure the prisoner and hustle him out! I'll meet yez on the street afther I've sifted for what this offers in the class of clues."

The four of us and Wells surrounded the confused native and marched him from the building. He seemed dazed and said nothing, only staring at his right hand, which I observed to be reddened and blistered.

"I think," Dark said, "that this must be the fellow—"

"Better drop that until . . . the Inspector comes out," Wells said.

Our prisoner emerged from his stupefaction at the sound of Wells's voice. "Which one are you?" he said sharply. "I don't know no Levinskys, or Napolitanos or Sullivans what talks like dat. Say, what kind of game is—"

Oxford now rejoined us, holding up a glittering shaft of metal. "This yours?" he asked Dark. "Found it in the cigar case. Dopey the Dip here"—I was surprised to find that he knew the little native's name, but I supposed that his work must have given him access to all sorts of information—"dropped it when his hot tip got hotter than he'd figured."

"All I done," the little chap whined, "was try t' write de horse down. But de pencil wasn't workin', and I give it a twist, an' den . . . "

"Quite a nice pencil," Oxford remarked musingly. "Where'd you get it?"

"Ah . . . Wanamaker's," the fellow said huskily. "Dey was on sale."

"Same place you got *this* and *this?*" Oxford reached inside the native's jacket, brought out Dark's notepad and wallet, and handed them to their owner.

"Say, you can't—"

"I just did, Willie."

The little man bristled. "Say, you ain't no bulls! What—"

Oxford nodded. "Right as rain, Raymond. We are not the bulls. We're with the Big Fellow."

The prisoner paled. "Not . . . ?"

"Not *him*," Oxford said scornfully. "D'you think that bozo has gadgets like the one you made the mistake

63

of heisting? No, *our* boss is so big you haven't even heard of him. And you'd better make sure, Chauncey, that he don't hear of *you,* get me?"

"O . . . Okay. I . . . I c'n go?"

"You'd better, if you know what's good for you. All right, boys, he won't—"

"Ha!" Dark exclaimed delightedly. He had been inspecting his restored property. "That idiot didn't hurt it at all. See—" He pointed the instrument at the pavement. A hole about the size of a vehicle wheel in diameter and about the width of three fingers in depth appeared in it.

We all looked at it with fascination, none more so than our prisoner, who seemed especially struck by the fact that the perimeter of the shallow crater intersected the tips of his footgear, exposing the ends of his toes. He gave a shrill cry, wrenched himself from our grip, and bounded across the street, heedless of the rushing vehicles.

"Huh," Dark said. "Guess I spoke too soon. He must've jiggled the focus setting a bit. It shouldn't have done that."

"*Shouldn't* it?" Oxford said with quiet politeness, stepping away from the indented circle. "Perhaps you'll be good enough to arrange that it doesn't do it again? Or to put it away where some damned pickpocket can't get at it?"

"No need to be stuffy," Dark answered. "I can't help it if some bungler gets hold of a good tool and misuses it. Anyhow, nothing much happened."

"Nothing much!"

Dark chuckled. "Now, if he'd turned it up to full power, number twelve focus, say, well that would have been a different story."

64

"Different?" Wells said. "Different in what way?"

"Well . . . the core of your planet is molten, right? So—"

"I think we'd best get back to the hotel, fellows," Oxford said, looking suddenly quite tired.

That evening, in our quarters in a place called the Waldorf-Astoria, Oxford turned to me and said, "So far *you* haven't given me palpitations, Raf. D'you suppose it'd be safe for you to accompany me on a little stroll through the purlieus? Most of the time it's okay, hanging around you fellows and thinking about the bylines I'm going to get out of it—but once in a while it really hits me that I'm hobnobbing with men from some star I can't even see at night, and I'd like to take a small dive off the wagon. You game, Raf?"

I understood from this that Oxford wished companionship in some excursion about the city, and readily agreed. We walked to near where the wedge-shaped building was, the evening being clement, and were soon at a large structure adorned with arches and constructed of a golden stone.

Oxford told me that it was called a garden, which I did not understand, and was named for an open space next to it, called Madison Square. We ascended to the roof, where we found a number of tables, trees in containers, and a raised platform where singers and musicians performed.

This, according to Oxford, was known as a roof garden. I was impressed with the flexibility of a culture which apparently had no difficulty in handling the concept of a garden (of one sort) atop a garden (of quite another), neither of them resembling a plot of earth for growing edible or ornamental vegetation, but it also

65

seemed to me to argue an imprecision of thought which boded ill for our hopes for this people's technical advancement. It would do us little good to have *Wanderer* refitted by a race which might well have three contradictory definitions of "aft control vane."

"Hey," Oxford said, "George M.'s here tonight—over there." He gestured toward a group at another table. "Bet you anything they ask him to do a number—sure enough, there they go."

The leader of the musicians who had been playing a lilting tune—having to do, Oxford informed me, with a woman who was cheerful in spite of (or perhaps because of) the loss of her mate—now came down from the platform and approached the table Oxford had pointed at. He spoke to a short man seated there, who, after shaking his head and smiling, arose and bounded to the platform.

The musicians struck up a lively air, and the short man capered about vigorously and sang in a loud, though not unpleasing, voice. His selections—involving, I recall, an announcement of his birth during the present month, called July, his preference for the name Mary, and a statement that he would soon be at a numbered street about a mile uptown from where we were—somewhat mystified me, but were received with great applause, in which I joined.

When the man came down from the platform and made for his table, Oxford called out to him, "Mr. Cohan!"

He approached us and said, "Hi. You're—oh, yeah. Ned Oxford. Hearst papers, right? Met you when you were going out to cover the Russky-Nip scrap. Say, you know I tried to work up a song about that, but never got to first base. Had a good line about the Yalu Peril, but there wasn't any heart to it. Main problem, audience didn't know which side they were rooting for."

Cohan looked at me sharply. "Heard something . . . yeah. You one of the fellows in this Hearst stunt?"

"Stunt?" Oxford said.

"Been talk around, last day or so, that your boss is up to something new, going to be a big story. This fellow part of it? Something about men from Mars, way I understand it. You from Mars, fellow?"

I looked at Oxford, nonplussed. He sighed and said, "There's no way of keeping a secret once the wise guys on Broadway start getting a sniff of it."

"Rosenthal and them are making book that Hearst is pulling a Barnum routine," Cohan said.

"Well, you could clean up pretty well if they give you odds," Oxford told him. "It's no stunt. Certified, proven fact, and the story breaks tomorrow. But don't put any money on Mars. Ambassador Raf, here, comes from a lot farther away than that. Listen, Cohan, you'll keep this on the Q.T., okay?"

"Surest thing you know," Cohan said. "I don't want the odds to drop before I've got a bundle down."

Oxford then took me to a place inhabited by members of his craft, among whom he circulated with great animation. I was left to my own devices at a counter much like the one at the Hoffman House, with nothing to amuse me but the view in a mirrored surface behind the counter and a glass of what Oxford called a "highball," arrived at by mixing a brown, aromatic fluid with water.

The taste was somewhat sharp, and the drink seemed to me to require further dilution. The attendant was in earnest conversation with a client some distance away, but I was pleased to see a large bottle of water within my reach. I withdrew the plug that closed its top and filled my glass, and was surprised to find that the taste was no less sharp, though different. The diluted drink in any case warmed me, and I looked with considerable interest and amusement at the images in the mirror, no longer minding Oxford's desertion.

The attendant, when he returned, seemed upset that I had helped myself to the water, but was mollified when I handed him the quantity of local currency he asked for. It seemed to me an excessive amount to pay, but I had no way of knowing the native customs on this point. And I had to admit that it was considerably more authoritative than any water I had yet tasted here.

Some time later we found ourselves at yet another counter, in a room of what appeared from the outside to be an elegant private house, but which, Oxford assured me, was the quarters of an organization of "players." I was about to ask him what game or games the members played, when my attention was drawn by the sight of Mr. Cohan talking animatedly to a group of people at the far end of the room. I pointed this out to Oxford, who invoked the name of one of the planetary deities, said, "I'd better give George M. the quietus on this again," and left me.

A native standing next to me at the counter sipped from his glass and said, "With a bare bodkin, preferably?"

I ran over the local expressions of inquiry I had assimilated and essayed what I hoped was an appropriate one. "How?"

"Oh, George is a good enough fellow. It's just that it offends me to the very soul that the theater has come to this pass. The song-and-dance stuff is all the go now, and trashy melodramas, and that fellow Shaw drawing the crowd by standing everything on its head. Nobody wants the real thing, the Bard. Women flock to the theater to look at me—''

I inspected him to see if I could determine the reason for this. He had wavy, thick hair; a straight, sharply pointed nose; and a firm, rounded jaw, and appeared to glare as he regarded me. I could see nothing really peculiar about him.

''—so all the managers care about is finding something that keeps my profile stage front. I could play Hamlet—''

''At what?'' I asked.

My neighbor turned his stare upon me. ''Not a joking matter; greatest role on the stage,'' he said truculently, and I realized my mistake. ''Play,'' both in this conversation and, presumably, in the name of the club I was visiting, was to be understood in the sense of acting a part in a drama, not engaging in a sport or contest. It was another example of the chaotic nature of this language, and it·struck me indeed that it might be possible to construct a whole sentence the significant words of which could be taken two ways.

''I 'played' in the 'garden,' '' I said, chuckling at the conceit.

The man next to me ignored my deft wordplay and said, ''Could do a Hamlet that'd knock their *eyes* out.'' He stared at the glass he held, then drank from it. ''Listen.'' I did so, hoping to learn something of this Hamlet matter, but he then changed the subject, advising me that being was the central question of existence (or possibly the other way round; his terms were elaborate and unclear) and that, in the face of certain conditions (which he enumerated), voluntary termination of life might be called for.

One advantage of the philosophical style of conversation is that, being both personal and imprecise, it requires little in the way of actual information, and I welcomed the chance to engage in a discussion which would not reveal my ignorance. "The ethics of self-ending vary from world to—from place to place," I observed. "But if you were to do as you suggest, how then would you get to play Hamlet?"

My neighbor looked first at me, then into his glass, apparently studying it deeply. "Either I've been having too many of these things, or you have," he said. "Maybe both. What the *hell* did you mean by— No, I don't want to know. I'll be as bad off as you are if I try to work out what you said. Are you on the pipe or something?"

"Your race's fluids affect my physiology differently from the way they do yours," I explained. "I find they cheer but do not inebriate. That may, of course, be a result of my internal modifications as an Explorer." I had a feeling that there was something wrong with what I had just said, but could not isolate it.

"An Explorer?"

"Why, yes, how did you know?" My glass was empty, and I took a good draught from the one Oxford had left behind him. "Speaking of Exploring, I am reminded of the story of the time Pado's crew dropped in on this methane-breathers' world. They breathe methane there, d'you see," I explained, wishing him to be clear on the point, "not as it might be oxygen or helium or whichever it is you people use—I forget just what for the moment." The anecdote was a good one, and I fancied it held my listener's interest fully, as he stared at me throughout it, his eyes fairly glazing with the intensity of his concentration.

Just as I finished, Oxford came up to us and said, "Sorry I took so long with Cohan, Raf, but I've got him to see he mustn't—ah, hello, Jack."

"Oxford," my conversant said in a low, plaintive voice, "this fellow's been telling me—to be fair, I should say I *think* he's been telling me—that he's a creature from another world. Has my mind slipped its clutch, or do you have the latest model in lunatics in tow?"

"Been spilling the beans, Raf?" Oxford said severely. "You know you shouldn't . . . ah, well, it's not that important. Jack'll keep it under his hat, I'm sure, and the story breaks tomorrow anyway. No harm done. Yeah, Jack, Raf's with a bunch of fellows that got stuck here when their, um, airship—only it goes through space—cracked up near Frisco, and Hearst's keeping 'em under wraps 'til he can spring the news right. They've already seen Teddy Roosevelt and been stamped 'passed.' Read all about it in tomorrow's *American* and *Journal*."

The man closed his eyes and drew in, then let out, a long breath through his mouth. "That's it," he said in a whisper. "When the ears go back on you and start feeding nonsense to the brain, then it's time to throw in the towel. Tomorrow I'll probably start hearing cues from some other play right in the middle of the second act." He pushed his glass from him. "Gentlemen, you have seen Jack Barrymore take his last drink, to be shortly followed by his exit, pursued by bugbears. Good night, sweet princes, and it wouldn't surprise me at *all* if I hear flights of angels singing me to my rest *this* night!"

I watched him leave the room, then turned to Oxford and said, "Sighbleshap."

"What?"

I was aware of points of heat at my nose and cheek-bones, the sudden physical manifestation of impatient anger at Oxford's probably deliberate obtuseness. "Excitable chap," I repeated with forced patience.

Oxford gave me an appraising look and, with an inconsequence I found alarming, demanded that I give him some particulars concerning a person who sold sea shells next to the ocean, which I refused to do, not being in any way informed on the matter.

"It doesn't show much," he said, "but my expert opinion, Mr. Ambassador, is that you're grandly sozzled, and it's time to toddle on home to John Jacob's palace."

The computerlike speed and precision with which I divined from this string of cant terms the insulting suggestion that the substances I had consumed had altered my mental state was in itself a refutation of the slander, but as I was about to deliver a stinging retort, all the accumulated stresses of our near-fatal arrival on this planet, the uncertainty of both present and future, our travels, encounters and adventures—all these suddenly manifested themselves on my over-strained system, and I lapsed into insensibility.

The reaction to my accumulated fatigue stayed with me much of the next day, marked by such symptoms as dryness of the mouth, a stabbing pain in the head, and spatial disorientation, and I thus missed much of the immediate excitement surrounding the release of the news of our presence.

I was aware of Oxford rushing in to where I lay, early in the morning, and waving a copy of a newspaper at me. The front surface was covered with large red letters and marks indicating emphasis, but they vibrated before my eyes, and I was content to accept Oxford's assurance that they announced our arrival and ostensible mission. Apparently the bulk of the paper was given over to material concerning us, prepared by Oxford and Wells, with only the necessary information on sporting events and a page of humorous drawings remaining of the paper's normal contents.

"Circulation's double normal, and they're fighting for 'em in the streets," Oxford announced happily. "We'll have to throw the others a bone, of course. I've set it up for some of the press fellows to interview you this afternoon; otherwise they'd claim it's all a fake, in spite of the President backing you—but they'll never catch up with us now! William Randolph and Mrs. Oxford's boy Ted have got the inside track for fair! O frabjous day! Callooh! Callay!''

At the thought of granting any interview in my present state, I gave a hollow laugh—which I regretted immediately, as it produced the illusion that the top of my head had suffered explosive decompression. When I pointed this out to Oxford, he looked at me closely and remarked, "Yeah, you're the original Katzenjammer Kid right now, I'd say, home address Hangover Square. What you want is a good, reliable corpse-reviver."

I gathered that this colorful, if repellent, term denoted a restorative for fatigue, and certainly the dark brown liquid he brought me after consultation with a number of the hotel staff had that effect. The taste was remarkably unpleasant, and it appeared to contain some corrosive substance which acted powerfully on the greater part of my interior surfaces, but I shortly found that my head had stopped pounding and that I was able to move from one point to another with reasonable accuracy and without the necessity of supporting myself on various pieces of furniture.

All the same, I was conscious of a certain weakness as I faced the group of about twenty reporters who crowded our suite a few hours later. They looked distinctly unfriendly and only begrudgingly impressed by the exotic appearance we made in our own clothing, which Oxford had insisted we resume for the occasion.

"What kind of fake is Hearst trying to pull off?" one man yelled, and there were approving mutters from some of the others.

"Before you boys get yourselves out on a limb," Oxford said, "you better have a look at these. Official government medical records, TR's statement, the works." He passed out numerous sheaves of paper, which seemed to impress the reporters, for their angry murmurs died down.

"This is one of the great news stories of the age," Oxford said, "and I can see you'd be sore, being scooped on it. But Hearst got it first, and that's the breaks of the game. Now he's being square enough to give you all your own chance at it, and I suggest you make the most of it. Gentlemen—and ladies; I see we have a few of you here today—I give you Ambassador Raf, who will tell you in his own words of his immense journey through the wastes of space to this planet and of his mission among us; questions afterward, please."

I gave them substantially the same account I had contrived for President Roosevelt, but it was received with less friendliness.

"How do we know you're not scouts for an invasion?" "What so-called benefits are we supposed to get when your masters come here?" "Isn't it true that your people will flood us with cheap labor?" "How does this stuff about life on other worlds square with Scripture?"

"His paper's for Bryan," Oxford whispered to me of the last speaker. "The Boy Orator's already come out with a statement saying you can't be so because you ain't in the Bible."

I fear that I did not make a vigorous response to any of these questions, as I still felt quite feeble, and they were fired with such rapidity that there was no time to compose coherent answers. This did not seem to matter much, for each questioner would start scribbling on a piece of paper or notepad he or she held as soon as the query was made, without awaiting any answer. "They know their own paper's line," Oxford muttered again, "so they've already got the story angle they need—it

75

don't really matter that much what you say. Teddy's for you, so the Republican papers'll make you out a cross between the Rover Boys and Andy Carnegie, and the ones that are backing Bryan'll come out for burning you at the stake.'' I hoped he was jesting.

Questions of a startling irrelevancy now emerged, and I was asked whether I thought certain giants (a class of being of which I had not been aware) would manage to gain a pennant they were apparently in search of (I suggested that their height ought to allow them to reach it successfully, if it was out of the reach of ordinarily constructed natives, which seemed to be the right response), my opinion of the city's tall buildings and whether I had as yet visited a public monument of some sort which they had placed in the midst of a large body of water.

"That's the color stuff,'' Oxford advised me in an undertone. "They use that to make you seem just like everybody else.''

"If they want to portray us as totally ordinary,'' I whispered to him, "what is the point of writing about us at all?''

He shrugged. "The whole thing is to persuade the readers that even the most remarkable people, or whatever, are something they can handle. A prince or a king or something, d'you see, they don't cotton to him unless they know he's got tight shoes or likes baseball or eats a hot dog—then they've got something in common, and don't feel they have to shy a half-brick at his head. And believe me, you fellows need all—oh, oh. You better field the sob sister's spitball pretty smartly: she's a flaming suffragette.''

A female native was waving energetically at me.

"Mr. Ambassador!" she called in a strident voice. "You have told us nothing of life on your world. Is there equality of the sexes, as there should be in an advanced civilization? What in fact is the position of women there?"

I confess that I had not anticipated questions relating to a life which now seemed so long ago and far away, and, for a moment, I was at a loss as to how to reply. Dark, who with my two other companions had been standing behind me, stepped forward, evidently tired of his subordinate role in the proceedings. "I think I can say something about that," he said. "Wells has been discussing the matter with me pretty thoroughly—it's the kind of thing he goes in for—and—" Wells, his face scarlet, plucked at Dark's sleeve, but was shaken off. "—I've got a lot of things pretty clear in my mind that I'd sort of forgotten, what with all that time I've spent in space. Now, as to the position of women among us, there are a number of them. My own favorite—"

He then gave a succinct description of certain of our folks' standard mating practices. The woman who had requested this information did not seem at all happy to have received it, for she turned white, swayed, and appeared about to lose her equilibrium. A man next to her took her arm to steady her, but she wrenched herself free and made a gesture as if to strike him with her writing instrument. The reactions of the other reporters included awe, hilarity, and dismay; several took notes on pieces of paper other than those they were using to prepare their stories.

"Boys," one of them said after a moment, "my paper's got a motto about all the news that's fit to print, and I think we have now come past that point. I don't know that I could keep my hand steady enough to write anything more down just now. Thanks, Oxford, Mr. Ambassador; I guess we've had enough.''

It was another example of how much we had to learn about this culture that I was surprised that it took so long for the results of the interview to become available; taking into account the widespread use of electricity, I had expected some sort of viewing of the news to commence almost immediately. However, I learned from Oxford that this was not the case and that the appearance of what he called ''Extras'' from all the newspapers within only a few hours marked an extraordinary effort.

It was certainly remarkable that they had managed to print so much based on the skimpy material the reporters had gathered, but Oxford assured me that this was a specialty of the craft, and not to be wondered at. Many journals contained highly imaginative drawings of the four of us, some of humorous intent. One showed us, ludicrously out of scale, grouped at the top of the planet and looking down at its surface. Dark was highly amused by the printed line underneath, which represented one or all of us as saying, ''It's a nice place to visit, but I wouldn't want to live there.'' I myself found it a distressing reminder of our situation.

''Ah,'' Oxford said with satisfaction, pausing in his rapid survey of the newspapers. ''I was looking for this. This fellow's stuff goes down awfully well with the public, and if he's written you up, they'll be ready to believe you're okay.''

He passed a page to me, indicating an item. There seemed, as I read, to be an element in the writing I had not yet encountered, though I could not be sure what it was. "These gents have come from outer space," it began, "to visit this poor human race, and, truth to tell, they're not so weird or sinister as might be feared. They seem like ordinary folks, and one of them likes risky jokes (at least we *hope* the guy was joking). Their presence sets old Gotham smoking—what they're doing, what they want, what they can do, what they can't, are things that no one knows for sure (we note not all their thoughts are pure!) . . ." There was more in the same vein, which I found hard to follow.

As Oxford had predicted, reactions differed according to the politics of the papers' owners. Readers of a journal favoring Bryan in the coming election might well receive the impression that we constituted a menace to civilization and to religion; one such suggested that since their cult considered Earth the spiritual center of the Universe, without making provision for the existence of life elsewhere, we must be regarded as supernormal manifestations of powers inimical to the cult, and that harsh measures toward us might be appropriate.

An opposing paper presented to its readers a glowingly optimistic account of the benefits to be expected once full contact with our supposed Empire was established, and called for what it referred to as an "Open Door Policy" toward space.

A journal called *The Times* contained a piece which made Oxford raise his eyebrows. "This'll get some backs up," he said. "Listen: 'With the coming of these ambassadors, so like us in appearance and behavior, yet emissaries of a realm unimaginably far and strange, a new age has opened for humanity. It is an irony of history that this has happened in the waning days of Mr. Roosevelt's presidency, for the vigor and breadth of vision which even his opponents have respected would

79

have meant much to the nation in the dealings with the astronauts. Whatever the virtues of the two contenders for the office, it cannot be said that either has demonstrated any qualities which will be outstandingly useful in handling a situation so utterly without precedent in history.' "

Oxford set the paper down and looked at Wells. "True enough," he said. "If a problem can't be solved by Bible-thumping and orating, it ain't up Bryan's alley. And Taft did all right pacifying the Philippines, but it's not the same thing. In fact, come to think of it, *we're* the little brown brothers in this setup. I guess there's a lot of people going to be wishing it was Teddy running again, not those two. And I'm not sure I'm not one of them."

"I wish I could disagree with you," Wells said thoughtfully. "I really prefer to look at history as being determined by large-scale things, such as science and invention, economics and so on—the whole business of making out that it's the fights between kings and such that's important irritates me. It's damned sloppy thinking, and is responsible for more . . . well, never mind that. But I have to say that this does seem to be an age of accidentally important men. Your President's one of them—I'm sure the history of the last eight years would have been different without him in office—and there are others. I can't imagine, for instance, anyone else affecting Germany the way the Kaiser has; without him on the throne, things would be quite different. It's an odd thought, you know, the changes one different circumstance could make. It might be rather amusing to work out what might happen if just *one* thing in history had gone differently. Say the South in this country had won the Civil War. Then the whole business of the transcon-

80

tinental railroad, the colonization of the Midwest, the destruction of the Indians, would never have happened. Instead of a world power, the United States would have been a moderate-sized republic, secondary in influence perhaps to Brazil or Canada, with the hegemony of the northern continent falling to the Confederacy, with its strong European ties. *That's* the thing,'' he went on animatedly, his bulbous eyes shining. ''It's almost like a chemistry experiment—make one change and, if you know what's involved, you can see what would or should or might or could happen as a consequence. And the thing is, if you make that one change—you don't need others—things are bound to happen. It wouldn't be . . . *what?* That's it''—he gestured with his right hand, occasioning the loss of some portion of the fluid restorative he held in a glass—*''elegant,* that's the word, otherwise. Slip one change into the equation and see how the rest all balances out; add one or two more, and there you are with the three-body problem, and who wants that, I ask you? I may do a piece on that for one of the papers, so I don't want you fellows pinching the idea in advance and flogging it to *Frank Leslie's* or *Collier's.* That's it; put in *one* change, and the most fantastic upshots will start shooting up. Next thing you know, given the right single change, Lord Alfred Douglas might be crowned Queen in Westminster Abbey, not that he isn't about halfway there already. What a marvelous idea!''

Ari, Dark and I looked toward Valmis, who appeared agitated at this unwitting echo of his obsession from a being who, in Valmis's view, was himself inhabiting a continuum created by just such an altered circumstance. Valmis seemed on the point of speaking to Wells, but Dark stepped between them and Ari spoke up. "Ah, yes, Wells, you were telling me something of the, um, Kaiser, was it? Most interesting, *most;* and I'd appreciate it if we might continue. We may leave looking through these tedious newspapers to Raf and Mr. Oxford." He drew Wells to a far corner of the room.

"Now, you shut up about this nonsense," Dark muttered to Valmis. "It's bad enough some of 'em think we're demons or some such. If you go prattling about how your mythical machine created 'em or split 'em off or whatever it is, they'll lock us up as lunatics if they don't believe you, or put us in that chair of Edison's if they do!"

Valmis nodded resignedly, and I felt safe in returning to Oxford and the newspapers. With a little effort, I might be able to puzzle out the significance of that curiously cadenced news story.

9

The President appeared more vigorous and buoyant than when we had last seen him. He crossed his office and extended his hand to each of us in turn, saying, "It's bully to see you gentlemen again, just bully! By George, you've stirred things up, haven't you?"

Behind me, Oxford whispered, "That stuff about dumping Taft's got to him, all right."

The details of the trip which was to introduce us to such of the American nation as chose to notice us, and them to us, had been worked out by discussion among the presidential officials and Oxford, and it had been agreed that the journey should start with an official meeting with Mr. Roosevelt in Washington. It seemed to me a strange proceeding, as Roosevelt, in common with the greater part of those involved in the government, had fled the capital to avoid the damp heat and noxious vapors of summer a day or so after his second private interview with us, and was now ensconced in his family home about twenty miles from New York City; but it was felt to be vital that images for reproduction in the newspapers be taken of us in front of the White House, and so he and our party had traveled, though separately, for several hours on the trains for the encounter.

"Well, I don't mind telling you that I'm taking a good deal more interest in these proceedings right now," the

President said jauntily. "I believe it may be that you people and I will have a lot to discuss in a few months. It's a little early to talk about formal treaties, of course, but I think we all might be keeping in the backs of our minds what's involved. We'd want, for one thing, to work out what sort of guarantees—"

At this point, his secretary, Mr. Loeb, entered with a whispered word for his chief, much as he had done just before the incursion of Mr. Morgan and Mr. Edison previously.

"Well, I . . ." the President said uncertainly.

"He says it's urgent, Mr. President."

"Well, I can't just . . . it's difficult, but, yes, I suppose you'd better . . ." He gestured impatiently, and Loeb left. "I think I know what this is," he muttered, looking at Oxford over his pince-nez. "Guess you do, too. There's been talk going around. . . ."

Mr. Taft entered the office, fairly shaking the floor with his tread. "Theodore—Mr. President," he said, "I've . . . they've been to talk to me." He sank into a chair, which quivered for an instant, but held firm. "The party bigwigs, and Cannon, you know, plus a couple of Senators. They . . . they . . ."

"Will," the President said softly, "you're a big man . . . in every sense. Don't let this get to you."

Taft threw Mr. Roosevelt a sharp look. "You've got some notion of what's going on, then? You seem to be taking it mighty coolly."

"Well, now, Will, it's a grave matter, and calls for calmness. What is it Kipling says, 'If you can keep your head when all about are losing theirs'?"

Taft looked at him again before replying. "If you're in the mood for poetry, Theodore, I'll tell you that *I* feel like that line in 'The Wreck of the *Hesperus*'—'"We are

84

lost!'' the captain shouted as he staggered down the stairs.' Rhymes with yours, too, come to think of it.''

"Just what's happened, Will?'' the President asked him. "What did these fellows who came to see you want?''

"I suspect you've got a pretty clear idea of that. These . . . *astronauts* here''—he threw us a glance bright with dislike—"have thrown a monkey wrench into the whole damned election. Bryan's all for having 'em exorcised or lynched or such, and *our* crowd's saying that I'm not the man to handle 'em so as to get something useful out of 'em. And the party feels that our line has got to be that we've got a candidate who can do just that. And, by God, they've got on the telegraph and polled a quorum of the delegates to the convention—the same fellows that nominated me on the first ballot last month!—and got 'em to agree to 'accept my withdrawal if offered.' ''

"Ah, Will,'' the President said, laying his hand on the big man's shoulder. "It's a heavy load to bear, but for the good of the country . . . And look at it this way: the presidency was always a second choice for you, I know. You wanted a place on the Court more than anything—well, I'll be able to see to that for you, by George! That business about not running again, well, that can't apply now, not with . . .'' He gestured toward us—with, I noticed, his right hand. I was pleased that he would apparently be able to accomplish his goal without sacrificing that useful member.

Taft looked up at him, then, impressive as a force of nature, rose from his seat until he stood, looking slightly downward at the President, seeming to dominate the room by his very bulk and gravity. "Theodore,'' he said, "you've only got the half of it. *You're* not going to

85

be the one putting up Supreme Court appointments to the Senate, any more than *I* am. The National Committee, well, they've been talking with some of the fellows in industry and finance, and they've all pitched on someone they think can work the best with our *visitors*—someone who knows science and so on—a man who—"

"Confound it, Will! What the devil are you trying to say?"

"Oh, *Lord!*" Oxford said behind me. "They can't be—but, oh, sweet spirits of ammonia, it makes an awful kind of sense. . . ."

"I have the honor to inform you, Mr. President," Taft said bitterly, but not without a note of satisfaction in his tone, "that the delegates to the Republican National Convention for the year 1908, electrically reconvened, are prepared to designate as their candidate Mr. Thomas Alva Edison."

The President's teeth and eyeballs shone vividly as both were bared by a sudden contraction of his facial muscles, but there was a dead silence in the room until Wells broke it with an awed murmur: "Gor*bli*mey!"

10

After the picture-taking, which was conducted in a subdued mood—I noted later that the results were quite striking, as the President bore an uncharacteristic expression of savage gloom—we returned to New York to prepare for our tour. On the way, Oxford and Wells animatedly discussed the startling political developments. We did not participate, but at one point Oxford said to me, "This'll smooth things for you. It was going to be a pretty dull campaign 'til this happened, and now it'll be a humdinger. The public will be grateful to you for gingering it up. You'll be as popular on the road as John L. or Christy Mathewson."

And so it proved. Wherever we went during the next months, we were greeted with enthusiasm, mixed with a certain derisive affection; evidently the Americans had in the main concluded that, whatever our supposed mission, our actual function was to provide them with some novelty and distraction. We—usually I, as it was agreed that Dark was too apt to say alarming things, that Ari had little interest in communicating anything except Metahistorical data, and that Valmis was still too high-strung—addressed crowds from the rear platform of our train, at banquets in cities and small towns, at picnic grounds, at county fairs; we shook hands, wrote our names in native characters and our own script in albums designed for the purpose; posed for pictures with local dignitaries, sometimes partly garbed in regional costume; spoke well of prominent features of the landscape and whatever manufactured or agricultural products characterized the area; threw out the first ball at baseball contests and threw curved pieces of iron, normally intended to protect the feet of work animals, at uprights set in the ground. All of this was recorded by a picture-taker accompanying us, written up at great length by Oxford and telegraphed each night to the Hearst newspapers in New York and San Francisco; and, as he told me, resulted in a substantial rise in circulation for what he called "the whole chain."

It took us from the beginning of August to the middle of October to complete the tour, which seemed to me an excessive length of time for the benefits that might be expected, and I told Oxford so. "We're dragging it out a little," he admitted, "but Teddy—and Edison, when he got into it—held out for that. They want you off the board for most of the campaign, and while you're whistle-stopping around like this, you aren't in any one place long enough for folks to get excited about you for more than a day. If you were where the news-hawks and politicians could get at you, there's no telling what you might say or what someone might pull, and the whole applecart could turn over. As it is, it's going fine. Edison's line in the campaign is to ignore Bryan, and it looks like the voters are doing that, too. Edison mostly sits out in Menlo Park and talks about the wonders of the future, and when he does stir to make a speech, it draws the crowds like flies. Bryan's making a fool of himself, pounding away on the same note—send you back where you came from and don't contaminate our pure old Earth with heathen ideas—and all he gets is half-empty halls, with the audience shuffling its feet and wishing he'd get back to Free Silver.''

Our quarters—a three-car private train—were a good deal more spacious than *Wanderer,* but the journey was so extended and filled with repetitions of essentially the same events that I found myself unable to retain any clear impression of the whole or to form any picture of the nation through which we were paraded, and could afterward recall only a few striking incidents.

I do remember our first stop, only a few miles from New York City, at Mr. Edison's establishment. Though the inventor was absent, to Dark's disappointment—he was, we later learned, in Washington, conferring with the President and his party leaders and at that very hour agreeing to accept the hastily offered nomination—we were shown about with great courtesy. It was somewhat tedious for Ari, Valmis and myself, as our interests did not encompass machinery, to which the place seemed to be devoted, but Dark was fascinated.

"This electricity stuff," he told me, "that's all very well, but it's really a pretty crude way of working with something they already knew about. What's really impressive is that talking machine thing—d'you know Edison thought it *all* up himself? Now *that's* inventiveness, that is. Of course, it's all wrong," he said to one of the staff, who stood nearby.

The man stiffened. "Wrong?"

"Well," Dark explained, "you aren't going to get really accurate sound reproduction by working mechanically, you see. No matter what you do, you're limited by the fact that you've got one solid thing bouncing off another. It's awfully clever, but it's like trying to get into space travel by shooting off explosives—you can make a start at the idea, but it won't get you far. What you want to do is, you want to get down the electric impulses, and then reproduce those."

"But . . . huh," the man said. "Say, you folks mind if Charley here takes you the rest of the way round? I've got something I want to get at."

Dark chatted in the same manner with a succession of guides, apparently boring them greatly, as each tended to pass us on to another on the plea of work to be done.

Certain other happenings of the tour remain with me, though it would be hard to say when or where they took place. I recall that Oxford was most impressed when we met with an ancient native, who was apparently held in great honor and affection because, in the course of conducting warfare on behalf of his nomadic tribesmen against the dominant culture, he had slaughtered a great number of Oxford's people and achieved a reputation for cruelty. It may be that I missed some element of Oxford's explanation that would have made it more logical.

The old man studied me keenly. "Your people sending a war party after you?" he asked. I assured him that this was not so, and he appeared disappointed.

"I saw the white men come with their trains and telegraph wires and fences, and the Indians vanished like mist. Wasn't their soldiers that ended us, but the things they had and the way they lived. I saw that—me, Geronimo. Saw it and fought it but couldn't stop it. Nobody could. I'd like to see the same thing happen to the white man while I'm still alive. Be a damn good joke."

I noticed that after this interview Oxford and Wells looked at me uneasily from time to time.

It was a constant habit of the natives to escort us

about such of their industrial establishments as were located conveniently near our stopping places, and we developed the custom of relegating this duty to Dark, as he was the only one of us capable of at least appearing interested in such matters. This generally worked well, but led to one unfortunate incident.

He and Oxford had gone off on one of these excursions, which we expected would take at least two hours. Wells, Ari, Valmis and I were taking our ease in the lounge car when we were surprised to see the vehicle in which they had left returning at a high speed. It stopped next to our car, and Oxford fairly dragged Dark from it and thrust him onto the train, then turned to an individual in a blue uniform who remained in the vehicle and shoved a sheaf of currency at him.

"Thanks, Chief," I heard him call. "This should help you keep a lid on what happened, right? And, say, listen, would you tell the engineer to pour on the steam and get us the hell out of here right now?"

"Surest thing you know, Mr. Oxford," the uniformed man said respectfully, quickly thumbing through the bills.

In a moment, Oxford and Dark entered our car, stumbling as the train suddenly started into motion. Dark had a bruise under one cheekbone, and his native jacket had a tear at the collar.

"Whatever's been going on?" Ari asked, peering at him.

Oxford glared at Dark. "Your friend here suddenly took a notion to cut loose and start beating up our hosts. Is he subject to fits or something? It cost me a lot of W.R.'s long green to square things with the police there, but I guess they'll handle it. What the hell did you think you were—"

"I couldn't help it," Dark said. "It just got to me. Listen, Raf, do you know what these people do?"

"All sorts of things, I expect," I replied.

"No, I mean—look, I know I don't get out as much as you fellows when we're—"

I broke in, for in his agitation he appeared to be about to say more than I thought prudent about our actual work, Exploration—it was still vital to keep up the fiction of being a diplomatic advance guard. "Oxford, Wells—would you mind if we discussed this alone? I promise you we'll get at this, but Dark's a bit upset just now, and I think we'll find out what's wrong more easily if we have him to ourselves."

When the two Earthmen had gone, Dark resumed. "You see, I stick with the ship mostly, while you three go out and sniff around the natives of whatever planet it is. So maybe it's that I don't get to see so much of what goes on in different places. But I tell you, this . . . I couldn't believe it!"

It appeared that he and Oxford had been taken on a tour of a factory engaged in producing textiles. There were a great many machines of commendable ingenuity, all creating a great noise and filling the air with an unwholesome dust composed of fibers of the material being processed. The work, Dark observed, was carried out by small creatures, perhaps half the size of the natives, who performed it quite nimbly. These he supposed to be certain members of a class of creatures known as primates, some of which, distant evolutionary cousins of the humans, we had seen in cages in a park in New York, assiduously trained for tasks which the natives themselves would find distasteful or perilous.

"That didn't set too well with me, for I could see that the job would wear the beasts out pretty quickly. But,

92

after all, that's the way it is with sentient races; the ones further down the ladder are going to be used for *something* by the fellows on top." What had really made Dark uneasy was what seemed to him the rather nasty-minded humor involved in removing the creatures' facial hair and dressing them in clothing similar to, though of poorer quality than that worn by the natives, so as to make them resemble their masters.

His disapproving comment on this was received with incomprehension by those conducting him through the factory, and he was finally given to understand that the workers were not what he had supposed, but rather were in fact juvenile humans.

"And it wasn't even as if they were being *punished,*" he said to us wonderingly. "Their own *children,* put out to work like that. They didn't look like humans any more, really—all sort of dried up, and some of them coughing. . . ."

As Dark told it, once this had sunk in, he had given a yell of outrage, struck out wildly, and felled two or three of those nearest him; only Oxford's quick action in removing him from the scene and "squaring" the chief of police had averted an extremely awkward scene.

"I am afraid you do get a narrow view, being confined to the ship," Ari observed. "Certainly, according to our own standards, what you observed is distressing, even outrageous. But there are practices among other humanoid races which we, as Explorers, have been obliged to witness calmly, beside which this pales into insignificance. I recall particularly the Pththn, who—"

Valmis and I recalled them as well, and begged Ari not to go into any detail.

"Well," Dark said, glowering, "it's all very well to keep up a detached attitude about these natives and what they do to each other. But I'm damned if it's going to worry me any more, this business of messing around with their culture; they could use some pretty drastic changes!''

Normally our encounters along the way were conducted with prearranged care and formality, but there was an amusing instance somewhere in the middle of the country, after our departure from a town, village or place called Dayton, when Oxford appeared in the lounge car, marching two natives before him. These were lanky, solemn-looking individuals, who looked at us with a sort of feverish eagerness.

"Stowaways," Oxford said grimly. "Nipped on board while the crowd was surging around you and hid under some seats up forward."

I was feeling pleasantly relaxed, having been treated during our halt to some few glasses of a local fruit drink known, I believe, as applejohn, and I spoke to the intruders in a friendly manner. "You wanted our autographs, then, my good men? You needn't have gone to all that trouble to—"

"They're not interested in souvenirs," Oxford said. "These chaps claim to have built an airship—"

"*Heavier*-than-air," the taller of the two said indignantly. "There's a difference. And it ain't a claim—Wilbur and I, we've flown it, shown it around, even demonstrated it to the Army, but nobody'll pay it any mind, not even you newspaper fellows, that'll write up a two-headed calf as if 'twas the biggest news since Richmond fell. Now, from what everyone says, these foreign gentlemen here, they've got the President's ear, and Wilbur and me, we think that if they was to tell him—"

94

"Ah, now, look," Oxford said. "This is that sort of kite thing you flew in North Carolina five years back? Now, I remember that; it got a line or so in the metropolitans, but what's so great about it?"

"Hey," Dark said. "You say you got something up in the air without, um, floating it? And you don't have gravity repulsion here, that's for sure—how did you manage that?"

As the two brothers explained it, they had joined together the unrelated concepts of a kind of airborne toy, a propulsion mechanism intended for boats, and a power plant used in road vehicles to construct their machine.

"My word," Dark said, "that's quite something. And you worked out the airflow stuff all on your own?"

He and the two strangers repaired to a corner of the car and talked earnestly for some time, all three of them frequently making swooping motions in the air with their hands.

At our next stop, about an hour later, Dark saw them off the train before our ritual greeting by the town's dignitaries. "You're on the right track," he called after them. "You've got to look for better power sources, d'you see, and ways to lose weight. All the rest follows, if you're going that way. You can't do much that's worthwhile unless you get hold of antigravity, of course, but that'll do to get on with. Really remarkably clever for natives," he added, turning to me, "but I tell you, it's discouraging to think that that's the best they've come up with. It's all very well for them to find ways to potter around in their atmosphere, but it's no indication that we're going to get these people licked into any kind of shape to help us out with *Wanderer*."

As I have said, the middle of the time period known as October found us back in New York City, and we spent two weeks recovering from the effects of our journey, undertaking nothing more in the way of exertion than short walks and one excursion to the statue about which we had been questioned at the news reporters' interview in August. This was a large structure of metal, shaped almost as if to represent a native female, located on an island near the city, positioned so as to dominate another island nearby, on which persons wishing to enter the country were detained for some time. The intent, both of the detention and the location of the statue, appeared to be to intimidate the newcomers and prevent them from causing any inconvenience to those already resident. This insight, which I arrived at almost intuitively, was borne out by an inscription at the base of the statue, which referred to the arrivals from other places as "wretched refuse." Though striking me as strong—it was admittedly difficult for me, at this point, to distinguish between one sort of native and another—the designation appeared to reflect accurately the opinion held by more established inhabitants of those who passed through what the same inscription mysteriously referred to as "the golden door."

Our travels and our relaxation from them had kept us from paying much attention to the election campaign, although we had gathered from occasional discussions between Oxford and Wells that there was hardly any chance that Edison would not get what Oxford called the nod. This was a relief, as it was clear that Mr. Bryan, if victorious, would deal with us harshly, as offenders against his cult's views.

We were, all the same, somewhat on edge as we gathered in our hotel suite on the night of the election to listen to the results. A newly installed device, something like an enlargement of the Communicator amplifier I had given Edison, hung on one wall, and transmitted to us the latest information.

After some time, I realized that the voice relaying it was curiously familiar. "Bryan's sicklied o'er with the pale cast of thought, ladies and gentlemen," it said. "Latest reports show that there's something rotten in the State of Georgia—by less than a thousand votes, it's gone Republican for the first time since Reconstruction. O! that this too, too solid South would melt—and, by God, it's doing just that! Hum; there's nothing else coming in over the wires for the moment. Just time for a quick—that is, in the ensuing interval, my sister Ethel will entertain all you hundreds of electrodiffusion subscribers out there with a rendition of her Broadway hit, 'Captain Jinks of the Horse Marines.' "

"Wasn't that . . . ?" I asked Oxford.

"It sure was," he answered. "Barrymore's got a great voice for this thing. Good for him—but what's it going to do to newspapers? These gadgets have only come out in the last month or so, so hardly anybody has 'em, but by the time the next election rolls around, they'll be all over the place—and then who's going to rush out and grab the papers out of the newsies' hands to find out what's going on? I tell you, this century's rolling on a bit fast for mine."

"It's a great medium for popular education," Wells said. "Imagine—the great men of the time speaking their thoughts into every home, the classics of the race brought within the reach of all. It'll be ten times more the cultural revolution that we had in England with the Popular Education Acts and the penny press."

Oxford gave him a tired look. "Maybe so," he said.

97

"But you'll notice that they don't have a great mind or even an experienced reporter handling the election coverage on this thing, but an actor. Barrymore doesn't know beans about politics, but he's got nice, pear-shaped tones, and that seems to be what counts. I think this gadget's going to be a way to get more drivel across to people than the papers ever dreamed of trying."

Ari, Dark, Valmis and I turned in, once it was mathematically certain that Edison had won the election; Wells and Oxford remained awake, intent on the electrodiffuser, until well past sunrise. As I left the sitting room, I heard Barrymore's voice saying, "It appears, ladies and gentlemen, that William Jennings Bryan, in the words of the Swan of Avon, must now be seen as a poor player that struts and frets his hour upon the stage and then is heard no more." At least, I thought, he had dropped his monomania, which I so vividly recalled from our encounter at the player's club, for someone he called the Bard, and had a new enthusiasm, this Swan, whoever he might be.

It was in a state of some discomfiture that I found myself, a few days after the election, in a horse-drawn vehicle ascending the winding road that led to President Roosevelt's home outside New York City—Sagamore Hill. I had been given to understand that Mr. Edison would not become President for some months, and I had hoped to defer my confession of our actual circumstances until that time. However, an urgent summons to Sagamore Hill to meet with the (soon-to-be-ex-) President and his successor to discuss "matters of mutual concern to the United States of America and the Galactic Empire," delivered the day before by a White House messenger, left no doubt that Mr. Edison meant, as Oxford put it, to "jump the gun."

I could not expect Edison to take at all well the news that we were not an advance embassy, sent to open the way for a profitable relationship between Earth and a mighty realm of spacefarers, but rather that we were merely a party of castaways with nothing to offer. And even this, of course, would not be the whole truth. Our intention of making every attempt to speed the growth of the planet's technology still presented our only hope of departure, though we had not yet been able to arrive at any clearly defined plans, and it did not seem to me to be prudent to go into this.

I looked uneasily at Ted Oxford, who sat next to me

in the carriage. I had wished to tell him of our problem, but Dark and Ari had been firmly against that. "Do it once and get it over with," Dark had advised. "If you spill it to Oxford, he'll likely start getting the jim-jams imagining what the government will do to him for being mixed up in it—prison, hanging, the Edison chair, or something else they might get up specially. The very thought would make the poor chap so nervous he'd be apt to do anything."

I could well believe this—certainly, similar thoughts centered on myself were producing very unsettling effects. I felt that I could have consulted Wells to useful effect, but he had been obliged to return to England the day after the election, as he put it, "to see to my affairs." Dark later told me that, from what he gathered from Wells's conversation, these affairs were apt to be political or sexual or a combination of the two, and I could understand the urgency which possessed the slightly built journalist.

I was roused from my brooding by the halting of our conveyance and a murmured "oh-oh" from Oxford. A large and elegant automobile, with a small American flag displayed on its front parts, stood in front of us, leaning at an angle, with two wheels in a ditch at the side of the road. Two uniformed men were laboring with long poles to right it, but did not seem to be making much progress.

"Them as takes their autos up this road always seems t' get stuck just about here," the driver of our carriage said dreamily. "Or if 'tain't here, then on the next bend. Station hack ain't *good* enough for 'em, my, no, got t' chug up here in their fancy gas-burners. Pride goeth before a fall and an haughty spirit before destruction," he further observed, which seemed to me an excessively harsh way of putting it.

"Hi! You!" With some dismay, I recognized a stocky, white-haired figure standing beside the stranded car as Edison. "I've got to get on up to Sagamore Hill to—oh, it's you fellows. Give me a lift, will you?"

"*Lift*," our driver muttered to Oxford. "It's farm carts, or as it might be your family buggy, that gives *lifts*. A hack, now, takes *fares*. There's a difference, you see, one bein' in the amateur line and t'other in the professional."

"Driver," Oxford informed him in a low voice, "the gentleman requiring our help is Thomas Alva Edison, President-Elect of the United States."

"Hmm," the driver said. "In that case, and seein' as we're most of the way there, he c'n ride for half fare."

To my relief, Edison did not plunge into the topic which I had been summoned to discuss. Looking back at the toiling chauffeurs as our carriage moved on, he said, "That's a fool way to do things, building cars that don't fit the roads they've got to run on. I expect *you* people"—he turned to face me with a sour look—"don't have that sort of problem."

"Our ground transportation is organized on somewhat different lines," I admitted. "I don't know the details, but the—"

"Don't *tell* me," Edison said. "Whatever you've got there, it wouldn't work for us, I'm sure. But there should be a way to get a narrower wheelbase that'd support enough weight and still be stable . . . let me see . . ." He fished a notepad from his pocket and became absorbed in making notes and sketches on it. "No, that wouldn't do it," he muttered. "Outriggers? A built-in jack . . . nope. Ha! *There's* a thought, now. You'd have to . . . Yeah, that'll make Ford sit up and take notice; I c'n get this off to him tonight. . . ."

He spent the rest of the journey on his rapid calculations, giving vent to an occasional pleased exclamation.

Mr. Roosevelt met us on the lawn in front of his house and ushered us into a room of considerable size, much more imposing, yet, as it were, personal, in atmosphere than his office in the White House. A large heating device in which pieces of wood were burned, providing both warmth and a decorative effect, stood at one end of it; that it was dangerous to approach this mechanism was indicated by the presence of the outer covering of a large animal, with intact teeth displayed warningly, stretched in front of it.

Another such skin, covered with irregular spots, but without the teeth, was thrown over the back of a type of wide chair, ample for two or three; this skin must have had a different significance, as Roosevelt seated himself and Edison on the piece of furniture with no sign of a qualm, and invited Oxford and me to draw up chairs to face them. I was glad to do so, as this position placed my back to the head of a large, horned animal protruding from one wall. Although the balance of its body was evidently contained behind the wall, so that it was prevented from entering the room, it had a fixed, unfriendly stare that I did not care for.

"Now that we don't have to worry about Bryan declaring you anathema," Roosevelt said, "we can get down to business. Most of it's going to be Edison's problem, but I imagine there are some things I can do while I'm still in office to get this business started."

"Right, Mr. President." It seemed to me that Edison

used the term with a certain sardonic relish. "For instance, Ambassador, just about how soon do you expect to be able to make your report to your people?"

It was clear that my last chance to temporize was
gone, that my only possible course was to be completely candid and forthright. "There is a . . . um . . .
difficulty about that," I said, suddenly feeling that
forthrightness could wait for a bit.

"Difficulty?" "Difficulty?" The two Presidents
spoke as one.

"Well, about this Empire . . . it . . . there isn't what
you could actually call an Empire, really. . . ."

Edison's face was unnervingly stony, Roosevelt's
even more unnervingly mobile, as I gave my explanation.

When I had finished, Roosevelt said slowly, seeming to bite off each word with his large teeth as if he
wished to destroy it as it was spoken, "Do you mean
to tell me that you have turned the politics and
government—the very history—of the United States of
America upside-down with this story? And that it's not
true? By Godfrey—"

"Well, we *are* from another planet," I broke in hastily. "That part's true enough, and there's really quite a
number of advanced civilizations about. It's that . . .
um . . . well, they don't do much in the way of trading
and such, especially with the . . . ah . . ."

"Primitives," Roosevelt said heavily.

"Well, yes; you see, it wouldn't be worthwhile . . .
It's not that your sort of world isn't *interesting*," I said.
"Why, that's what the Explorer Service is all about, to
gather information about places unlike our own planet,
don't you see? It helps the young people so much, and

103

quite a few adults consult our archives, too, when they've nothing better—when there's something they want to know about, that is."

Edison jammed his hands deeply in his trouser pockets and regarded the tips of his shoes. "Well, well," he said mildly. "Ten thousand or so years of human history, a few billion souls, the great republics, kingdoms and empires of a planet—a rainy day's amusement for the kiddies, that's what we are, huh?"

"Our climate differs from yours in that—" I began.

"Keep *quiet,* by George!" Roosevelt said. "You'll pay for—"

Edison lifted a hand. "Now, Mr. President," he said. "Just put yourself in these fellows' place. When you're off to Africa next year, why, s'pose you got lost in the jungle, lost your supplies and so on. And you came to some tribe you couldn't be sure was friendly. Now, wouldn't you maybe try a tall story on 'em so's you could count on their help? You didn't have any big stick to carry, why, you'd have to bluff, right?"

Roosevelt evidently did not care for the comparison, but apparently could not fault it. He gritted his teeth, then turned to Oxford, who had sat quite still beside me since I had begun my confession. "By Godfrey, were you in on this? Was Hearst? Was it a put-up job between you and these . . . derelicts?"

"It's news to me, Mr. President," Oxford said, with a forced attempt at his normal jauntiness.

"Well, it had better not be news *for* Willie Hearst!" Roosevelt declared. "If a *word* of this gets out in the papers, it'll be an almighty embarrassment to the government and to me personally—but it'll be the devil to pay and no pitch hot for Hearst, let me tell you!"

"Mr. President," Oxford said earnestly, "let me tell

104

you straight out that I had sooner take passage on the *Flying Dutchman,* and steerage at that, than to explain to Mr. Hearst that the stories I've been getting my bylines on for the last couple of months have been all moonshine. My lips are sealed, believe me.''

"They sure are,'' Edison affirmed, sitting up suddenly. ''Now, I'm counting on you to back me on this, Roosevelt, 'cause it's the only way to handle it. Oxford, you're not working for Hearst any longer, effective at close of business, as of even date, and business has just now closed. You are an officer in the United States Army, bound to official secrecy by whatever appropriate acts and ordinances, et cetera, et cetera. Roosevelt, swear him in—you can have Loeb do the paperwork and figure out what rank he is later on.''

''But I don't see—'' Roosevelt began.

''Don't *have* to see it, man! *I'm* goin' t' be carrying the can on this, and you've got to help me!''

Both Roosevelt and Oxford appeared bemused as the one administered and the other received the oath confirming the impromptu commission.

''Fine!'' Edison said. ''So you're our man now, Oxford, not Hearst's. And your job's to ride herd on this bunch of castaways—keep 'em happy *and* out of sight until after I'm inaugurated, and make sure there's nothing about 'em gets in the papers that hasn't been there already. I don't have the least idea in the world what I'm goin' to do about 'em, but now's no time to start rocking the Ship of State. Once I get to the wheelhouse, I'll have worked out what to do. There'll be something, I don't doubt. I've lit up the world, startin' with a piece of burnt bamboo for a filament, and it'd be mighty strange if I couldn't figure a use for two brace of astronauts!''

105

12

Although he appeared to have relegated Mr. Roosevelt to a minor role, Edison did turn to him for help in finding quarters for us, and the President was able to place us in a house some miles from his own, without alerting the owner or the townspeople to our identity. The cost of our housing and maintenance, including an elderly couple named Bonacker who saw to the cooking and housekeeping, was paid out of the public purse, again by some means arrived at by Mr. Roosevelt.

By the time we were settled in the large house, on a bluff overlooking a harbor, the foliage had fallen from the trees, and we were able to see some distance, down to the water and across to the opposite shore. It was a lonely place, sparsely built up, with a huddle of houses and a shipyard and a dock on the shore below us—the name of the place, Glenwood Landing, appeared to derive in part from this last feature—and an establishment which combined the functions of provision store and post office a little inland. A couple of miles' walk up a long hill led to a larger cluster of stores and houses, called Glen Head, and a station on the railway. Oxford told us as we debarked from the train from New York that we were seeing this station for the last time until he had further word from the President or Edison. "You fellows are free to stroll around the shore and so on, but the station area's off-limits, by order of Lieutenant Colonel Oxford, Commanding."

He spoke lightly, but it was evident that he felt the gravity of his hastily conferred military rank. "I tell you, Raf," he confided to me about that time, "it's not that it makes me all that nervous that I could be shot for insubordination or something if I pull a bad boner now; I mean, if you get W. R. Hearst down on you, why, shooting'd seem like a week by the beautiful sea compared to that. But I am now, by presidential order, an officer and a gentleman. Lord, if the Market Street crowd in Frisco heard that Ned Oxford was a certified gentleman, it'd hand them a laugh, no kid!"

We now settled into a time of quiet, which I at least found restful, occupying myself mainly with invigorating walks through the nearby area. A few miles away, past a large lake on a private estate, guarded by large swimming birds which appeared ready to attack any intruder, or even passer-by, lay a small village at the head of the harbor. There was in this place a refreshment establishment with a convivial crowd of habitués, from whose conversation I was often able to pick up much information on the culture—which was, after all, a part of my function—although it often developed that after spending some time there and joining in the refreshment, I was unable to retain any very accurate impression of what I had heard.

Valmis spent most of his time reclining on a stuffed piece of furniture on a glassed-in porch, regarding the trees and sky outside. He claimed that this was the best way to Integrate, given our circumstances.

Ari was happily busied with going over great piles of books and journals which Oxford had sent from New York City and elsewhere, and he declared that he was beginning to arrive at an understanding of the principles of Metahistory as they applied to Earth.

Dark also studied some of the journals, though little of their text; he was fascinated by pictorial representations of mechanical devices, especially those of self-powered land vehicles. "Wouldn't it be great to drive one of those," he said wistfully on one occasion. "The thing about running a spacecraft is, unless you run into trouble, there's no *feel* to it. But imagine pushing yourself through the atmosphere, just ramming through it, the engine roaring in front of you, feeling every bump in the road, the landscape spinning past you, and you controlling the whole thing! But Oxford won't let us have one, damn it!"

I thought I might divert him with an excursion to Roslyn, the neighboring village, as I had noticed next to the tavern a large mechanical device of a sort I thought he might find interesting. "Ha," he said when he saw it. "The water coming down off the hill there turns it, and that shaft it's connected to runs inside that building, where it does some work. My word, these people like to do things on the cheap—all that power, and not paying for it. Hmm—interesting arrangement of slats or whatever . . . catches the water so it turns, but lets it out so it doesn't slow the motion down. How . . . ?"

He leaned forward to examine it, but his interest was dampened—as indeed, was he himself, as I humorously pointed out afterward, though he did not seem to understand the jest—when he slipped and fell onto the wheel, which rolled him down into the stream that fed it, then carried him beneath it and expelled him into the waters of the harbor.

A native in a boat nearby caught him when he surfaced, hoisted him aboard, and brought him ashore. As a needed restorative measure for Dark, and a reward for his rescuer, I insisted that both repair with me to the tavern. In short order, Dark, wrapped in a blanket while his sodden clothing steamed in front of the fire which warmed the room, sat next to me on a bench, while our guest faced us across our table and sipped a warming drink.

Dark took a gulp of his—it was made, I believe, with a distillate of fermented molasses and adorned with a lump of animal-derived fat, and had been heated by plunging a piece of hot iron into its container—and said, "Ha! What *power* that thing had! Just *whooshed* me along under the water and flung me out! Those slat things really bite into the water. Say . . . that'd work the other way, wouldn't it? I mean, look—you could put a power source onto one of those wheel things, d'you see, and stick it into the water. And if you had it on the side of a boat, when it turned, why, the boat would just push through the water like mad!"

Our guest looked at his glass and at ours before he spoke. "Seems t' me you'd just sort of spin round if you did that," he said carefully. "Hangin' it over the side, the way you seem t' be suggestin', why, it'd turn your boat in circles, 'stead of goin' ahead, as I s'pose you'd want it t' do."

"Oh." Dark thought this over. "You're right, I guess. What a shame."

"O' course," the other went on wryly, "you *could* put a pair of 'em on, one on one side, one on t'other. That way they'd balance out, an' you'd get more power, too, I expect."

"Hey, that's a *great* idea!" Dark exclaimed. "Listen," he said to me, "do you think we could do ourselves some good with these people by putting them onto that? Or maybe," he went on, lowering his voice and giving a quick glance across the table, "if things

109

don't go so well when You-know-who gets inaugurated as You-know-what next March, and we have to make our own way, we could sell the notion. We'd cut this chap in on the profits for helping, of course.''

"There was talk,'' said Dark's rescuer, looking at a point somewhere above our heads, "about sellin' off the William Cullen Bryant place down the shore road for a lunatic hospital. Either of you fellers hear if that ever come about? Or if there was any other such enterprise openin' up hereabouts?''

"No,'' I answered. "We don't, ah, get around very much, and don't get to hear what the na—what you people talk about.''

"Did seem t' me that was the way of it,'' the man said, standing up. "Been interesting talkin' to you fellers. I don't know when I've had a conversation just like it. Thanks fer the drink, but I think I've had enough. Suggest maybe you have, too.''

"Ah,'' Dark said, "but look at it this way. If one of these things gives me a whole new approach to water transportation, what wouldn't another one do?''

The native seemed to have no adequate response to that, and left.

Our walk home, an hour later, began pleasantly, though the sky was covered with clouds and the brisk wind was bitingly cold. After a bit, though, I had the uneasy impression that the unfamiliar stimulant we had taken at the tavern was affecting my senses; it seemed to me that I saw several white spots whirling through the air, and at the same time I experienced a chilly, stinging sensation on my face and hands. Worse, it appeared to me that the ground and trees were gradually becoming tinged with white, as though my ability to perceive color were draining away.

110

"Well," Dark said loudly as we trudged along. "This is interesting countryside, the trees and all. They look different from our trees, don't they? The fronds or whatever they are falling off them like that."

"They aren't the same as at home, no," I agreed.

"*Quite* different, in some ways," he said. "And the ground, too. One notices, from time to time, so to speak, some differences about that." I saw him give a quick sidelong glance at me. "And it isn't to be expected, I suppose, that the air would always be the same, either."

"How do you mean?" I asked.

"Nothing in *particular,* Raf, but—whoop!" One foot skidded from under him, leaving a trail in the illusion of whiteness on the roadway, and he nearly fell.

I stooped and ran my hand along the ground. A scraping of white matter gathered on it, which quickly resolved itself into a clear liquid which I recognized as water.

"Hey, this stuff's real, isn't it?" Dark called, having made the same experiment.

"It seems so," I replied. "It's like rain, I imagine—of course, it'd naturally come down frozen when the temperature drops." I was irritated with myself for not having foreseen this phenomenon, which now seemed natural enough. It does not occur on our home planet—nor does the climate there change with time, as on Earth, which I suppose accounts for its absence—and I had not encountered it in the course of my Exploration duties; but still, given the factors involved, I ought to have been able to predict it.

"That's good," Dark said. "I thought that stuff we drank was making me see things."

"That would be extremely unlikely," I told him.

"Our implants are specifically designed to keep us from being affected harmfully by anything we ingest." I spoke with some severity, I fear, as I was reproaching myself for having forgotten this.

"That may be," Dark said, "but I don't know that they were meant to handle anything like that rum stuff."

In spite of our enforced leisure, the time passed swiftly. Shortly after we marked the turning of the year with the ceremonies Oxford insisted on, which for some reason resulted in all of us being afflicted by a temporary return of the fatigue I had experienced at the players' club in New York, I realized that there was not much time remaining before Mr. Edison's inauguration as President.

I sought out Ari. "Listen," I said, "hadn't we better start working our plans out? I don't know what Edison will do with us, but it seems to me we've got to be ready to get at this business of speeding up the native technology, or we'll never get away from here."

"I think I've got an approach," Ari said. "Mind you, it's not completely clear in my mind yet, but it's coming. This is a remarkable world, remarkable. There are some very intriguing possibilities. . . ."

As an experienced Recorder, I have to say that this sounded as though what was being communicated was that Ari was completely baffled, but in fact only a few weeks later, he called us together out of Oxford's hearing to lay out his proposed course of action.

"One thing that has fascinated me," he began—Dark rolled his eyes; we all knew from experience that whatever fascinated Ari was likely to take a lot of time in the telling— "is the attitude toward warfare. It seems to be a general assumption that, in spite of the disastrously prolonged wars of the planet's past, modern weaponry and transport will result in wars which, if they are fought at all, will be short and sharp. All the major nations have secret plans, which journalists are able to ferret out only with some effort, calling for swift movement of troops by railway, automobile and bicycle to deliver decisive blows to an adversary. At the same time, there is a worldwide interest in peace, with many nations cooperating in a running conference designed to assure it in one of the smaller countries in Europe. The almost unanimous opinion of informed people is that wars are on the way to becoming a thing of the past and, if they occur at all, will only be temporary and local.

"Yet," he went on, "I have discerned a Metahistorical pattern in some of the very measures designed to assure this. In Europe, for instance, all the major powers are allied with others, the notion being that no one will go to war with any one nation, as several others are pledged to assist it, presenting a joint antagonist too powerful to deal with."

"That doesn't seem like such a bad notion," Dark observed. "I've gone to lots of refreshment places and such on different worlds that I wouldn't care to enter unless I had a couple of friends with me to discourage some disorderly chap from seeing if he could take me apart for fun."

"Quite," Ari said. "But I recall a few occasions on which such friends have had to deliver you to *Wanderer* in a fairly used-up state."

"Well, that was when the disorderly chap had some friends with him, too, and . . . oh."

"Precisely. This balance of alliances may well deter

one power from making war on another—but if it does *not*, it then assures that any war becomes a general war. And that, gentlemen, is what is about to happen."

We would have taken his word for it, but he felt impelled to go into detail—I suppose to have some fun after all those months of research. There was a lot about the effects of industrialization and public health work, but the interesting bits concerned the fairly odd people who ran some of the big countries. There was one in England, where Wells came from, who seemed fairly sensible, but he was getting on and not well, and so would have to be considered as a temporary element. For some reason, which I didn't understand Ari's explanation of, two of the other important rulers were relatives of this King Edward's, by blood or marriage. One of them, the Emperor of Germany, was apparently a highly excitable type and much given to doing alarming things. He claimed to be an absolute monarch, but all the same had nearly been thrown out, within the past few months, owing to a lot of odd goings on. Apparently he had been at a party where one of his generals, dressed in a woman's dancing costume, had dropped dead; and this and similar matters had not set well with the Germans. The other was also an emperor, in a place called Russia, and while not as active as his cousin or whatever the relationship was, was almost as alarming, as he had a tendency to do nothing much and pay attention to whomever had spoken to him last. This resulted in many countries being under the impression that they had agreements of various sorts with Russia—agreements which turned out not to be effective.

These and several of the other kings, emperors and such in Europe had possessions and alliances in other parts of the planet. "So the whole point," Ari explained, "is that once *anything* happens, it's going to spread all around the world. And, given the factors I have already pointed out and the extremely unstable temperament of the principal personalities involved—Wells was right about that, you know—why, that *anything* is bound to happen. This Nicholas, the one in Russia, for instance; he could get nervous about keeping his people under control and decide to start up a war to give them something to keep busy at. He tried it a few years ago, and it didn't work, but that doesn't seem to bother these people. If he went into what they call the Balkans, say, that would bring Turkey into it, and England would get nervous about India, and likely join with the French to stop him; William in Germany might lend a hand either way, and they'd all draw on their colonies and friends and relations, and you'd have—"

"Hey!" Dark said. He had been studying the map Ari had provided, trying to keep track of the countries involved in the discourse. "Here's something interesting."

"Interesting as opposed to *what?*" Ari said testily.

"Look here. This Russia place, a bit of it runs all the way to this ocean here, see? And on the other side of that, you've got San Francisco, which is near where those ham-fisted natives sank poor old *Wanderer*. Well, then, this part here, what they call Siberia, that's where we near as anything crashed. I think I could work it out . . . Ha! Right here, a place called Tunguska. We'd have blown a damned big hole in it if we'd impacted."

Ari and I looked quickly at Valmis, expecting him to get into his familiar routine about the morality of using the Probability Displacer and point out that in one continuum we *had* created an impact crater in the Tunguska

115

region, but he merely shrugged and said, "What is, is. Or perhaps it isn't. But we might as well act as if it is, as there isn't any way to act as if it isn't."

There isn't much you can do with a statement like that, and I rather welcomed Ari's resumption of his lecture.

"The main point is, this whole place is close to critical mass, so to speak. It's going to go up, to explode in general warfare, and soon. Probably not for another three years, but certainly within six or seven—say, 1912 to 1916. Every principle of Metahistory dictates that, in spite of what the natives may think. There will be wholesale destruction and slaughter; much of the civilization on this planet will lie in ruins; all the energy, wealth and ingenuity the major nations possess will be expended on an effort which will drain them completely and achieve none of the objectives they intend."

We contemplated this dire picture for a moment, then Dark said, "Ah, then, what we've got to do is work out a way to get them to stop it and set about learning how to do what they've got to do to refit *Wanderer*. How do you think we could—"

"No." Ari shook his head. "On the contrary, we must bend every effort to get them into this war as quickly as possible!"

13

I am no Metahistorian, nor would I care to be, so I could not fault Ari's logic as he explained it; but the idea did seem a bit raw to me.

So it did to Dark. "It makes sense the way you put it," he said dubiously, "but I can't say I like it. I mean, it's all very well to say that they're going to have the war anyhow, and if they start it up now, it'll go faster and be done with, so we get the benefit of the speed-up in science and so on without everything getting used up—all right, you're the Metahistorian, and I expect you know what you're talking about. But all the same, prodding them into it, that seems pretty shabby."

"True enough," Ari said. "It was not an easy decision to arrive at, either ethically or, I may point out, in terms of long hours of study and calculation performed whilst you, Raf and Valmis were amusing yourselves. It represents my best effort and thought, but I should of course be glad to hear of any more acceptable alternative you might have to offer."

As he was well aware it would, this effectively silenced our objections, and he proceeded to the next stage of his plan. It was necessary, according to him, to pay personal visits to certain of the important rulers—mainly Edward of England, Nicholas of Russia, William of Germany, and possibly Francis Joseph of Austria, though this last, being advanced in years, might well not

117

be in any condition actually to comprehend much of what was said to him—and, using Metahistorical principles and techniques, to act upon them so as to speed up their war plans. He refused to be more specific than this, saying, "I'm a Metahistorian, and you're not. It's all I can do to handle the responsibilities of my craft, and I can't imagine what it might do to you to have to deal with it. I'm certain I don't want to be an Integrator or a Captain or a Recorder."

"How are you to get to see these fellows?" Dark asked. "Or is that a secret, too?"

"On the contrary," Ari replied. "It is a matter of practical detail, not of Metahistory, and so does not fall within my scope. Getting us from one place to another, setting up appointments—that's the sort of thing Recorders and Captains traditionally do, as I recall, and I am sure that you and Raf can manage it. I am perfectly willing to handle the really difficult parts of the enterprise, the actual dealing with these monarchs."

Dark and I found after a few moments' discussion that the solution was easily arrived at. That is not to say that it struck either of us as very good, just that it was the only possible one.

"Everyone still takes us for ambassadors, bar Oxford, Edison and Roosevelt," Dark summed it up, "so there'd be no trouble about getting at the kings and such, once we were where they are. So we've got to get Edison to let us go over to this Europe and go see them. Not, of course, telling him that we want to stir them up into shooting at each other—I don't suppose he'd go for that—but, oh, saying that they might want to help out in doing something to get *Wanderer* refitted. That's what we actually will be after, of course, in the long run, so it's not that far off the truth."

118

When we told Oxford what we felt prudent to reveal of our plans, he said, "I don't know why he wouldn't go for that. If you're traveling around hobnobbing with the Kaiser and so on, that'll help keep up the fiction that you're what you're supposed to be a while longer. I don't know what he'd do with you otherwise. I have to say, it tickles me that you guys put such a big one over on both those big guns, Teddy and Edison. And, for that matter, I'm a little easier in my mind thinking of you as beached sailors instead of a sort of advance guard of a whole new civilization. It kind of got to me when old Geronimo said what he did, because that seems to be the way of it—even if the civilized fellows come in with the best of intentions, the ones who are there already get it in the neck, one way or another. They just can't compete, and they sort of give up and turn themselves into carbon copies of the new people. *We've* done that often enough, Lord knows, and I don't favor poetic justice one bit, not when I'm on the short end of it."

As our intention was precisely to create drastic change in the society of the whole planet, though not quite in the way he spoke of, his comment made me uneasy. I liked Oxford—we all did—and had reason to be grateful to him, and it went against my grain to have to conceal from him that we proposed to act in a way he would find upsetting. On the other hand, concealment was necessary if our interests were to be served, so there seemed no choice; conscientious action, it seemed to me, ought always to be founded on rationality.

"It is a sort of ordeal," Ari observed, "perhaps a survival of customs I have read of in Levels Two and Three in this planet's cultural evolution. They conduct the ceremony in the open in this abominable cold to

119

show that both the old President and the new one are hale enough to stand it, and I suppose it works well enough; I believe only one of them ever died of it."

I was more interested in the content of Edison's inaugural speech than in its setting, though my ears and face were painfully chilled. We had been invited to witness the ceremonies, and Oxford had taken us down to Washington—rather faster, I noted, than the trip had taken us seven months before, as the newly installed electric turbine locomotive cut considerable time from the run. As we had been bidden to a White House afternoon reception immediately afterwards, I had determined to put our proposition to the newly installed President then, so paid special attention to his references to us in his speech.

"We have this past year," he said, his voice carried to the extensive crowd—and, I realized, to many parts of the country—by the rapidly growing network of electrodiffusion devices, "been privileged to encounter the greatest opportunity and challenge mankind has yet had to face. Men from another planet—from another star, one we cannot see—are among us. What they bring to us, and how we deal with them and their gifts, will mark our future. That future is far more varied and exciting than it appeared to be before last summer. We have had our eyes opened to the fact that we are not alone in the Universe, and even, in some ways, may not count for very much. Well, it will be the main work of this Administration to see that the American people aren't counted out—that we use the presence of these visitors from unimaginably far away to secure a place in the future fitting to our glorious past."

Quite gracefully put, I thought, and neatly avoiding any awkward references to the nonexistent Galactic

Empire. Perhaps if nobody mentioned it any more, it would be forgotten; the people of Earth did appear to manifest somewhat flighty intellects. The rest of the speech did not hold my attention, as it dealt with such parochial matters as the establishment of a national scientific academy, the regulation of electrodiffusion, and the granting of independence to some Pacific and Caribbean islands obtained in a war ten years before, on the grounds that they were more trouble than they were worth.

This last item appeared to agitate Oxford, however, for an abrupt movement he made in the chair next to me nearly caused the tall cylindrical hat he was wearing for the occasion, as all of us were, to fall off. "If he can do that, he's a wonder," he muttered. "The fire-eaters in Congress'll be after him in no time. But if anyone could bring off turning the Filipinos and the Porto Ricans loose, I guess he could—all he's got to do is tell 'em it makes scientific sense and dollars-and-cents sense, too, and who's to argue with the genius who's electrified the world and made a fortune at it? Imagine, we've finally got a President who means to do things because they're sensible—who ever heard of that?"

The reception at the White House was a crowded affair, and the new President was so much in demand that I did not get a chance for a word with him for nearly two hours. I drove off the effects of the cold with several glasses of a warming beverage that had the peculiar quality of bubbling in the glass, something like the Würzburger Oxford had recommended to us at the Hoffman House, except that it was paler and had a more delicate taste.

President Edison spent a good deal of time with a somewhat younger man, thinner and notably shrewd-looking. I later saw this man talking with Dark, to their apparent mutual interest; he then drifted over to Ari. I joined them in time to hear Ari say, "Mr. Ford, I cannot agree with you. The study of the past is the only key to the future and, indeed, to the present."

"I'll tell you again," the man said, "history is bunk."

"Your opinion as to the worth of the scholarship extant on your own planet," Ari said with determined politeness, "is, of course, your own business. However, looking at the principles expounded and tested by the discipline of Metahistory—"

"And Metahistory is metabunk, I guess," the man said. "This fellow here one of you? He know how any of your things work?"

"I am a Recorder—as well as being an ambassador, of course," I added hastily, still wishing to keep up our pretense. "Recorders Record and Communicate; they do not study mechanics."

"Huh," the man said. "How about the fourth one of you? Has he got any notion of mechanics?"

Ari explained to him the function and methods of an Integrator, and the man shook his head. "Four of you, and only that Dark fellow's got the know-how to talk about any of the things you use. What a way to run a railroad!"

"What did he mean about a railroad?" Ari asked after the man had left us. "We don't have anything to do with railroads. Nor does he, from what he told me; he makes those car things, not trains."

"These people, even the brightest of them, have a way of lapsing into inconsequence," I told him. "They start with one thing and finish with another. I expect

122

their brains work differently from ours. Remember that, as it may work to our advantage."

I finally found the President alone, leaning against a wall and looking rather tired. I had acquainted myself with the name of the drink being served, and I gestured cordially with a glass of it as I approached him. "Nice champagne, this," I remarked.

Edison curtly said, "I s'pose it is. Would have liked to've had American stuff, but they tell me it isn't good enough yet. That's another thing we'll see to in time; no reason we can't put out wines as good as anything that comes from France."

"Ah, France," I said, pleased that a natural introduction to my proposal had presented itself. "That's in Europe, France is."

"*I* know that," Edison said.

"We ought to go to Europe, d'you see?" I went on. "A good idea, visiting Europe. See the kings and whatnot. Being ambassadors."

"But you darned well aren't ambassadors!"

"Ah, but *they* don't know that," I said, shaking an admonitory finger at him. "Wouldn't it be nice if we all went to see them, see, and . . . and, well, got them to see if they could help us get poor old *Wanderer* back together. I should think any king or emperor would want to do that, if he was the right sort of king. Or emperor," I added, wishing to be fair. I had not given Mr. Edison the closely reasoned presentation that Dark and I had worked out, but in the festive circumstances of the occasion, it seemed to me that something more informal was called for. Also, I found that I could not quite recall the full details of my intended argument.

"You fellows want the U.S. government to stake you to the Grand Tour? Go call on royalty and chat with 'em

123

about your problems, the things you know, and so on? That what you've got in mind?''

"In a nut-husk," I said, pleased that he had understood so quickly.

"That's about the size of it, I'd guess," he said, with a glance at me. "Well, I'll tell you. Let's see, you're all going back tonight to that Glenwood place?"

I assured him that we were. "Fine. Well, you'll have my answer in the morning, you can be sure of that."

Our late afternoon journey back to New York was enlivened by the presence of Mr. Roosevelt, who for a while abandoned his family, traveling a car or so ahead, and joined us.

"By George, I was pretty sore at you fellows for a while," he told us. "But I'll tell you, just as Edison was taking the oath today, and I was telling myself how sorry I was for myself, I saw in a flash how I'd be feeling if *I* was taking it—and that was pretty darned glum. I could've taken another four years of it in my stride, in the ordinary way of things—there's the Canal to see through, and the trusts could do with a little stampeding still, politics and all that—it would have been lots of good fights of the kind I'm used to, and maybe some good coming of it, which is all you can ask. But this business with you people—I have to say that's 'way off my range. I expect I know more than most men about this Earth and what goes on on it, but I'm not geared to look outside it, and I guess Edison's the right man to see to it, after all. . . ." He looked at the landscape speeding by outside the window for a moment, then turned to us, shedding his pensive mood.

"Well, I'll be busy enough, anyhow," he continued.

"My son and I are packing and sorting things for the African trip, and I don't suppose I'll have an unoccupied minute for the next three weeks. Oxford, why don't you bring 'em to Hoboken to see me off?"

Oxford said that might be a good idea, as we had travel plans of our own and might wish to acquaint ourselves with the general aspect of a ship before embarking. Mr. Roosevelt questioned us about these plans and gave us much information about King Edward, the Kaiser, the Czar, and Francis Joseph, who was also called a Kaiser. He explained this by informing us that "kaiser"—and, indeed, "czar"—were derived from the family name of a native chieftain who flourished two millennia previously. He then discoursed on language, giving me some most valuable insights into the mental workings of the natives; on political and social experiences he had had, which quite fascinated Ari; on naval gunnery and the construction of battleships, to Dark's great interest; and even drew Valmis out of his customary Integrator's state of withdrawal—which in persons of other crafts would be known as torpor—and into an animated discussion of the relationship of philosophy and the workings of nature as exemplified in the behavior and construction of animals.

"By Godfrey," Roosevelt said, standing and rubbing his hands together, "I feel the better for our little chat. Be interesting to see how Edison handles you fellows for the next four years. Always good to match wits, isn't it? If he's not up to snuff . . . well, 1912 isn't all that far off. I'll be seeing you."

Tired after our journey to and from Washington, we slept late the next morning. I, in fact, did so to a lesser extent than I should have preferred, as I was awakened from a comfortable, sound slumber by Oxford's hand shaking my shoulder.

"If a fellow's been on the trains for hours and frozen his ears and nose in some primitive ceremony, and hung about a reception and all that," I said, "it seems to me that that fellow ought to be able to sleep a bit and not have a fellow shaking a fellow's shoulder."

"I believe," Oxford said, "that you told me the President said you'd have his answer about the trip this morning?"

"Oh," I said, sitting up. "It's come, then? What is it?"

Oxford strode to the window of my room, raised the shade and then the window itself, admitting a gust of chilly air. "Take a look."

I got out of bed and went to where he stood. When I leaned out the window, I could see the front entrance to the house. I could also see the two uniformed men who stood in front of it, each resting on his shoulder a firearm equipped with a sort of knife on the front part.

The two others at each visible corner of the house were similarly equipped.

"*That's* the answer," Oxford said grimly. "A detachment of Marines—to keep us under house arrest!"

14

Oxford showed me the letter the officer in charge of the party of intruders had presented to him upon their arrival about a quarter of an hour before.

Lt. Col. Oxford:

You and the so-called astronauts in your charge are hereby ordered confined to your present quarters until further notice, said orders to be enforced by the detachment of Marines who will bring you this letter. I am using Marines as I don't think there will be any question of your trying to pull anything funny about your rank with any of them. Marines don't pay much mind to the Army, and I am told that holds true for Capt. Thatcher especially.

I have got nothing against you, but you are needed there to keep an eye on them and for other purposes I will explain, and remember that you are in the Army, which means I am your Commander in Chief, so it is not just a matter of a pink slip in your pay envelope if something goes wrong. You know what I mean, I am sure.

Now, these astronauts have had more than half a year's board and room and travel and per diem and so on, at U.S. expense, and most of it under false pretenses. It is time they started earning their keep. I suspect some of them are not playing with a full deck

"What does that bit mean?" I asked Oxford.

"It's one of our terms dealing with, ah, cultural differences; don't worry about it, just go on reading."

but there is knowledge there that is bound to be useful to the U.S.A. I certainly do not propose to have them gadding around the Old World, telling anything they might know to a crowd of foreigners. We have got to get what we know from them and develop it, and then we can decide how much of it we can sell—not give away—to other countries.

You have a great opportunity to be of service to your country, and I am sure you see that you had better take it. Set these fellows to work writing down what they know about their machinery, power sources, weapons, and so on. Get any stuff they have away from them on some pretext so that our technicians can work on it, but be sure to find out if there's anything dangerous about any of it first, as I do not want Menlo Park to burn down again. The engineer one and the simp I know have some interesting things, but do not overlook the other two, as even what they might use as a toothbrush might turn out to be something we haven't even thought about here yet.

I emphasize that these people are a vital resource in the possession of the U.S.A., and with them in your charge, I expect that you will get good results. You had better.

I am sure I do not need to tell you that disclosing the contents of this letter to any person, and especially to the astronauts, is a court-martial offense. I have not asked anybody to look me up the military law on that point, for I don't doubt that the President can find a way to make sure that an officer who disobeys a direct order is not just in hot water but in superheated steam.

Yours in confidence,
EDISON

There were a number of points about this missive which seemed to call urgently for my attention, but one stood out above the others.

"Why did you show this to me?" I asked. "Now he'll boil you or whatever he meant."

128

"I don't *expect*," Oxford said, "that you'll put a call through to the White House to tell him about it. I have to admit that some of the things you do and say make me less sure of that than I'd like to be, but I'm banking on it all the same. The thing is, I didn't *like* that letter. I don't like being pushed around, and I don't like having you fellows pushed around and milked like cows. And I damned well don't like the President—a man I've been brought up to revere since I was a kid, and that I voted for—pulling a stunt like this. No President should do that, and Tom Edison especially shouldn't—it's not worthy of the office or the man—it's a cheap business, and I don't mean to go along with it."

"Well," I said uneasily, "that's very square of you." It was certainly useful that Oxford had chosen to side with us, but once again I felt a momentary oppression at the thought of the necessity we labored under to change his world around him without his consent.

"I can see his point, of course," Oxford went on. "He's under an awful lot of pressure—it'll be the devil's own job to pull the fuse out of that business about your nonexistent Empire, now that folks have got hotted up about it, and there's no denying that you've got some pretty sharp items in your luggage—Lord, I don't like to *think* what Edison'd do if he got wind of that jim-dandy little tool Dark uses to take notes with! And that agate-type-sized ear trumpet you gave him, why, he's used that to build those electrodiffusion gadgets that're all over the place now. But all the same, it seems to me he's got to stand the pressure and find a way to do things that's fitting for him and for the country. And holing you up here and making you produce information he thinks he needs to know isn't that. And I'm feeling just enough of a patriot to see that he doesn't get away with it. If this be treason, he can make the most of it, and I imagine he will, but what the hell?''

There seemed to be a considerable number of contradictions and logical flaws in this statement, such as the notion of patriotic treason, but, in spite of his erratic mental capabilities, it was clear that Oxford was prepared to be of help to us, which was nice to know. It would be even nicer, it seemed to me, to gain some idea of how he proposed to do that.

His next words bore on this point. ''All right. We want to figure out what to do next. It seems to me that this dodge about you going to Europe is the thing to look at. I mean, once you're off there, I see Edison as being pretty well stymied, and that's what we want. It might even give him time to come to his senses, which I'd like. I still think the old boy's basically a great man, even a good man, and he's just got some unexpected pushes that have turned him the wrong way for a while. Now, how do we work that?''

''I don't imagine Edison would let us off to see Mr. Roosevelt start his trip,'' I said. ''If he did, I suppose we could find some way to get on a boat that would take us to Europe.''

''No, I don't see him doing that . . . but hold on a minute! You've given me a notion, Raf!'' He dashed from the room, returning perhaps ten minutes later.

''I didn't think they'd have bothered to do anything about the 'phone,'' he said, seating himself on the edge of my bed. ''And so they haven't; it's working fine. If they've put wiretappers onto it, we're in trouble, but I didn't hear any clicks. You'd better get yourself and the others looking presentable; we're going to have a pretty considerable visitor in an hour or so.''

''From the tone of Mr. Edison's letter,'' I ventured,

130

"it seems unlikely that our guards would wish us to have visitors."

"I don't think they'll make any trouble about this one," Oxford said with a tight smile.

And indeed Mr. Roosevelt was greeted most deferentially by Captain Thatcher, the Marine officer who commanded the small detachment. "Since these fellows are in the neighborhood, thought I'd look them up and have a good gab with 'em," the ex-President boomed. "With your permission, of course, Captain."

"Certainly, Mr.—that is, Colonel," the officer said. "They're restricted, but I don't see that that applies to you, sir."

"Quite right, so it doesn't, by George," Mr. Roosevelt agreed, and was ushered inside the house.

Oxford quickly apprised him of the situation and handed him Edison's letter. "Now that's a bad business, a bad business," Roosevelt muttered, scanning it. "Edison's gone off the rails about this; he's going about it all the wrong way. You people may have been pretty sharp with us, but that doesn't mean he's got any call to mew you up and pick your brains."

"I'd hoped you'd feel that way, sir," Oxford said. "And that you might be willing to do something to help."

"Help?" Roosevelt demanded. "*Help* contravene the direct orders of the duly elected President of the United States of America? *Help* these scamps escape the consequences of their actions? Put myself in hazard merely because I believe the President is acting hastily and unfairly? Get involved in God knows what kind of a scheme that probably wouldn't work anyway? By George, I believe I will!"

This decision once taken, Mr. Roosevelt and Oxford worked out their plans with remarkable swiftness, while Dark, Ari, Valmis and I looked on. The details seemed fairly simple, and I supposed that any of us Explorers might have come up with an equally good idea had it been expected of us.

"That's it, then," Roosevelt said after a while, standing up. "I'll see to my end of it on my own, and you get these fellows ready for what they have to do. It'll all be set up for the right time and day—if there's any hitch about that, I'll get word to you some way. I'd rather not use the telephone any more, as I think you're on a party line here, even if there's no tapping. By Godfrey, this is a bully wheeze, so it is! And the best of it is, Edison'll thank me for it someday when he's seeing things clearer, just the way they all did after all that Panama business died down. They were all after my hide then, for slicing Panama out of Colombia and seeing to it that the new government gave us the rights to the Canal, but you don't notice anyone whining about it now, do you? This is one of those things—the man that's got the vision to see what needs to be done does it, and the consequences sort themselves out afterwards."

The ensuing weeks of inactivity were a strain on my nerves. This period did not differ in any substantial particulars from the months before, but the knowledge that it was soon to end—and end extremely actively— preyed upon me. It may have done the same on Ari, Dark and Valmis, but we found that we tended to be uncommunicative among ourselves during this time.

A visit from Mr. Roosevelt's son Kermit, ostensibly to present us with some large migrant birds his father had killed and wished us to eat, signaled that the end of our waiting was near. "Dad's got it all set," the youth told Oxford. "Five passages on the *Pavonia,* leaving Thursday from Pier Fifty-Six at four. So you work your end of it out to start at just about noon. Here's the schedule for everything." He handed Oxford a sheaf of papers. "Good luck!" he said, and left.

In accordance with the plan Roosevelt and Oxford had determined on, at about ten on the appointed morning we all repaired to the stable next to the house and hauled out the carriage stored there. It had been deprived of its animal motive power by our guards soon after they arrived, the beast having been sent off to enjoy a sort of holiday on a nearby farm, and our sole ordinary contact with the outside world had thereafter been the once-daily arrival from the nearby store of a wagon bringing ourselves and our guards necessary provisions, all this being considered needful to prevent us from entertaining ideas of unauthorized departure.

His mind having been bent to mistrust by his orders, it was only natural that Captain Thatcher should stroll over to us to ask, "What do you people think you're doing?"

"Tests, Captain," Oxford said genially. "I've finally got 'em out of their sulks, and they're willing to start in to work, the way the Commander in Chief wants. They've got some concepts that could revolutionize metallurgy, but they've got to test out the tensile strength of our steel, see? So what they've got to do is work out how strong these buggy springs are, as a starting point."

"Right," Dark said, slinging his equipment into the equipage. "I'll activate the parodbmnis here, and once the fleegle is adjusted, we'll set this other stuff going" —here he grabbed the cases containing our previously

133

packed equipment and threw them into the body of the carriage—"and then we'll all get in and bounce in it a bit and see how strong the springs are. After that, we'll be able to invent up a storm for Uncle Tom."

"Well, you've got it in a pretty slim location there," the officer observed, giving Oxford a sharp look. "You get to jostling it, that buggy could roll right down the drive and into the road. And I kind of doubt you'd want that, Colonel. And I know for *sure* the C-in-C wouldn't, so why don't I just take a little security measure about that?" And within a moment or so he had fetched a length of chain and a padlock, with which he fastened the carriage to a stout tree.

"There, now," he said, standing back. "You can experiment all you want, and no bother about rolling away."

"That's dished us," Oxford whispered to me.

"Don't worry," muttered Dark, who had overheard him. "Just carry on as planned."

Accordingly, we all climbed into the carriage and began jouncing up and down in it, as if to test the strength of the springs. Dark clambered into the rear seat, fumbled in his pocket, and brought out his writing instrument. He twisted the barrel slightly, then leaned over and held it against the chain stretched taut between the carriage and the tree. A portion of it glowed white, and it parted and fell away.

The Marine captain called, "Hey, what're you—"

Dark sprang to the ground, gave the carriage a mighty shove, and leapt aboard again as it began to roll down the slope of the drive.

As we gathered speed, confused shouts came from behind us.

"It'll take Thatcher's men a while to get organized,"

Oxford told us. "That's the advantage of surprise. TR said—"

A sharp crack sounded, followed by the sound of something whipping through the air over our heads.

"They recovered fairly fast," Dark said.

"Well, that's just a *warning*," Oxford said.. "They wouldn't want to take a chance on harming us—you're too important to the—"

Another couple of cracking noises came, and Oxford jerked his hand away from the side of the carriage, where a large splinter of wood had sprung up, quite near his fingers.

"On the other hand," Ari observed, "they might well feel that they would be better off having us on hand severely damaged than not at all."

"Well, we'll be out of their line of fire in a second— *hold on!*"

The rapidly moving carriage encountered a turn and struck the low wall which lined the drive a glancing blow, thus changing its direction. The curve put a screen of trees between us and our now running pursuers.

The remainder of the drive was steeply pitched and led to the main road; we gathered speed at an alarming rate as we approached it.

"Isn't this faster than you figured?" Dark called.

"Some," Oxford answered grimly, holding on tightly—as we all were—as the carriage bounced over the rough surface of the drive.

"How are we going to stop?" Dark asked.

"From the looks of it, by crashing into that tree on the other side of the road! Lord, TR and I calculated it'd be just a fast sort of coast down here, not a runaway!"

"Well, we don't want that, do we?" Dark said. He

135

leaned over first the right rear side of the carriage, then the left, and straightened up. "I think we'll be—"

The carriage suddenly gave a lurch, then tipped backwards, the rear of its body slamming onto the driveway with a force that sprang several of its parts and jarred us all horribly; it scraped along a few feet farther and stopped.

Ahead of us, two detached wheels ran crazily down the drive and across the road and into the trees.

We untangled ourselves and our possessions from the wreckage and at Oxford's urging ran down the short remaining length of the drive. "I didn't *think* it'd go far without a full set of wheels," Dark panted, running beside me. "So . . . *zip!*" He flourished his writing tool, then tucked it back into his pocket.

True, it had been a quick and effective solution to the immediate problem, but it did seem to me that a person of Dark's mechanical ingenuity might have come up with something that did not involve quite so many bruises as those I was now becoming aware of.

I was gratified to see, as we came onto the road, a large closed automobile with a figure in the driver's seat, waiting a few yards past the drive; it quivered and rumbled, a welcome indication of its readiness to move.

We piled into it; Oxford sprang to the seat next to the driver and called out, "Drive like hell!"

With a jerk the machine started off, and we were soon fairly flying down the long hill. Dark twisted to look behind us. "Those Marine fellows got down the drive just in time to get a glimpse of us—now they'll know what kind of car we're in!"

"Good," Oxford said. "Be a shame if they didn't."

I was not particularly interested in this cryptic obser-

136

vation, being more concerned with the discomfort and alarming nature of our journey. The car bounced and swayed, and made quite an unsettling screaming sound as it made the sharp turn at the bottom of the hill without noticeably slackening its excessive speed.

We tore along the shore road, in the direction away from Roslyn, and were soon in a sparsely inhabited, heavily wooded area. Perhaps five miles—and about four minutes, as I calculated it—along, we drew up at a deserted pier and were instructed to leave the vehicle.

A larger one, with a boxlike body bearing in ornate gold letters the legend OSTERMAIER'S—THE ALE THAT PUT FLATBUSH ON THE MAP, stood at the side of the road. We were ushered hastily into the interior, which was crowded with large pungent-smelling barrels, among which we were hard put to find space; the driver swung the rear doors to, and in a moment we were once more being jolted uncomfortably, only this time in total darkness and with a very penetrating, though not unpleasant odor.

"Where's that lamp?" I heard Oxford ask. "That fellow was told to leave one—ah, here it is." There was a rattling, a clinking, and a scraping sound; a light flared and then steadied as Oxford adjusted the oil lamp and set it on the floor of the vehicle.

"It's going just fine," he announced. "They'll find that car within an hour or so, and they'll have to cover the chance that we got away by boat—that'll give 'em some extra trouble and cover our trail a bit. We'll cut over to Glen Cove and head back for New York by the high road. If the truck's stopped, we'll duck into those empty barrels toward the front there, but I don't think we'll need to do that. Now you better start getting into these."

He dragged forward some paper-wrapped bundles, which proved to contain native clothes of a style distinctly different from what we were wearing, and we followed his instructions. After we were garbed, he surveyed us. "You look like a bunch of farmers in from upstate who've been snagged by a sidewalk tout for a Grand Street clothes store—great! Nobody'll give you a second glance, even supposing there's somebody watching out for us." Oxford did not bother to assume a different costume, contenting himself with affixing a large moustache to his face, this item having been included in the bundles, along with our clothes.

"Say," Dark said, "isn't Roosevelt going to get in trouble over this? I mean, he and his son were the only ones to visit us, and I don't see Edison not thinking that that's something that has to be looked into."

"For one thing, TR and Kermit sailed for Africa yesterday," Oxford replied, "so it'd be pretty hard to ask him any embarrassing questions just now. But the main thing is, I've left behind a pretty ripe red herring for Edison and his people. When they search the house, they'll find all sorts of scraps of paper left behind in my room, covered with mysterious jottings and lots of telephone numbers. Aha! they'll say, and go about finding who's on the other end of those numbers—and they'll learn that most of 'em are foreign consulates. Germany, Austria-Hungary, Japan, Servia, Russia—lots more, too. I made calls to all of 'em, the last couple of days —asked 'em a few dumb questions—so the local operator'll remember having placed them. And to add to the fun, I put down a number I happen to know—a New York City cop, a high-up fellow, who's known to be in with some of the gangs. So when they piece this all together, won't they have a nice Conan Doyle plot all laid out for them? Turncoat Oxford solicits help from foreign agents anxious to get U.S. secrets, makes contact with corrupt policeman, and contrives escape with aid of gangsters! They can't *help* swallowing that, or at least spending most of their effort looking into it for a long time. Especially," he added thoughtfully, "as the car that picked us up belongs to a dead rabbit."

"Pull yourself together, Oxford," Dark said severely. "What would even a *live* rabbit want with a motorcar? You're driveling, man!"

He was not, though, as it developed. The persons actually responsible for the confusion were a group of criminals who had chosen to call themselves the Dead Rabbits. We were all of us seasoned enough to Earth's ways not to bother inquiring into their motives for this; if they were by chance known, we probably would not understand them. The car had been appropriated clandestinely in New York earlier that morning through the agency of an officer whom Roosevelt had known while in charge of the police force some years previously and whom he was able to bring into the scheme in confidence.

"He was tickled to do it," Oxford said. "The Pinkertons or whoever Edison uses will trace its ownership in no time, so that way, the Rabbits'll have an awful lot of pressure on them from the Federal government, which will please the cops mighty well—at least the honest ones, and they won't mind a bit if Lieutenant Becker, the one whose phone number I jotted down, gets a bit of a grilling, too."

He fingered his moustache morosely. "Of course, I don't like it that this casts *me* as the twentieth-century Benedict Arnold. But I guess it'll blow over sometime, and the fellows that know me won't believe I've sold out, and I don't much care what anybody else thinks. And anyway, what the hell; you can't make an omelet without breaking some eggs.''

His comment on cookery, though irrelevant to what he had been saying, as was so often the case in his conversation, was an unwanted reminder that, out of nervousness, I for one had eaten skimpily of breakfast and had had nothing since. There seemed to have been no food brought along for this journey, though I should have thought it would have occurred to Oxford to make such a provision, and I was obliged to make shift by inhaling the vapors emanating from the empty barrels, which, while not satisfying hunger, at least after a while induced a sense of well-being and indeed a tendency to slumber during the remainder of the trip.

I was awakened to be deposited with the others on a stone-paved street in the city, lined with large sheds and the prows of ships.

"Let's hustle!'' Oxford said, and, grabbing our belongings, we followed him into the nearest shed, while the ale truck sped away down the street. We then climbed a slanted sort of walkway and found ourselves on board a large vessel, in which we were led to assigned sleeping compartments.

As was the case with the train on which we had traveled, the *Pavonia* was staffed with persons willing to perform a number of personal services, especially bringing some food and drink to those who desired it; and I was soon happily combining my modest unpacking with a needed light meal and a quantity of ale—the aromatic journey in the truck had made me curious about this substance, which I had not encountered before, but it proved to be not dissimilar to the

140

Würzburger I had previously enjoyed. To test out this perception, I requested the servitor to bring me some Würzburger, and by judicious alternation I was able to arrive at a clear understanding of both the similarities and the distinctions between them.

The sky was darkening as the *Pavonia* steamed out into the city's harbor and passed the statue we had visited so many months before. Standing at the rail, as seemed to be the obligatory custom, though I should have been quite happy to be reposing in my sleeping place, I recalled the phrase in the inscription on the statue's base about "yearning to breathe free," and had to admit its aptness; now that I was departing from this alarming America, with its rapid journeys, weapons-using guards, complex ruses, and really quite unreasonable President, I was certainly beginning to breathe more freely.

"Just *look* at that, would you!" Dark caught my upper arm in a painful grip as he spoke. With his free hand he pointed to one side, where another vessel lumbered over the broad waters. It was facing pretty well at us, though not, I was glad to see, moving at a speed which carried any suggestion that it might run into us; and I could see, on either side, a large wheel turning about and dipping into the water.

"That damned fellow in the tavern!" Dark growled. "He's gone off and sold the idea on his own, and cut us out completely! Well, that does it! If Ari wants to get these chaps shooting and blowing each other up, more power to him! It might not be a bad idea, even if it doesn't get us off the planet, just on general principles."

15

Of our journey, which occupied some six days, there is little of note to Record. One stretch of the ocean looked much like another, and the regular succession of ample meals, two out of the daily three accompanied by an interesting variety of wines, marked the passage of time in a soothing but not especially lively manner.

On Oxford's advice, we mainly avoided contact with our fellow passengers, as he did not seem confident that we could sustain an extended conversation without revealing that we were other than we purported to be. "It was hard enough getting you on board under fake names," he observed, "without chancing blowing it now. Lucky the U.S. don't have a passport system, the way they do in Russia and other places, or we could never have done it."

Dark may have been unlucky, or perhaps less conscientious than the rest of us, for he found himself in frequent conversation with a female who, seated at a table next to us at meals, gradually insinuated herself into our group, concentrating her attention upon Dark. It appeared that she had lost, or perhaps mislaid, her mate—whether voluntarily or otherwise was unclear—and so was perhaps one of those "cheerful widows" I had heard the song about, in the "garden" atop the "Garden."

On the third night of the voyage, Ari, Valmis and I were relaxing in the smoking lounge when Dark, whom we had not seen since dinner, approached us. "Damned woman wanted me to take her for a walk on the deck to look at the moon. I told her it was no great shakes, all a lot of rocks and dust—you remember, fellows, we got a close look at it as we came in?—and that anyhow it was confoundedly cold outside. And she said the weather wasn't the only thing that was cold and flounced off to her cabin. Now, what was that all about?"

"It is hard to tell, without full awareness of the larger Patterns," Valmis said, "but, looking at, as it were, the micro-Patterns, I should hazard a guess that she had undertaken an early step in a mating ritual, to which your response indicated a lack of any interest whatever."

"Do you really think so?" Dark said. "Ha!" He strode from the lounge, and the three of us resumed our desultory conversation. I had obtained a measure of something called brandy and was investigating its properties when he returned, some twenty minutes later.

"You were right," he told Valmis.

"How were you able to arrive at that conclusion?" Ari asked.

"Well, I went on down to her cabin, which she'd let me know the number of some time back, and banged on the door, and when she opened it and wanted to know what I wanted, I asked her, was that nonsense about going for a walk something to do with a mating ritual? and she laughed and said she guessed it was, so I said, Right, then! and so we did. Closing the door, first, of course; she told me she preferred it that way."

Valmis seemed pleased that his assessment of the

situation had proved accurate; Ari looked at Dark with interest, and I with alarm.

"What was it like?" Ari said.

Dark shrugged. "Much the same. When you have this sort of standard humanoid structure, there aren't many surprises that way. I had an idea that would be the case, from what Wells told me. Wells seems to know a lot about that end of things, though it gets him in trouble from time to time."

"And he's not the only one!" I cried. Intimate knowledge of native females was, for a variety of reasons, discouraged firmly by Explorer rules; and, to this end, our biosurgical implants had, on recent voyages, been extended in scope so as to remove this problem from the area of free choice. "D'you mean to say the implants don't function?"

Dark's face bore a contented smile as he looked at me. "Not," he said, "if you work hard at it."

As the *Pavonia* edged up to its berth, I was cheered to recognize the diminutive figure of Wells waving at us from the pier. He had brought along a large chauffeured motorcar into which the six of us, with our possessions, fitted comfortably; after the formalities of debarkation had been seen to, we sped away. I was surprised to see that shop signs and other visible examples of writing were largely indecipherable, and said so.

"Well, they're in French, you see," Wells explained.

"Why is that? I understood you had the same language in England as they have in America."

It was then that I learned we were in France and not England, even though we were to call on the King of the English. The King, it appeared, made a habit of leaving his country for substantial periods of time, especially during the uncertain weather of late winter and early spring, which he spent in France, but also in summer and autumn. His subjects, far from resenting this, were gratified, as most of them would themselves have preferred to be elsewhere much of the time, and so took a prideful vicarious pleasure in their monarch's travels.

"It was quite a to-do, getting this all arranged," Wells said. "Roosevelt's cables—he shot them off to the King, the Prime Minister, and the President of the Board of Trade—set everyone by the ears, and they all had to come to *me* to get a line on what they should do. Dear me, didn't it go hard with Asquith to have to get advice from a 'horrid little Fabian sensualist'!" Wells spoke the phrase with relish, as if he gloried in each descriptive term, as I suppose he did. "But he had to, all the same, to get my assurance that you were the real article and some tips on how to get on with you. Asquith's all for seeing what can be got out of you for the benefit of the Em-pah, but young Churchill, at Trade—Roosevelt got him in on it 'cause he thinks Winnie's the same sort of chap he is at bottom, though right now they don't agree politically, Churchill being for the moment more to my way of thinking, or says he is—is all for letting whatever joy you've got flow unconfined, for the benefit of all mankind. Anyhow, it's worked out that you're to see the King at Biarritz, which is where we're on our way to. He's a dear old chap, really—knows what he likes in food, wine, cigars, horses and women, which makes him beloved of all good Englishmen. About women, by the bye, if you should meet a Mrs. Keppel whilst you're there, you've got to strike a sort of medium between being quite

145

cordial and not seeing her; she's an awfully good chum of the King's, if you take my meaning, but nobody's supposed to take any notice of it."

"Speaking of women," Dark said, "there was a funny thing happened on the way to France, about this widow. . . ." He and Wells were for some time occupied with a discussion which appeared to absorb them, while the rest of us watched parts of France whirl by the car.

When they had done, Oxford spoke up. "Wells," said he, "there's something you ought to know. Our friends here don't come as emissaries from any star-girdling Empire, no, indeed." When he had completed his explanation, Wells looked at us oddly. "As far as I'm concerned," he said, "I haven't heard that. When it comes to getting in to see the King with one story, and then telling him the facts have got to be altered a bit, I'd sooner leave that up to you. If there's a flaming row about it, I stand ready to pick up your remains, but not to get into the middle of it."

The journey took the remainder of that day and part of the next, the hours of darkness being spent at an inn in a small town which afforded little of interest. I took a turn around it in the evening and found a place marked with what I was told was the French word for "coffee," a mild stimulant I had enjoyed in the mornings in America, but the range of coffees here was considerably larger than I had before encountered. There was one sweet kind, called "absinthe," which went down quite smoothly, and another, called "cognac," which was harsher in immediate effect but appeared to produce quite a bit of internal heat, which was useful in driving off the chill the air carried.

This air must have possessed soporific qualities, as it

was only with the greatest difficulty that I was aroused early the next morning for the resumption of our journey.

We drew up before a large hotel in Biarritz shortly after ten in the morning and were quickly ushered to a large suite of rooms on the first floor. The hotel was called by the French word for "palace," which I suppose is why the King had chosen it. Oxford remained behind in the lobby, as it was felt that his status as a fugitive U.S. Army officer might later present embarrassments for the King.

A large man, somewhere between Roosevelt and Taft in bulk, and sporting a moustache as impressive as Roosevelt's, plus a beard, was sitting at the head of a large table on which were spread various kinds of meats, condiments, breads, beverages, sweets and utensils.

Wells, at this point the head of our party, bowed low and said, "Good morning, Your Majesty."

"You're Wells," the King stated, pointing a fork at him. "Socialist, aren't you? Trouble over women, too, hey? I've heard about that. No harm in it as long as you don't behave meanly, no harm. And these are the gentlemen from outer space, are they? So." He regarded us with his slightly bulging eyes. "You don't look any stranger than a lot of people in my Empire," he said, "or, for that matter, in my court. But if Mr. Roosevelt, whom God preserve, vouches for you, I must accept it that you are what you say." He spoke in a very different way from Wells, and I made a note that the aristocratic, or royal, classes in England used a mode of speech that emphasized the impact of the "r's" and turned the "w's" very nearly to "v's."

"It would have been interesting to see what my

mother would have made of you," the King said, studying us. "I expect she would have been gracious, and full of advice, but not at all amused. My father, now, he would have been the man for you—interested in everything, he was, machinery and progress and so on. He'd have been fascinated by the idea of talking with people from another world. Though he might have had some trouble reconciling your existence with his firm belief in the Bible."

"Mr. Bryan had something of the same difficulty about us during the American elections," Ari said, absently taking from a dish a piece of something that might have been fish, and chewing on it.

King Edward looked at him coldly and said, "If I had not already been persuaded by Mr. Roosevelt and my Prime Minister—and, for reasons I do not see, but shall make it my business to find out, the President of the Board of Trade—that you are what you purport to be, I should now be convinced of it. To compare William Jennings Bryan with Albert of Saxe-Coburg-Gotha, Prince Consort to the Queen of Great Britain and Ireland, Empress of India, and Defender of the Faith, that is believable only in a person not of this Earth! My dear man, you'll want to take the bones out of that trout, or you'll choke on them—here, let me show you how."

At the King's invitation, we joined him at his breakfast, of which there seemed plenty to go around.

"Now," he said at the conclusion of the meal, "we have some business to get to, eh? Strange circumstances, I must say, strange circumstances. Roosevelt sent some devilishly long cables, but they really didn't make everything too clear. I gather that you left the United States rather hastily?"

"Our talks with Mr. Edison were not proceeding

satisfactorily," Ari said, which was certainly true enough. "He wished to bring them to a conclusion as soon as possible, but we felt that we should be better able to go on with them once we had a greater store of information about your planet. He was most pressing, unfortunately, so in order to avoid unpleasantness we . . ."

"Stood not upon the order of your going, eh?" the King said. "Well, I don't want to do anything to upset our relations with the United States, God knows, but I don't see how Mr. Edison can make any sort of issue out of this—I mean, the whole thing about ambassadors is that they've got to be able to move about freely, or diplomacy's nowhere at all, eh?"

Both Wells and Ari looked uneasy at this. I reflected that this situation would take some delicate handling. The King still took us for ambassadors, which Wells now knew we were not. We would have to convey our true aims to the King, while keeping them secret from Wells and Oxford, at least at this stage. I hoped Ari considered this problem as falling within the scope of a Metahistorian, as I did not see that any of the rest of us was qualified to handle it.

"Very well," the King went on. "Which of you do I talk to?"

"Myself, Your Majesty," Ari replied. "I am the spokesman for our, ah, embassy. And if I may, I should like to have my colleague Raf with us. He is the Recorder for our mission and should be present to set straight any confusion that may arise."

"A good idea," the King agreed. "I wish there had been someone else than my nephew William to take note of my talks with him in Berlin two months back. We spoke of our navies, and he convinced himself that I

149

had made some most remarkable statements on that subject! Now, as for the rest of you, why don't you take a drive about the countryside this morning? You'd enjoy that; I always do. You might drop in on the *pelota* matches at Anglet, and there's some good racing at La Barre. They're excellent cars, Mercedes, most reliable.''

"Would they be the big reddish ones I saw outside?" Dark asked.

"My machines are claret-colored, yes," the King said.

"Ah, I'd like a spin in one of those," Dark said. "Tell me, what's the gear ratio for the highest speed? I think American cars—"

"You might ask my chauffeur that," the King said. "I find the things fascinating, but haven't the least idea how they work."

Having put the others in the care of one of his attendants, the King led Ari and me to his study. "Ah, good," Ari said, looking about the large room. "Maps and things—that round one there, the model of the planet, with everything on it; that's useful, I expect. I was hoping you'd have plenty of maps. Lots of people don't, I gather."

The King eased himself into a large chair behind his desk and looked at Ari severely. "Lots of people aren't kings, either," he said. "How do you expect I could reign over an Empire that's spread over the whole world if—well, never mind. Gentlemen, as you are representatives of another Empire, one which, I gather, is substantially larger than my own, I think you might begin by telling me something of your intentions and interests here, toward the British Empire first, and then the rest of the world."

I admired Ari's aplomb as he outlined the actual facts of our situation as opposed to the fiction by which we had gained admittance to the King's presence. King Edward listened gravely, his face showing neither anger nor astonishment. At the conclusion of Ari's statement, he lit a cigar carefully and drew deeply upon it, occasioning a momentary fit of coughing, then looked at us.

"Some of my predecessors would have had you hanged in chains or racked for presenting yourselves falsely as ambassadors," he remarked. "And I must say I am not pleased by your imposture. However, one must be flexible in dealing with persons from another world, I suppose. And I shall say that it's a relief to me that you're not what you said you were. We have quite enough to go on with, with the Empires we now have, and coping with another one from off the Earth entirely would probably drive all the foreign offices clean mad. Those that are not already," he added.

"Very well, then," he went on, "what you're really after is some aid in refitting your airship, or whatever it is. We ought to be able to do something about that. Our British shipyards are the envy of the world, and I make no doubt that they ought to be able to do something. I dare say the government would be willing to underwrite the cost, as it would be an excellent advertisement for our industry. I'll have it brought to the attention of the Board of Trade—Churchill would probably be all afire for it."

"With all respect, Your Majesty," Ari said, "there's no chance that any shipyard could help *Wanderer* just now. The planet just doesn't have the technology for it. There's got to be a lot of progress, what you might call a great leap forward, before anything can be done."

I was awaiting with considerable interest the unveil-

151

ing of the arcane Metahistorical techniques by which Ari proposed to manipulate the King to our advantage. To my surprise, he launched baldly into his thesis on the inevitability of an imminent major war, the destruction it would work at the same time as it promoted science, and the desirability of getting it launched quickly so as to minimize the worst effects while preserving the favorable (from our point of view) ones. I had to admit he made his point convincingly, bolstering it by darting from map to map, outlining hypothetical movements of armies and fleets, demonstrating the role that the nature of continental land masses would play, citing statistics of industrial and agricultural production, but it seemed to me that it was not the most tactful method of persuasion.

The King apparently shared my feeling. Though obviously shaken at the ghastly picture Ari had painted of what lay in store for his civilization, he squinted at him and asked slowly, "And what did Edison make of all this when you told him?"

"Ah, we didn't do that, of course, Your Majesty," Ari said. "You see, the Americans *elect* their leaders. They just did that with Edison, you know."

"I am aware of the American electoral process," the King said grimly.

"That's good; then you'll see that their main job, really, is getting elected, not running the country, so naturally they never get to be really professional at it. I couldn't be candid with Edison, you see, as he couldn't possibly be prepared to understand and act on what I would have told him."

"An interesting viewpoint," the King said, looking at the cloud of smoke emanating from his cigar. "And . . . ?"

"Well, *you* people, emperors and all, you're brought up from birth to rule, and you know that you'll be on the job for life, unless something upsetting happens, as with bombs in Russia or beheadings, like your Charles. Though come to think of it, those people left off being Czars and whatnot only when they were dead, didn't they, so it comes out to the same thing. Anyhow, it stands to reason that a hereditary monarch is in the nature of things better equipped to look at matters of state logically—to comprehend, if I may put it that way, the principles of Metahistory that underlie the growth and decay of cultures."

The King drew on his cigar, then, removing it, pursed his mouth oddly and emitted a quantity of smoke, which assumed the shape of a ring and hung in the air for some time. "It isn't every time I can do that," he observed, then turned to face Ari directly. "My good man, if we monarchs are as clear-sighted as you seem to think, why ever are you visiting us with this appalling idea of a world war? Don't you think we'll do everything we can to *stop* it? And that would, of course, make us perfectly useless from your standpoint, I gather."

Ari chuckled and answered, "Dear me, no. I do hope you all will see the logic in what I say, and make your dispositions so as to have your war over and done with without wrecking your civilization completely, as that would involve us in a more extensive delay than I care to think about, but there's no chance of *averting* it. Look," he said, pointing toward the window. "D'you see those hill things out there, with the white on top?"

The King looked in the indicated direction and said, "Yes. They're the Pyrenees, in fact, if it matters."

"Well, now, imagine you've got some big stones on top of one of them, quite a few, scattered about. And

153

they're all on one of the steep bits, if you follow me. Now, if one of those stones comes loose and starts rolling, it's going to bang into another one and jar it loose, so you've got two of them going. They'll hit some of the others, and pretty soon you've got a bunch of stones rolling down the mountain, going faster and faster. And whatever's in the way, a person or an animal, or as it might be a village, now, that's going to get smashed. And even if you catch sight of the rocks when they're about halfway down, and you *know* they're going to smash the village, you can't do a thing about it. And my Metahistorical examination of your situation on this planet shows that the rocks, so to speak, are rather more than halfway down, and gaining speed.''

"But, damn it, man,'' the King said explosively, "people and nations aren't *rocks!* We are thinking beings! We *choose* our actions, I tell you, and we need not—'' At this point, he fell to coughing once more, which allowed Ari to speak without the discourtesy of interrupting.

"Individuals, of course,'' Ari said, "may behave in any number of unpredictable ways, the humanoid types especially, which is what makes them the most interesting races to study Metahistorically. I mean, there's not much challenge in working out what a race of sentient crystals is going to do, is there? They spend most of their time forming lattices; quite decorative, but not affording much scope for the Metahistorian, I can tell you. But this humanoid diversity, taken in the aggregate, adds up to complete determinism, if I may put it so. The courses of nations and of worlds may be charted with complete accuracy, as I have charted yours. You've got Russia *here*''—he tapped on the map with an extended forefinger—"Germany here,

Austria-Hungary there, France, Turkey and so on, and yourselves spread all over the place. Given everything I've gone into before, you're bound to have a most remarkable disaster, millions dead and ruins all over the place, and there's nothing you can do about it. That's what Metahistory shows quite clearly, and if it weren't so, it wouldn't be Metahistory, would it?''

The King looked pale and tired. ''We have all told ourselves that it would not come to this,'' he said in a low voice, ''that we could keep everything balanced somehow—that we could go on building ships and guns so that we should not have to use them, that our generals could devise cleverer and cleverer plans, that—''

''Well, that's one thing,'' Ari interrupted, careless of etiquette. ''Generals and such. They've got an inherent error factor built in, you see. I mean, suppose you have two countries; you could call them A and B, to keep things clearer. Now, there's a dispute between them, and the generals on both sides make their plans. Now, assuming they're pretty nearly equally matched— otherwise they'd be silly to try a war, wouldn't they?—well, then, at least half the generals have got to be wrong.''

''How is that?'' the King said faintly.

''Well, obviously, each lot of generals, A's and B's, tells their government that their plans will work, or they wouldn't start up the war. And, as one side or the other loses, the generals on the losing side are proven wrong. It's usually worse than that,'' Ari went on reflectively, ''as even the winning ones are quite often wrong about what will happen, how long the whole thing will take, and so on. You had that in South Africa, as I recall—won the war, but it was much harder than you expected, so your generals were *half* wrong, and the Boers' generals *all* wrong, which works out to about twenty-five-percent accuracy for the trade, if I have got my figures right. I don't think you'd be at all happy if your chauffeurs or your cooks got things correct only half the time or less, so that's the difficulty in working with generals, you see."

The King considered this proposition for some little time, then roused himself to say, "I had never thought of it quite like that. It makes a dreadful kind of sense, though I think that you people's brains must work rather differently from ours."

"Thank you, Your Majesty," Ari said, pleased with the compliment.

"It is a terrible prospect you show me," the King continued. "Terrible—and I fear that I cannot dismiss it. You confirm what I have begun to dread, and yet you offer no escape. . . ."

"Well, no, there isn't any," Ari said. "That's Metahistory for you."

The King chewed gloomily on his cigar. "If it must be so, it must. God grant I do not live to see it."

"That's about an even chance," Ari said, looking at him appraisingly. "If you were to get at it pretty quickly, as I recommend, which would serve your planet's people's ends as well as our own, as I have tried to make clear, you'd probably see it pretty well launched. If you and your fellow kings just let things drag on another couple of years or so, why, I'd have to agree that you'd probably be pretty well out of it."

"What!" the King shouted, rising to his feet, his aristocratic accent making the word come out nearly as "Vot!"

"Well, that coughing, and the way your face changes color. A moment ago, it was quite pale, and now you've

156

got a nasty flush about the cheeks. From what I learned when Mr. Hearst's doctors looked us over, you people function about the same as we do, so I'd say your heart's in *very* bad shape. A year or so, that's about what you'd be safe in counting on.''

King Edward's face was indeed now a most startling hue, more toward the purple side than the red; his eyes protruded even more than they had before, and he began to splutter at Ari, evidently an expression of anger. This changed into another bout of coughing, and he sank back into his chair, his massive body heaving as he tried to stem its force.

"Dear me,'' Ari said, "I hope I haven't upset him.''

"I believe you've upset *us* properly,'' I observed, watching the writhing monarch strive to catch his breath. "I shouldn't be surprised if he died right here and now, and I don't care to think what happens when two strangers are closeted with a King-Emperor and are later found with his corpse. Something tells me that the upshot would be regrettable.''

"Well, we certainly don't want that,'' Ari said. "Let me see, did I bring—ah, yes, here they are.'' He drew a small metal container from a pocket of his costume.

"What have you got there?''

"Those things I take from time to time, you know. It's all very well for you young fellows to get along with the implants, and they do you very nicely, I'm sure; but I'm a bit older than you, and I'd start going wrong inside in all sorts of ways without a little extra treatment to clear out dead cells and other bits of rubbish. So I take one of these once a voyage or so, if I start feeling run-down, and it gets rid of everything that doesn't belong there.''

"Will it work the same way on him?''

157

Ari looked at the King, whose face had darkened further and who now seemed scarcely able to breathe at all; his feet drummed on the carpet. "Well, if it doesn't, I can't see that he—or we—would be any worse off. Here, give me a hand."

I stood behind the feebly twitching King, holding his head steady, as Ari forced a capsule into his mouth. "Mmmm—wharyer . . . ?" I heard him mumble; he stiffened and then relaxed. I feared the worst, but as I went to stand beside Ari, I saw King Edward's face resume a more normal hue and his contorted features become smooth.

After a moment he sat upright in his chair, looked at us, and said, "Good Lord, what did you do? What *was* that? I haven't"—he placed a hand on his chest and took a deep breath—"been able to breathe that easily in years. And I don't feel that sort of pain right here . . ."

"Well, I'm sorry, Your Majesty," Ari said uneasily. "But you did seem to be in immediate trouble, and I thought I would try . . . That is, this is something the older fellows like me take along on these trips we go on; they sort of wash out accumulations of poisons and fats and things. They take a while before they're fully effective—"

"Do they?" said the King. "*Do* they? There is more of this effect to come, then?"

"If you've been having stiffnesses in the hands and elsewhere, as I expect might happen," Ari said, "you'll find that's a good bit less, or even all gone, in a day or so. The same thing with any problems about seeing and other senses, I should think."

"Indeed?" said the King. "Tell me, do you have another one or so of those you could spare? I feel tremendously fit right now, but it would be nice to have one or two on hand to use when this one wears off tomorrow or next week."

"Next year, more likely," Ari said. "That's going to go on working until it's undone all the stuff your system's accumulated over the last . . . however many years it may be. It'll take a while, even with all the smoking and food and such, to get it all back, if ever. But you might as well have a couple, certainly—here you are."

"Thank you." The King looked at the capsules in his palm, then back at Ari. "I am grateful, of course. But tell me, how is it that, just before my attack, when you were talking about my condition with such exemplary detachment, you did not think to suggest the use of one of these?"

"Well, we don't like to interfere, you know," Ari said, with some evident embarrassment. "We're trained not to do that, interfere with na—with persons on other planets. And especially when it's something like that, you know—a condition you've built up over the years. It's hard to know why you'd want it, of course; I certainly wouldn't, but if you hadn't, you wouldn't have done all the things that brought it on, would you? So it was really none of my business to do anything about it, but it really didn't set well to let you choke to death like that, as you seemed about to— turning purple and twitching and fighting for breath and—"

"Quite, quite," the King broke in testily. "The experience was sufficiently vivid in itself; I do not require that it be rehearsed for me."

"It's bad enough," Ari went on, "that we're coming around to set you right on this war business—we're not

159

supposed to do that, either—but interfering with what you've chosen to do to your own body, that's really fairly intrusive, and I can only say—"

"If you attempt to *apologize* for saving my life and restoring me to a state of health I have not enjoyed for years, perhaps decades," the King said, "I warn you that I shall be positively uncivil." He looked at us once more and shook his head slowly. "You people do indeed think differently from us. Be that as it may, I am in your debt. Your proposal that the nations of the world fling themselves at one another's throats in order to oblige you by some scientific advances that might result strikes me, I must tell you candidly, as repellently cold-blooded—although I admit our world can display some parallels—but I shall at least see that you get a chance to present it. You ought to see my nephew William next, the Kaiser. I believe he might be even more impressed by you than I am. William's an original thinker, for royalty, and I believe it might do him good to come up against minds even odder than his own. It should take no more than a day to make the arrangements for him to receive you, so you should plan on being in Berlin the day after tomorrow."

He rose, walked to the window, and leaned out. "I can smell the spring in the air, and the sea," he said. "It's a long time since I could do that . . . and the mountains—I can see them more clearly. It's as if I were young again. . . . Well, I shall set about advising my nephew that he is to receive some very curious visitors and would do well to listen most closely to what they have to say; I can't do better than that, can I, eh?"

The King summoned two aides, one of whom led us away to rejoin our friends. As we left his study, I heard him instruct the other to inform his guests that he would not join them on a proposed automobile outing that afternoon, and to advise Mrs. Keppel that he would be calling on her after lunch.

"Look here," I said as we walked down the corridor. "You told us all that about how oddly these emperors went on. I mean, the Kaiser and the ballet-skirted general, and so on—that all came into your Metahistorical predictions. How does that square with this business of them being more rational than Edison?"

"Metahistory is not your field of endeavor, my dear Raf," Ari said kindly. "Personality, which is infinitely variable, has nothing to do with the reasoning powers, which exist and function independently. I myself, while hail-fellow-well-met to a fault in my personal dealings, am yet a remorselessly logical intellectual machine when circumstances require me to fulfill my ordained function. Thus it is with these monarchs."

16

Wells was impressed by Ari's carefully edited account of our conversation with King Edward and his promise to arrange an interview with the Kaiser.

"You're artful, you are," he told us, "getting round the old boy like that. I should have thought he'd have had you flayed or something for passing yourself off as ambassadors."

"His Majesty is, naturally enough, a most reasonable man," Ari explained, "and so was able to deal with our problem reasonably. I expect it will be the same with the Kaiser."

"What a hope," Wells said. "Look here, I'd better go along to Berlin with you chaps. If you rub the Kaiser the wrong way, you're likely to end up in a fortress, and you'll want someone on hand to send you in a sausage now and then."

Oxford had collected a pile of journals during the motor outing and was going through them rapidly. "Nothing in yesterday's London papers," he observed. "And I don't make out anything about Edison or whatever the French might be for 'space' or 'astronauts' in the heads in today's French papers. So it looks as though Edison's keeping the lid on this. Very sensible of him, and a good thing for us. It'd be awkward, having the U.S. raising a hue and cry after us. I imagine he's thought better of the whole idea."

162

In spite of King Edward's expressed fondness for the resort, Biarritz was not a particularly interesting town, and a few strolls around it soon exhausted its attractions, at least for me. Thus, when Oxford, Dark and I were taking yet another walk along the promenade the next afternoon—Wells being busied with our travel arrangements, Ari with refining the details of what he proposed to tell the Kaiser, and Valmis with contemplating the significance of what Patterns were perceptible on the ceiling of his bedchamber—we welcomed the distraction provided by an automobile that drew up alongside us, the driver of which beckoned to us urgently.

He was, it appeared, in the business of taking tourists for trips into the countryside, and as the rate he mentioned seemed surprisingly reasonable and he spoke English fluently—I had not yet gone to the trouble of using the Communicator to equip myself with any other language, having been given to understand that any monarchs we might encounter would be well versed in our first native tongue—we agreed to his proposal and entered his vehicle.

We were soon out of the town and climbing a winding road into the hills. "I don't see that this is all that interesting," Dark said, looking about.

"There's a swell view from up ahead," the driver called back.

"That fellow speaks pretty good American-style English for a Frenchman," Oxford remarked. "I suppose he's spent some time in the States."

The excellent view the driver had promised did not materialize. Instead, as we rounded a bend we saw a large closed automobile with pulled-down blinds drawn up at the side of the road, with its front parts opened to

163

expose the engine; a man was bent over as if to examine its workings.

"Hey, I don't think we better stop," Oxford said as our own vehicle slowed. "I've heard there's lots of bandits in these hills, and this could be—"

"Got to stop and see if we can help," the driver answered. "Law of the road." He pulled up beside the other machine, and we got out. Dark went to peer into the engine over the shoulder of the man working on it, fascinated as always by mechanical details. Oxford and I, for want of anything better to do, joined him.

"Now, how does this thing work?" Dark asked the native, poking at some part with his writing tool. "What seems to be wrong? Is it this thing here? I can see that there might be something that's got loose—why don't I—"

At this point, we were startled by the noise of a car engine springing to life—quite obviously not that of the one we were examining. We turned—Dark exclaiming "Oh, *damn!*"—and saw the machine which had brought us to this spot moving rapidly down the road and soon vanishing around a curve.

"Here, what's all this about?" Dark said. "Why did he . . ." He stopped, noticing, as we all did, a hand-held projectile weapon which the motorist had produced and was now pointing at us.

"I can explain that, gentlemen," a voice from behind us announced, and turned once again. Stepping down from the interior of the car, and holding another, somewhat larger weapon, was Captain Thatcher, the Marine officer from whose custody we had escaped a week before.

"We're in the soup, I'd say," Oxford muttered gloomily.

164

"Into the car, you men," Thatcher said, gesturing with his weapon. Seeing no really practical alternative, we obliged him. He remained outside and called, "All right, Olson, crank her up and let's get going!"

"*Been* doing that, Captain, but damned if there *really* ain't something wrong with her!"

"Well, get it for God's sake fixed fast! It can't be anything serious; you went over it before we started out." He turned toward us again.

"You fellows weren't as clever as you thought," he said. "That was a mighty nice dodge you thought up, all that gang and foreign stuff, but what ditched you was a fisherman out in the harbor—saw you changing from the car to the brewery truck. He didn't come ashore until 'way later that day, so the Pinkertons didn't get it out of him until it was too late to stop you from sailing. But we traced the truck to the pier—a cop there noticed it specially, 'cause Ostermaier's don't deal with the saloons around there, and he was wondering if something new like that mightn't mean some graft for him—and had a talk with the steamer line's passenger people. And don't you know, there was five passages bought at the last minute, so it seemed pretty clear what you'd done—and don't think Colonel Roosevelt ain't going to have some fancy explaining to do when he gets back from the Dark Continent, I want to tell you!

"Now, thanks to you folks, I had the signal honor of a personal interview with the President of the United States, and that don't come the way of a Marine captain very often. And Mr. Edison laid it out nice and clear. 'Captain,' he says to me, 'I don't hold one mistake against a man. So you've got your chance to go and get me these people—pick a couple of men to help you, anything you need. But get 'em back from where

165

they've gone to. If you don't, why, that's another mistake, and that I do hold against a man. And the man I hold *that* mistake against is going to be personally supervising sanitary facilities in the Canal Zone for the rest of his hitch, at the lowest possible level.' So you can see I got a stake in bringing this off—and so does the President, I'll tell you; he got me and Olson and Dyer, him that drove you up here, over to France on a fast destroyer, boilers supercharged all the way. Docked ahead of the *Pavonia* and trailed you down here, and now, by God, I've got you! The important ones, anyway," he said, looking at us as though he found that hard to believe. "The President was mighty particular about you two, not so much about the others—and he's got some special treatment laid away for Mr. Lieutenant Colonel Oxford, here. My, he just didn't care at *all* for what you done, Colonel, and he means to let you know it. Hey, *Olson!*" he called. "Isn't that damn motor fixed *yet?*"

"Well, *you* come and have a look, Captain! It *should* work, but it don't."

Captain Thatcher said something that had not been included in the vocabulary which the Communicator had instilled in me, and slammed the door. "Now, don't you get any ideas about running off," we heard him say. "So much as a *head* gets poked out the door, and there'll be a bullet in it."

In the darkness of the enclosed car, we could hear the clinking sound of the two men examining the engine. "I don't think they're going to get it to go," Dark remarked after a while.

"Why not?" I asked.

"Well . . . when I was having a look at it, I thought I spotted something loose. So I was just going to give it a little weld to hold it in place, d'you see?'' He produced his combination writing instrument and portable tool. ''And when our car ran off like that, it startled me, and I gave it more power than I'd meant to. I think it fused a couple of bits that are supposed to move.''

"*That's* nice," Oxford said. "Now, not only are we kidnapped, but we'll have to be walked to wherever Thatcher wants to take us instead of being driven there, unless he feels like plugging us right now to save the bother.''

''I am sure he wouldn't want to do that,'' I reassured him. ''Mr. Edison seems to want us pretty badly, and I don't see that our cadavers would be much use to him.''

''Considering what Edison's likely to do to me, I might be better off if Thatcher gets it over with right now.'' Oxford sat back, lost in gloom, but presently he brightened and said, ''Say, I think I hear—''

The door was pulled open and Thatcher scrambled into the car with us, and shut it again, covering us with his weapon. ''I can hear a car coming up the hill,'' he said. ''Now, don't anybody get funny—no calling for help or such. Edison wants you alive, but I guess he can get along just as well if you're shy a finger or a knee-cap. And you wouldn't want the blood of some poor Frenchman on your hands, would you? For if I've got to start loosing this off to keep you folks quiet, I don't mean to leave any witnesses behind.''

In silence we heard the approaching car grind its gears as it negotiated the turn below us, then the growing noise of its engine as it came near our vehicle. The three of us sat upright as the noise changed character, indicating that the new machine had stopped; Thatcher glared and flourished his weapon.

167

A booming voice asked, "What seems to be the trouble, my good man? My chauffeur may be able to help; I'll send him over. Ponsonby, fetch me a campstool; I do love to watch people fixing cars."

Dark and I turned to each other. "That's . . ." we said in unison.

"Who?" Oxford asked, whispering in deference to a savage wave of Thatcher's weapon. "Oh, wait—you can't mean . . . ? You do, don't you?" Reading the expressions on our faces correctly, he turned to Thatcher.

"Thanks for the ride, Captain, though it didn't get very far. We'll be taking our leave."

"*Will* you, now?" the Marine demanded thoughtfully, sighting his weapon between Oxford's eyes. "I kind of doubt that. You make any moves, and you're going to get damaged some. Plus I might just help myself to that nosy jasper's car to get out of here with."

"Captain," Oxford said, "the gentleman who is taking such an interest in your breakdown is Edward the Seventh, by the Grace of God King of Great Britain and Ireland, and all that. Further, I understand that he travels on these excursions with another car, loaded with French policemen, fully armed and alert—I may say *nervously* alert—to any possibility of violence in the immediate vicinity of His Majesty. Your program of plugging us and then stealing his car therefore seems to me impractical."

Thatcher raised the blind on one window, looked out, and cursed. Before he snapped it down again, I caught a glimpse of two large red cars, the rear one crowded, as Oxford had predicted, with several tough-looking natives in blue uniforms and flat caps.

Keeping his eyes on Thatcher, Oxford slowly reached for the door handle, then eased the door open. "We've played the King, Captain," he told him softly. "Unless you've got an ace, it looks like you'd better fold your hand."

17

The King very graciously invited our party to return to Biarritz with him, as the motorcar did not seem likely to be fixed at any time in the near future. Oxford contrived it so that he, Dark and I rode with His Majesty, and Thatcher in a following vehicle along with a number of French policemen; the unfortunate Olson was left behind to protect the disabled car until help could be sent from the town.

Once we were under way, the King looked at Oxford shrewdly. "There was something about all that that didn't quite look like a spin in the countryside," he observed. "For one thing, it doesn't seem to me that you'd get much benefit from the view in a closed car—with drawn blinds." His aide, seated beside him—the three of us were ranged on a sort of padded bench opposite them, obliging us to ride backwards, which, it being his automobile, seemed reasonable enough—also gave us an inquiring look.

"Well, it's an odd business all right, sir," Oxford admitted, and explained briefly the circumstances of our abduction.

"Dear me," the King said, stroking his beard. "That won't do, will it? But it's deuced awkward—I can't very well cause a complaint to be made, I suppose—it's just not done to take official notice of these things—and yet those men will doubtless try to impede your travels if they're free to do so. And I'm beginning to feel that it's rather important that you go on with your plans to see the Kaiser and whatever else you might choose to do afterwards. . . ." He raised one eyebrow as he looked at me, from which I divined that he assumed we had not revealed the full truth about our intentions to Oxford and that he did not himself propose to enlighten the reporter.

"If I understand the problem aright, Your Majesty," the aide said, "there need be no particular difficulty. The French legal system, unlike ours, is admirably designed to deal with inconveniences to important personages without undue formality."

"Well, I wouldn't want those fellows guillotined or any such thing as that, you know," the King said.

"No need for that, I'm sure," the aide replied. "But there's no reason the police couldn't manage a few days' detention, and nothing written down about it. They'd probably be pleased as Punch to do it; nobody's tried to assassinate you, and I expect they're getting a little bored."

Upon our arrival back at the King's quarters, the occupants of both cars disembarked, and the aide went over and exchanged a few words with the police. These were in the French language, so I did not understand them; evidently, neither did Captain Thatcher, who ignored the conversation and stood glowering at us. The police seemed to take the meaning quite clearly, which was only to be expected, they being French and therefore adept at the tongue, for they seized Thatcher and bore him away, struggling and shouting.

"I think you and your companions should have a clear track to Berlin, gentlemen," the King remarked.

In this he was accurate, for we experienced no trouble on our train journey, and drew into the German capital about mid-morning of the next day but one and were swiftly conveyed to what we were informed was called the Old Palace, somewhat away from the center of the city.

Our reception there was in marked contrast to the almost furtive way in which we had been brought in two closed cars from the railway station. We were ushered through gates into a large garden with a long path running through its center. On both sides of this stood a number of men in colorful uniforms holding cutting weapons upright—Wells relieved my mind considerably by claiming that these, in this setting at least, were purely decorative in function—and wearing metal hats with a spike on top of each, which it seemed to me might prove quite useful in warfare, as they would discourage an enemy from dropping onto you from above.

As instructed by the persons who had met us, we walked slowly between the files of men toward where a flight of steps ended the path. At the top of this stood a tall figure dressed in white, fairly ablaze with bits of bright metal and cloth in the area of the chest. Like Roosevelt and King Edward, he wore an imposing moustache, differing from theirs in that the ends turned upward to form sharp points, quite like those on his soldiers' metal hats, though it seemed to me they could hardly serve a similar purpose. He wore a highly ornamented cutting weapon hanging in a container from his belt, and his right hand rested on its handle. I noted with some surprise that his left arm was held close to his body in an awkward fashion, and appeared to be somewhat shorter than the other.

"He's being cagey, you see," Wells muttered to me.

"No public fuss about your arrival, in case he should decide that he doesn't want to acknowledge you, but just enough pomp here so that you'll feel well done-by if it turns out you're worth it. He's got a terrific sense for that sort of thing; I imagine he'd have done well as an actor-manager, probably better than he has as Kaiser."

The Kaiser greeted us cordially, declaring that as we came recommended by his uncle and Mr. Roosevelt, whom he claimed to admire above all men, he would listen with great attention to what we had to say, although he felt obliged to point out that it was difficult to see any way in which Germany might benefit from intercourse with another Empire, as it already contained everything necessary to civilized life.

He ushered us through some portions of the palace, pointing out with evident pride many pieces of furniture, woven wall hangings, paintings, and a profusion of smaller objects in cases or on tables; all these, he declared, were of the best quality, and furthermore, many were associated, in ways which would interest us remarkably, with his personal and family history.

"Nice jar, this," Dark said, picking up a ceramic container adorned with representations of birds and flowers, which the Kaiser had informed us had been taken by his troops from a place called China during what I understood, perhaps incorrectly, to be an uprising of prize-fighters.

"Put it *down*, man!" the Kaiser said. "It's worth thousands! *Everything* here is quite expensive, and I should be obliged if you would remember that. I don't come to your planet and fiddle about with your *objets d'art,* and I don't see why you should feel free to do so with mine!"

173

Dark's action may have been fortunate for us, as the Kaiser, still somewhat nettled when we reached his study, made a point of excluding Oxford and Wells from our deliberations. "What the Emperor of Germany and these men from the stars have to say to each other is their affair, and not that of Great Britain or the United States," he said stiffly. "You gentlemen will be taken on a further tour of the palace, and mind you don't touch anything." We were thus enabled to continue avoiding revealing our true purpose to our friends, a course I preferred, as I still felt that they did not have the breadth of view that would allow them to perceive the necessity of hastening the destruction of their civilization.

Nor was the Kaiser notably sympathetic to this notion when Ari laid it before him. King Edward had indicated, he said, that we had matters of grave consequence to discuss with him; he had not expected to be subjected to an inundation of pig-dog nonsense.

"The peace of Europe is assured!" he told us, striding back and forth behind his desk. "I have the guarantees of my cousin the Czar; I have an understanding with the Turkish Sultan; the might of my Army and Navy is such that all must see the clear choice between the hand of German friendship and my Empire's mailed fist! I am called William the Peacemaker, and I assure you it is for good cause!"

All the same, Ari's presentation of his thesis began to intrigue the Kaiser. Both Wells and the King had told us that William possessed an inquiring mind, and he was evidently caught up in spite of himself as Ari expounded on Metahistory, pointed out what the maps showed, and in the main brought up the same arguments that he had with King Edward.

"I don't like this," the Kaiser commented after Ari had done. "I don't believe it, but I can't altogether dismiss it. I know what my blood tells me is the correct destiny for the German people, for Europe, for the world—but you turn everything on its head, and make me begin to doubt. . . ." He walked to the window and looked out, then turned back to us.

"Gentlemen, we have been too long in this room, and my head is not so clear as it should be. Let us all take a turn in the fresh air and let it blow away some of the cobwebs you have spun about me. A few breaths of God's good ozone, and we shall all look at this differently, eh? We Germans are great believers in the doctrine that the healthy body houses the healthy mind!"

I saw Dark glance sharply at the Kaiser's left arm, and I experienced a sinking feeling about my midsection. Our Captain, though a very capable man, was not so versed as Ari and myself in the ways of tactful association with persons of alien planets and was all too inclined to say things which, while perhaps true, produced alarming effects.

And so it proved. We had scarcely walked past a bend in one of the graveled paths through the garden, which put us in the midst of a grove of trees, when he spoke up. "Look here," he said. "That healthy body business—how does that square with that arm of yours?"

The Kaiser wheeled and glared at him—and, I was sorry to see, at the rest of us. "What!"

"I've been noticing the way you hold it, and you don't use it at all, so it can't be good for much, can it?"

The Kaiser's face contorted remarkably, which caused his moustache to assume a variety of configurations. "This is unheard of!" he gasped in a low, hoarse voice, as though something were blocking his throat. "Disgraceful! Barbaric! A piece of not-to-be-borne insolence!" He clapped his right hand to the hilt of the cutting weapon at his side and drew it partway from its container, at the same time taking a step toward Dark. The container somehow impeded his leg movement, and he stumbled and fell heavily to the path.

"There, you see?" Dark said. "If you'd been able to use that arm properly, you'd have very likely kept your balance."

The Kaiser gave a sort of low, wordless howl as he attempted to struggle to his knees. I exchanged an uneasy glance with Ari. It did seem that the monarchs we encountered were an excitable lot, and I found myself wondering if there were not some flaws in his theory about their greater-than-normal rationality.

18

"Here," Dark said, "let me give you a hand. As you've got only one that's any use to you," he added, in what struck me as an ill-advised attempt at relieving the situation with a touch of humor.

The Kaiser gritted his teeth and muttered, "No— don't need it—*lèse-majesté* to touch the Emperor's person, anyhow, except under prescribed circumstances. . . ."

When he regained his feet, his rage seemed to have subsided, and he looked at us in bewilderment, apparently careless of the gravel which clung to the knees of his uniform breeches. "I can't imagine what the devil made you say that," he said wonderingly. "It went *past* rudeness, past mere insult, past anything I have ever known or heard of. Old Bismarck had an edge to his tongue, especially when I had to sack him, and I've had some bluff conversations with honest peasants whilst inspecting my estates—who may well have been taking advantage of an opportunity to get in a safe dig at the All-Highest, though that's by the way—but I've never *ever* . . ." The Kaiser fell silent and looked at Dark as though he were for the first time truly realizing that he (and therefore the rest of us) were beings outside his experience.

"Well, I'm sorry if I somehow seem to have hit a sore point," Dark said, "but I do think machinery ought to work properly—that's my craft, you see—and I suppose I do speak my mind when I see something out of order like that."

"The human body," the Kaiser said, "is *not* a . . . a steam turbine or a railway train, as you appear to be suggesting."

"Not at *all*," Dark said. "Different entirely—fuel, materials, control system, just about everything. But all the same, it's machinery, and it seems to me to be pretty slovenly to let it get out of whack like that. Don't people laugh at you about it?"

"They do not, I assure you," the Kaiser answered grimly. "Not in my hearing, nor in that of any man who has pledged his sword to me. I may say that the rigors I have forced upon myself in order to make myself an accomplished horseman in spite of this"—he slapped his left arm with his good hand—"have won me much of the respect I command from my subjects. The greatest strength is the overcoming of weakness!"

"If you say so," Dark responded. "But it seems to me that it'd have been simpler to have it put right."

The Kaiser closed his eyes briefly. "I cannot imagine why the physicians who delivered me, not to mention their many successors who tormented my childhood with their remedial measures, never thought of that," he said.

His tone did not seem to me to carry any appreciable degree of sincerity, but Dark replied indignantly, "Well, they darned well ought to have! It'd have been a lot easier to take care of it at the beginning than it would be now."

"Take *care* of it? Do you mean to tell me . . ." The Kaiser stopped speaking and looked intently at Dark.

"Are you saying, sir, that you consider that this . . . condition could have been corrected by some means you know of?"

"Of course. It's a part that's not working, so what your technicians *ought* to have done was work out why, and fix it. It's all very well to talk about being strong by overcoming weakness and so on, but you've just now got your knees all dirty, and, I ask you, is it worth it?"

The Kaiser took a long look about him. "I appear to be on the grounds of my own palace, and not on the moon or in Cloud-Cuckoo-Land, so I must behave as though what I have heard is what has in fact been said, and make some rational response to it. We Hohenzollerns are not subject to demented fancies, unlike some of the Habsburgs and others I could name not a thousand miles from here. . . . I have the impression, Herr Dark, that you somehow believe it is by *choice*—"

"Say!" Dark cried. "I've got it! Of course; you people aren't onto a lot of things that we know about, so you get stuck with things like that you can't help. Dear me, what a pity. I don't suppose," he asked diffidently, "now you've grown up with it and all, that you'd care to get it working properly again? I don't want to be pushy, but I *hate* to see things not doing what they're meant to do."

"My arm," the Kaiser exclaimed angrily, "was ruined at my birth! It was wrenched from its socket, and by the time it was restored to its place, the nerves and muscles were destroyed!"

"I thought it might be something like that," Dark said. "You'd want to reestablish the nerve connections, first thing, then get in a supply of protein to build up the muscle tissue. I don't expect you could do very much about the bones at this late date, perhaps add an inch or two onto them, but I don't see getting a really accurate match with the other arm.''

"You can *do* this?" the Kaiser whispered.

"Well, yes." Dark looked surprised. "We Captains have got to be ready to maintain all sorts of equipment, and that naturally includes the people on the team. There wouldn't be much point, would there, in having your ship in good order if the crew got bent or broken or something? Mind you," he added, "most of my stuff's on the ocean bottom with *Wanderer,* so I couldn't do you a brand-new arm or anything like that. But I do have what you might call a first-aid kit in my gear, and that should be enough to let me do a sort of makeshift repair job like that. If you wouldn't object to the trouble, it'd take about three of your days, I'd say—and it *would* be rather a treat," he added wistfully, "to get back in practice again. I get this feeling that I'm going stale without something to do.''

Ari and I found it quite amusing that someone who valued precision so highly as Dark was so far off in his calculations. (Valmis, as usual, took little notice of what was going on with our endeavor, preferring to watch the Berliners go about their business from his vantage point in a place called Café des Westens; he said they formed Patterns unlike any he had yet seen.) It took not three days to rebuild the Kaiser's arm, as Dark had so confidently stated, but four; a thirty-three and one-third percent error, far beyond what a trained engineer ought to encounter.

On the Kaiser's instruction, we did not inform Wells or Oxford of what Dark was doing with him. We put it about that they were having extended talks on topics of great import, which did not require the participation of anyone else.

Wells expressed some perturbation about this supposed state of affairs. "I'm not, of course, taken in by the fiction of nationalism," he told me, as we sat over a couple samples of a local refreshment called Schnapps at the Café des Westens, where we had joined Valmis (who reported that it was quite effective in aiding the Perception of Patterns), "but I'm bound to say that it makes me uneasy that Dark's been *en tête-à-tête* with the Kaiser for such a time. I'd hate to think that Germany was getting all sorts of plans for long-range guns or land ironclads or things like that that might be used against England. Or for that matter against America— what d'you say to that, Oxford?"

Oxford, who had contrived somehow to find a glass of his favorite Würzburger so far from home, remarked mildly, "It'd have to be a mighty long-range gun to worry *us*, I expect. With three thousand miles of Atlantic between us and any worthwhile enemy, I guess we can afford to consider your wars as sporting events we can get good newspaper copy from."

Recalling Ari's sure prediction of the involvement of all nations in the coming conflict, I once more felt a pang of distress at the dissimulation we were obliged to practice, and ordered a double portion of the Schnapps restorative, which immediately exercised a calming influence on me.

"*Dark* wouldn't do a thing like that," I said. "He's as straight as they come, straight as a . . . whatever it is you have here that's *very* straight. If he knew anything about long-range guns, which I know for a fact he doesn't, and he told the Kaiser about it, which he wouldn't, why, then, he'd tell King Edward the same,

181

if he was asked, and Edison, and Geronimo, and Mr. Hearst, and Captain Thatcher, and that chap who so kindly drove us in the brewery truck, and Mr. Barrymore, and the lady he met on the boat—Dark, that is, not Barrymore, for I'm sure he wasn't traveling with us—and . . ." I went on a bit more, being rather pleased with myself for remembering so many of the very interesting people we had run across during our enforced stay on this planet. But both Oxford and Wells lost interest in the topic of conversation and turned to talk of other subjects, particularly the varieties of evening entertainment Berlin offered.

They embarked on an exploration of these, on which I accompanied them, although I have no precise recollection of what happened during it. In different establishments, a number of persons, both male and female, sang or spoke prepared speeches, which aroused generally favorable reactions, but as this was done in the German tongue, to which I was a stranger, I did not attempt to arrive at any opinion about what I saw. Refreshments were available in copious quantities, and I tried several sorts of them. Most were quite good, and I resolved to make a list of the best, but later lost it, or perhaps forgot to write it out.

It was the next morning, the fourth after our arrival in Berlin, when Dark came to the quarters that had been allotted to me in the Palace. I did not welcome him, as I was once again experiencing excessive fatigue and suffering apprehensions about whether some element in this planet's atmosphere might not be overcoming the protective effects of my implants.

"Here, you'd better come along," he said. "I'm just finishing off the last bits on that Kaiser fellow's arm, and he's likely to carry on some when he comes to."

182

I followed him reluctantly to the Kaiser's study, where Dark had been conducting his repair work. The Kaiser was stretched unconscious on a couch, his upper body bare except for the left arm, which, wrapped in a protective sheath, lay extended on a low table next to the couch.

"Most of the stuff worked just about as it does on us," Dark said, peeling the sheath off. "Needed a bit more anesthetic, but the tissue materials worked rather faster." Indeed, the Kaiser's arm now looked quite normal, aside from being opened deeply, exposing the bone.

Dark inspected the cavity with some small instruments and pronounced himself satisfied with the operation of the nerves and muscles, then deftly closed it and sealed the surface.

"That was quite a job," he observed, as he stowed his implements in his medical kit. "I hope not too many of us need any major repairs while we're here; I've about used up a number of things I doubt I can replace, though I expect I can synthesize the basic stuff locally. Ah, he's coming out of it."

The Kaiser stirred, then opened his eyes and slowly sat up. "Ah, I'm . . . oh, yes." He looked blearily at Dark and me, as though attempting to focus his eyes.

"You'll be all right in a minute," Dark assured him. "That stuff wears off fast."

The Kaiser's repaired arm hung limply by his side, and he reached for it with his right hand as though to position it more comfortably. The left arm twitched, and its lower part struck him smartly on the chest.

"Lieber Herrgott!" he said, looking at it. He clenched and unclenched the left hand, spreading the fingers as wide as they would go. Then he stretched out

both arms in front of him and looked from one to the other, his eyes wide.

"It takes some managing, since you haven't had the use of it," Dark said, "but you'll get accustomed, once you've run it a bit. I'm afraid it's still a trifle shorter than the other, by not quite an inch, and the flesh is rather firmer than on the other one, but I think you'll find it in quite good working order."

The Kaiser said nothing, but sat looking at his arms for a moment. Then he reached for a white shirt which was folded over the back of a chair, and, with a practiced motion of his right hand, slid it over his shoulders and inserted his right arm into the sleeve. "If you would be so kind . . ." he said to Dark, then stopped. With considerable difficulty and several false starts, he placed his left arm in its sleeve and drew the garment around him. He was now quite pale.

He put his hands to the front of the shirt near the top and began fumbling with a button and the hole through which it was meant to go. "If you'd like some help with that . . ." Dark began, but the Kaiser snapped, "No! Do you realize this is the first time I have ever been able to use both hands to do something so simple as *button my shirt?*"

"Or *will* be able to, anyhow, once you get the hang of it," Dark observed.

It took the Kaiser very nearly a minute to manage the first button, but fastening the others went more quickly.

His shirt properly arranged, he stood and surveyed us solemnly. "Thanks would be meaningless," he stated gravely. "So would honors or money. I shall not insult you by offering them." I rather wished Ari had been there, as he would have appreciated better than either of us the subtle delicacy and graciousness of the Kaiser's statement.

He walked to his desk and stood behind it. His white shirt was caught in a flood of sunshine that came through the window, and he seemed almost to blaze with light. "Be assured that you have earned the gratitude of Wilhelm Hohenzollern and his House," he said earnestly. "And perhaps of . . ."

He did not conclude his statement, but looked down at his left hand, which lay upon the desk in a patch of sunlight. He lifted it somewhat and contorted it, studying the shadow it cast. "My word," he murmured. "That's quite a good rabbit. And how do you . . . yes, that's it, a goose, no doubt about it. And *here* comes a wicked wolf to eat him up. . . . Excuse me, gentlemen, I was distracted for a moment."

He brooded awhile (keeping his hands still), then looked up at us. "Though you, Herr Dark, and I have been occupied with other matters these last days, the words and arguments of Professor Doctor Ari have not been absent from my mind. I have tried to make myself consider them nonsense, but the knowledge he has shown of the forces of history have made it impossible to dismiss them so easily. I do not accept what he says completely—if I did so, it would be difficult to continue living, even with . . ." He glanced again at his left hand.

"However, it is his and your wish to bring your theories to the attention of other world rulers, and I cannot deny you this. It shall be arranged that you go to St. Petersburg and talk with my cousin the Czar. I know not what may come of it, but . . ."

He moved from behind the desk and paced slowly

across the room. When he spoke, it was so quietly that I could hardly hear, as though he addressed himself rather than any audience. "It was the scorn that was hardest," he murmured. "The electric treatments and such, they hurt, really hurt, but *she* couldn't stand her first-born not being perfect, and she let me know it early and often. . . . When Papa knelt before Grandpapa at Versailles and gave him homage as Emperor—the first of our line, newly crowned in the heartland of the foe he had defeated!—it came to me that *I* should one day have that crown . . . and that my arm was a sign of my own destiny and my people's." Though his voice had risen, he did not yet seem to be talking to us directly. "The strength to overcome misfortune—the strength to deny weakness—the strength to fight for a rightful place in the sun—the strength to weld a stiff-necked people into a joyously obedient instrument of the racial will—I drew *that* from my withered arm! It was God's sign to me that He had touched me as He did Jacob at Peniel, and threw his thigh out of joint, that he might be no more Jacob but Israel, and would prevail. . . ."

He stopped his pacing and looked once more at his left arm, turning the hand over slowly. "And now I am as other men," he said, again so softly that he could hardly be heard.

19

It was quite comical to see the expression on Wells's and Oxford's faces as the Kaiser bade us good-bye that afternoon, coming to each of us in turn and grasping our right hands in both of his. They responded in an absent manner to his wishes for a good journey to St. Petersburg and to his expression on his regard for the great nations they represented, or at least came from; as we walked to the carriages that were to take us to the railway station, they kept glancing at their right hands in apparent bewilderment.

"You saw that, too, Wells?" Oxford asked, once we were in the train and leaving Berlin.

"*And* felt it," Wells replied. "It hardly seems fair that Raf should have tried to drink Berlin dry last night and it's us that gets the hallucinations. Only," he went on, looking at Dark, "it's *not* a hallucination, is it? You mended his arm somehow, didn't you, during those 'talks' you put it out you were having? Or did you graft a new one onto him, like some Frankenstein? I don't know if you realize what you've done. . . . I'm not in fact sure that *I* do, either. . . ."

Dark shrugged uncomfortably. "Well, it seemed to me something that wanted doing, so I did it. What's the harm in that? Look, it cheered him up enough so that he's sent us on to this Czar person, which is what Ari wants, and what you're along for a look at, so it's all worked out right, hasn't it?"

187

Neither Wells nor Oxford seemed totally satisfied with this, but neither did they appear able to find any adequate further comment on it, and the conversation became desultory.

The trip was almost as devoid of incident as the landscape was of interest; both were in the main flat and featureless. There was a moment of near-excitement when we were obliged to change conveyances at the border between the Russian and the German empires, owing to both nations' inability to agree on how far apart a train's wheels ought to be and the determination of each to have its own way on the matter within its borders.

At this halt, many passengers stood about on the platform and were questioned by Russian officials before being allowed to proceed to the next train. As we bore letters requiring our free passage, we were not so examined, and proceeded toward the waiting Russian train without hindrance. I heard a hubbub behind us and turned to see Captain Thatcher and Sergeant Olson being surrounded by shouting Russians.

"What's all that?" said Wells—who, it will be recalled, had not encountered either of the pair of far-traveled Marines—and ran down the platform to see.

When he came back, he said, "They've caught a pair of anarchists—fellows trying to sneak into Russia whilst carrying pistols. What a damn fool thing to do—even if they're not anarchists, they ought to know that the Russians won't take 'em for anything else, if they're armed."

Oxford and the four of us exchanged glances. Evidently Mr. Edison had not given up on his plans to retake us.

Nicholas Romanov, Czar of All the Russias (I had not been told there was more than one Russia, but that seemed to be his official title, all the same), was not nearly so impressive a specimen as his two royal relatives that we had met. He was a shortish, slight man, with a moustache and beard which, unlike King Edward's, appeared to be designed to conceal rather than to adorn his features. He was also, after we had gone through the by now familiar preliminaries of being closeted with him in his place of work—these emperors appeared to spend a lot of their time behind desks—a good deal less attentive to what Ari had to say.

"It's really too much for me," he said peevishly. "I can't think what Willy and Uncle Edward were about, asking me to receive you. I have the Duma, and the Court, and the peasants, and the Army, all at me all the time, and now you people, with this talk of wars and so on. *I* don't want a war, and I don't know anybody who does. We had one with the Japanese a few years ago, and it was most distressing, most; it very nearly meant the end of the monarchy, and I don't propose to have *that* happen, no matter what anyone says. No, no; it won't do, and it's really too bad of the Kaiser and the King to send you on to upset me this way. My family and I come out here to have a little peace and quiet, and next thing you know, I'm expected to listen to beings from another world tell me I'm supposed to go to war for some reason I can't at all understand. It's *not* the way to do things, and I'm not at all pleased."

This interview occurred at a place called Tsarskoye Seloe, some distance from St. Petersburg, where the Czar and his wife and children frequently retired to enjoy what they considered a simpler manner of life

189

than that obtaining in the capital city. The palace they inhabited seemed to me fairly elaborate, but emperors doubtless look at these things differently. Wells and Oxford had not taken too kindly to being excluded from our deliberations, but the Czar, on hearing that his cousin the Kaiser had made the same proviso, insisted on the point. "I don't see the reason myself," he had said, "but William knows about these matters, so I'd best be guided by his example."

Now he clearly appeared to regret having agreed to see us at all; he was certainly looking at us in a most unfriendly manner and moving papers about on his desk as though he wished us to leave but had not quite worked up the resolution to ask us to do so.

Ari was beginning to look rather discouraged, but he still persisted. "The findings of Metahistory, Your Majesty, leave no room—"

"Don't *plague* me with your Metahistory, sir! I won't be hounded in my own palace, not for the King or the Kaiser or anyone! It's really not fair to—"

The Czar's complaint was interrupted by the opening of his study door and the entrance of a small boy, who rushed toward him, calling impatiently, "Papa!" Then he saw us and stopped. "Everybody must stand up when the Heir to the Throne comes in," he announced importantly.

"But we are standing," Dark said, as we were, since the Czar had not invited us to do otherwise.

"Then sit down and then stand up," the boy advised. "I like it when people have to stand up."

"Alexei," the Czar said fondly, reaching for the lad. "You know you're not supposed to come in when Papa is talking business. However, I suppose it doesn't matter; I believe we have concluded our talk. It was good of you to come to see me, gentlemen, but I must not presume on your valuable time any longer. You may—"

At this point, the boy Alexei, in attempting to climb into his father's lap, slipped and struck his head a glancing blow on the desk. He gave a snort of pain and impatience, and a trickle of blood began to flow from his nose.

I understood this to be a common enough reaction to a minor injury, but the effect on the Czar was startling. He turned pale, grabbed the boy up, and darted over to a couch at one side of his study, yelling loudly enough to be heard outside the room, "Send for Grigori immediately! Grigori must come! The Czarevitch . . ." His voice broke. He laid the boy tenderly on the couch and began dabbing helplessly at the continuing flow of blood with a handkerchief.

In a moment, several persons entered, following a huge and hairy man clad in a rough robe. He strode to the couch and bent over the boy, speaking soothingly in the Russian tongue. As he passed us, I got a whiff of a rank odor, which, taken together with his appearance, suggested that he had somehow been prevented from washing for some time.

The Czar stood back, relief evident in his expression. Valmis, looking alert for once, drifted over near the couch and stood by as the hairy man, presumably the Grigori called for, continued to speak to the boy, at the same time stroking his forehead and gazing at him intently.

In a moment the trickle of blood stopped. Grigori wiped the stains from the boy's face with the Czar's handkerchief, which he crumpled into a ball and dropped, took him in his arms, and walked from the room, followed by the attendants who had come in with him. The Czar, sighing deeply, sank back into his chair.

"What was that all about?" Dark asked. "Wasn't it rather a lot of fuss over a kid's nosebleed?"

The Czar looked at him somberly. "I must ask you," he said, "to keep secret what you have just seen. It must *not* be known that the Czarevitch, who will one day rule in my stead, suffers from . . ." He sighed. "My son . . . there is something wrong with his blood. The slightest injury or cut is dangerous to him; the blood flows and will not stop, or it seeps under the skin, causing huge, inflamed bruises. The doctors can do nothing—only that holy man, Grigori, who has been sent from God to help us, can preserve him. It's a pity," he went on, with a return to his former querulous manner, "that he's got to create such a fuss wherever he goes, though. What he gets up to with the ladies of the Court is something shocking—and, worse, some of them don't seem to mind it! But the Empress turns a blind eye to it all, and so must I. It's upsetting having Rasputin here, but it would be unthinkable for Alexei to be without him."

"He's quite good at it," Valmis said. "From what I could see, it looked as though he were getting the boy to relax his consciousness enough to take control of the small veins and get them to tighten up and stop the blood. Very sound Perception of the Patterns involved, I have to say; I've seen nothing like it here."

The Czar looked at him in bewilderment. "Nobody knows how Grigori exercises his healing effect. It is a holy mystery."

"Not especially," Valmis said. "It's seeing what the Patterns are, you know, and acting with them.

192

Every sort of organization of matter has its Pattern, whether it's a single cell or a galaxy, or anything in between. Once you sense the Patterns fully, you're able to Integrate. That's my specialty, Integration, you see."

"Valmis," Ari broke in, "I cannot think that His Majesty cares to—"

"One moment." The Czar held up his hand and looked gravely at Valmis. "I don't understand you, but you seem to be claiming some knowledge of my boy's illness. That is hard to believe, but . . ."

"Well, it follows. It's part of the Pattern of blood to clot when there's a flow of it out of a puncture of some sort, so as to seal the wound off. And if it's not doing it, then the Pattern is off in some way. Your Grigori's work is most impressive, but I don't think he's getting at it directly enough. Where the Pattern's gone wrong would be in the blood itself, I should say, something extra or missing in the cells."

"The doctors have said something like that," the Czar replied wearily, "but what good does it do to know this? And in any case, they can't identify just what it is that *is* wrong."

"Perhaps I ought to have a look, then," Valmis suggested. "I'm not a medical technician or anything like that, but I should hope I haven't lost my touch at getting hold of a simple cellular Pattern! Dark, would you let me have the use of your kit for a bit? I'll want to use that viewer thing you've got in it to get a good look at the cells."

Though plainly at a loss to comprehend what was going on, the Czar gave orders for Dark's gear to be fetched. When it had come and Valmis had extracted the instrument he required, he pushed aside some pa-

193

pers to make a clear spot on the Czar's desk and spread out the crumpled bloodstained handkerchief Rasputin had left behind. Adjusting the viewer from Dark's medical kit, he inspected this closely for some time, muttering to himself. When he had done, he straightened up and said, "I believe that's it. There's a sort of—is it 'protein' you call it here?—anyhow, something the cell's Pattern seems to call for, and it's not there. I'd like to make sure of that, though. Do you have a clean pin or something like that about you, Your Majesty? Ah—" He went to a wall map and pulled out a pin with a brightly colored head, one of many inserted there.

"That's the Twenty-third Regiment!" the Czar cried in some agitation. "You can't—"

"Don't worry, I'll put it back in the right place," Valmis said. "I've got the Pattern of all those pins clear in my mind—though it's not a very good one; I should think you'd want a lot more of them over on the left side, near Germany. Now, put your hand on the desk, palm up, please . . . there!"

The Czar gave a start and a sharp cry as Valmis jabbed a fingertip with the pin and blotted up the resulting spot of blood with a piece of paper. This he also inspected with the viewer.

"As I thought," he said after a moment. "It's *here*"— he pointed at the blood spot in the paper—"and not *here*." He indicated the handkerchief.

"You have found the cause of my son's disease?" the Czar asked wonderingly.

"Well, yes," Valmis replied.

"Amazing! But . . . what good does it do to know this? The fault is in the blood; very well, we have learned that. But it is still there, and . . ."

Valmis, ignoring him, was rummaging through the

194

medical kit. "Dark, where is that synthesizer thing? I've forgotten what it looks like. . . . Say, is this it, the one with the yellow bands near the top?" He held up a complex-looking object.

"That's it," Dark told him. "Look, you shouldn't be fooling around with—"

"Don't *nag*," Valmis retorted. "It puts me off when I'm Integrating. You don't seem to understand that Integration's not just a matter of sitting about and Perceiving things, though that's a lot of it, but there are times when you've got to get your hands dirty, too, and that's Integrating just as much as the other is, so I'd be obliged if you'd refrain from putting me off my stride."

It was not only the Czar who was gaping at Valmis now; Ari, Dark and I were almost equally perplexed. We had rarely, if ever, seen Valmis so energized, and certainly not since our precipitous arrival on this planet. His mystical, melancholy obsession with his fancied distortion of reality seemed to have vanished.

He looked up from a further inspection of the paper and the handkerchief and caught our gaze. He grinned and remarked, "A very pretty problem, this. I must say it does me no end of good to have something to sink my teeth into. There's a lot of Integrators who don't think it's worthwhile bothering with anything this size, but I always say a Pattern's a Pattern, no matter where you find it, and it doesn't do anybody credit to ignore even the smallest ones. Either snobbery or laziness, that's what it is."

He turned to the Czar. "Look here, do you think you could let me have some blood? About a . . . what *are* your measures, now? As much as would go into this cup here?" He held up a moderate-sized vessel from Dark's kit. "It won't hurt, I assure you, and I don't believe

195

you'll miss it at all—your system'll replace it in no time. All you have to do is take off that jacket and roll up your shirt-sleeve."

"I don't understand," the Czar whispered. "What are you . . . what would you do with it?"

"Well, it's obvious," Valmis answered. "I'll put it through the synthesizer, to activate those protein things you've got and your son hasn't, so they can make replicas of themselves. Then we inject some of it into the boy, and the protein things start grabbing onto his blood cells, so that in a while they've all got them, and the new cells he produces are the way they're supposed to be. It's a clumsy way of doing it, I grant you, but it'll do the job well enough. Now, if you'd rather we got someone else in to let us have the blood, I suppose—"

"No!" The Czar spoke more firmly than I had yet heard him do. Staring wide-eyed at Valmis, he began undoing his tunic. "If this thing is to be, then my son shall have *my* blood!"

20

To my disappointment, and I suppose to the Czar's, Valmis said his process would not be immediately effective, and we should have to wait until the next morning to test its results. As a result, we were obliged to spend a most tense afternoon and evening. The Palace was in an uproar, with the Czar, pale and defiant, overriding all argument and insisting on Valmis being allowed to treat the boy Alexei; the Czarina, a very excitable lady, alternating between tearful hopefulness and angry objection (also tearful); the doctors and Rasputin, for once in agreement, bellowing and railing against the whole idea; and the general run of other people, from equerries and generals to the men who drove the carriages, arguing, expostulating, calling out, singing, praying, weeping, rushing about, whispering in corners, flinging themselves onto couches and off again, drinking quantities of a very warming stuff called vodka, and, in short, carrying on as though demented.

By common agreement, they left our party strictly alone, whether because of the Czar's decision to trust us or because they regarded us as possibly supernatural and dangerous beings, I could not be sure. Rasputin gave us some quite ugly looks when he chanced to stride by us, but did not make any approach. I was glad of this, as he had not yet found occasion to wash, and his presence in a place could be detected for some time after he had left it.

We contrived to get something to eat from the obviously reluctant and apprehensive servants. The meal was accompanied by some of the vodka, which I welcomed, as I found that its warming properties relieved much of the unease and tension which surrounded us.

"You people have got us in the soup properly if this business doesn't work," Wells predicted gloomily as we ate. "Whatever possessed you to meddle with the boy?"

"Well," Valmis returned defensively, "I saw the Pattern of it, and it just sort of came to me that I should do something about it. I've been keeping myself pretty much unaware here, as it's upsetting to see so many distorted Patterns and not be able to set them right—it's not all that easy, being an Integrator, don't think that for a minute—but there this one was, wasn't it? Besides," he added, "the Czar was awfully sulky, and I thought that doing something about this might cheer him up so we could get on with . . . with what we were talking about."

Wells breathed heavily. "I daresay it might. And if it doesn't work out, *sulky* won't be the word for the way he'll be feeling! That man doesn't have a great supply of backbone, but he *is* a near-absolute monarch, and if he's badly disappointed, we're going to find that out, and quite unpleasantly, too. My will's up to date, thank goodness."

"Oh, it'll work, all right," Dark assured him. "Look how nicely the Kaiser's arm worked out."

"Ah, yes, the Kaiser's arm," Wells repeated distantly. "You do get into the way of doing these things, don't you? I don't suppose," he went on, "that you had a chance to do anything drastic to the King, did you? He, at least, has not been . . ." He stopped what he

198

was saying and looked at Ari, who had suddenly developed an intense interest in the contents of his plate. "Oh, *no*," Wells said softly.

"Well, the man was choking," Ari said. "Be reasonable, can't you? I mean, it would have gone awfully hard with us if they'd come in and found Raf and me there, and the King dead on the floor; surely you can see that? And we didn't do anything drastic, the way you said. Just gave him a little something I take myself to keep the system working properly, so he won't have to be bothered again, worrying about his heart."

Wells rose from the table. "You people are too much for me," he said. "The Martians I invented aren't anything like as odd as you are, tentacles and all. I could never write you up properly, though Shaw might perhaps be able to do you justice. I believe I shall find my way to my bedroom now and try to get some rest. I find I'm *quite* tired."

As there was nothing much to do, with the Palace in such a turmoil, and as dinner had been given us very late, the rest of us repaired to our assigned rooms as well.

I composed myself for sleep, but found it evaded me. It seemed clear that our mission to Europe was not going as we had hoped. Ari's theory about hereditary monarchs being, as it were, the summit of rationality was not, in my view, being borne out by experience. They seemed quite as prone to confusion and emotion as other humans, if not more so. And, if that were the case, it was understandable that they were not properly impressed by the inexorable logic of his Metahistorical arguments and would therefore not be likely to see the advantages of accelerating their inevitable war. So it appeared that our venture might well turn out to be

199

fruitless, and our wait for the planet's technological improvement as protracted as we had feared. Still, the war, whether it came quickly or in a few years, would be the needed first step; once it was going, we ought to be able to do a few things that would help achieve our ends. . . .

This was fairly bleak comfort, and as I have said, I could not get to sleep at all easily. After some time, I rose and attempted to find the room in which we had dined. I recalled that there had been a bottle of the vodka there and believed its refreshing qualities might lighten my mood of worry sufficiently to allow a good night's rest.

I did not encounter anyone in the dimly lit corridors and hallways, the hour being advanced, although I could have done with some information, since after obtaining and sampling the bottle I had gone in search of, I discovered that I could not readily retrace my steps.

After a while, I found myself near what I recognized to be the Czar's study, the door of which was partially opened. I could see a dim light from inside; hearing a low murmur, I approached to see if I could be directed to my room.

When I peered in, I saw the Czar, his back to me, seated in front of a communications instrument, something like a telephone, into which he was speaking urgently, but in so low a tone that I could not catch any actual words. On a panel attached to it, I could see a flickering black-and-white image, which, by squinting, I could make out as that of King Edward; His Majesty's lips moved, but I could hear none of his words, which were evidently being transmitted into the earpiece the Czar held. I had not seen this particular sort of instrument before; I supposed that they must be quite expensive and therefore used only by the wealthy.

As the Czar seemed intent on his conversation, I did not disturb him, but left, taking a thoughtful pull on the bottle. I wondered what he might be discussing with King Edward, and I hoped that it might bode well for our aims. I took some comfort from this thought and from the vodka, and, upon regaining my room after some wandering, fell quickly asleep.

21

It seemed to me curious that when, after an hour of exhaustive tests the next morning, the physicians normally charged with the care of the Czarevitch wonderingly informed the Czar that his son bore no traces of his disease, the reaction was hardly to be distinguished from that which the decision to embark on his untried treatment had occasioned on the previous day. There was quite as much running, praying, crying, and so on; in addition, someone caused a number of cannons to be let off at intervals throughout the day and several loud bells to be rung very nearly continually. The Russians appeared to be an alarmingly volatile people, given to expressing joy as well as consternation in an extreme manner.

Although the bottle of vodka had aided me to attain a healthful night's slumber, I had somehow acquired a severe pain in the upper and rear portions of my head, and this ominous suggestion of malfunction on the part of my implants led me to feel quite dispirited, as well as irritated at the constant volume of noise.

This was added to, somewhere toward the middle of the day, when, on the Czar's orders, Rasputin, yelling most horridly, was driven from the palace and dispatched to St. Petersburg. He had, it appeared, attempted to assault Valmis and to accuse him of being in league with ill-disposed supernatural entities, and of an unwholesome cleanliness of person; and, when diverted forcibly from this, he had tried to mate with one or more of the Czarina's female attendants, who raised objections to this course of action.

"He was a false prophet," the Czar said sternly, watching the struggling robed figure being escorted away by a considerable number of soldiers. "It is to my shame that I tolerated him here; now that I need not, my court is cleansed of a stain which I had not allowed myself to see. Thank God, we have seen the last of him!"

I agreed heartily with this sentiment, as he seemed to be the noisiest of a noisy crowd.

I did not follow the events of the next day or so at all closely, as I was attempting, with only indifferent success, to rid myself of my lingering malaise by a judicious administration of the vodka refreshment. This, while occasionally effective, was not always so, for many of the symptoms, such as sensitivity to noise, head pains and the like, would return in full force after a period, and increasing the dose seemed to do little or no good.

I gathered, though, that Ari was encouraged by the progress of his talks with the Czar. "He's cagey, no doubt about it," he told me, having come unbidden to my bedchamber. "He won't let on what he means to do, but he's been on that picture telephone thing a good deal, talking with the Kaiser and King Edward. It must be that they're working out what they want to do to arrange their war, though I'm not allowed to listen in, which seems unfair. But that's royalty for you."

On the third day after the results of Valmis's treatment of the Czarevitch had become apparent, we were summoned to the Czar's study. I was feeling somewhat better, in spite of the professed inability of the servants to supply me with any vodka for the preceding twenty-four hours, on the claim that somehow most of what had been on hand had unaccountably vanished, and was beginning to hope that my implants, after a period of malfunction, had started to operate properly once more.

"I have grave news, gentlemen," the Czar said. I noticed that he bore himself in a more decisive manner than when we had first met him and that this was reflected in his speech. "I owe you much, and on that account have even gone to the length of giving careful attention to the remarkable proposition with which you approached me, abominable though it is. I have conferred with the Kaiser and King Edward as to courses of action that seem appropriate in the light of what you say, and you may be assured that there will, in due course, be certain results from those discussions which you will find significant. There is, however, another point which requires our immediate attention. Rasputin has evidently been telling his troubles all over St. Petersburg, and his highly colored account of your presence here has come to the attention of the Ambassador from the United States. My Foreign Minister, Isvolsky, has within the hour come to me with an urgent communication from President Edison, demanding your return and that of Mr. Oxford, as a military officer under serious charges, to his custody."

He frowned at a piece of paper he held in his hand and said, "He is most pressing about this. But I could not, in all conscience, allow you, who have done so much for me, to be taken captive against your will. Nor can I, as ruler of Russia, take such a provocative step as outright refusal against a powerful nation with whom we have many dealings. Therefore you must disappear."

"How do we do that?" Dark asked uneasily. It seemed to me, too, in light of what Wells had said about the Czar's autocratic powers, that "disappear" had a sinister ring to it.

The Czar gave a tight smile, as if divining what had passed through our minds. "I mean leave here, *and* in quite sound condition. Especially," he added dryly, with a look at me, "as our vodka supply appears to have been exhausted. You shall quit Russia, and in such a manner that there will be no official involvement of my government—ordinarily, I should have sent you off in a naval cruiser, but you will see why that is out of the question in this situation. However, there is a Spanish nobleman resident in St. Petersburg, owner of a seaworthy yacht and well known to me. I have arranged with him to put this vessel and its crew at your disposal for a fast sail to England, where you will be quietly received and sequestered until matters have developed further. The King is on his way home now and has promised to make all necessary arrangements for your secure accommodation there."

"Won't Edison's crowd figure out pretty quick what's going on?" Dark wondered.

"It may be so," the Czar replied, "but he won't be anxious to make a public outcry once you're away from here, and I can truthfully maintain that I am free of any official involvement. And he won't be likely to protest to Spain about your use of the yacht, as the Americans have already had one war with that country, and the public would not take kindly to beating a dead horse."

When we conveyed this news to our friends, along with the Czar's instructions to pack immediately, Wells bore it more philosophically than Oxford did. "At any rate, I'll get back to England," he observed, "and that's more than I felt like counting on a day or so ago."

Oxford was on the edge of surliness. "I've been smelling something fishy for some time," he said. "There's a lot going on I don't like the look of, and this is part and parcel of it. If what you've been telling all these king people is just that you'd like their help in getting your ship back in shape, how come it's so secret? And how come they're getting themselves all worked up over you? If we're to be whisked to England and hidden, that makes it seem as though there's more in it for the King than what you say. I'll stick by you fellows, for I don't seem to have a choice right now, but I'm bound to say that I don't think you're being square with me and Wells."

"They're not, of course," Wells told him mildly, arranging some clothing very neatly in a container he was packing. "That's one of the things that encourages me. It makes them seem more like us, doesn't it?"

"You will understand, I am sure," Ari said smoothly, "that what has been discussed between ourselves and the monarchs who have been kind enough to grant us their attention must of necessity remain confidential, and that what you take for a furtive secrecy is in reality a matter of necessary diplomatic courtesy. I trust this will allay your unworthy suspicions."

"See what I mean?" Wells said. "They're getting more human every day."

It was dusk when we reached St. Petersburg, after a comparatively brief train journey, and the carriage conveying us to the waterfront district, where we were to board the Spanish yacht, passed along a wide street lit by softly glowing lamps which cast pools of brightness onto the pavement.

206

As we approached one of these lit areas, Dark took a close look at a group of people outlined by the light. "My word, there's that Rasputin fellow!" he exclaimed. When we were nearly up to them, he leaned from the window and called jeeringly, "Hey, monk, had your bath yet? He won't have understood, of course," he said, sitting back in his place once more, "but I expect he caught the tone pretty well."

I looked back and saw the huge robed figure glaring after us; I also got a clear view of the two men with him. "If he didn't," I told Dark, "Captain Thatcher and Sergeant Olson will very likely explain it to him."

Though we had naturally anticipated pursuit after this encounter, it did not materialize, so far as we could see, and we gained the yacht's mooring place, boarded it, and stood out to sea without any hindrance.

"All the same, I don't like it," Oxford said as we stood on the deck and watched the lights of St. Petersburg dwindle behind us. "Thatcher and Olson are after us to save their hides, and Rasputin'd like to drink our blood for getting him thrown out of his cushy berth in the Palace."

"True enough," said I. "But now that we're out of Russia, there's nothing they can do, is there?"

Next morning, which broke gray and damp in the open reaches of the sea, I congratulated myself on having put this observation in the form of a question rather than a definite statement. Had I not done so, I should have been quite abashed at the sight of a large ship, bristling with guns and flying the ensign of the United States, cutting through the water to intercept us.

A loud voice, amplified, I imagine, by some mechanism, emanated from the ship, instructing our vessel to halt its progress. When, at Oxford's urging, the yacht's captain refused to do so, Oxford's order was effectively countermanded by a shot which raised an impressive spout of water not far ahead of us.

The warship drew up alongside us, and the captain yelled up at it, "This is piracy, *señor!*"

"Not at all, Don Diego, or whatever your name is!" the voice boomed from the ship. "We're following the orders of the President of the U.S.A. and Commander in Chief of the U.S. Navy, and I guess that makes it legal enough for me! We want your passengers, and we're going to have them. Far as I'm concerned, you're just a leftover we forgot to sink at Santiago Harbor, and I don't mind adjusting the error now, if you've a mind for it."

"This would *not* hold up under international law," Wells muttered.

"And this ship wouldn't hold up under a four-inch shell through the hull," Oxford said dispiritedly. "I guess we've been trumped, fellows. Edison wants us, and he's got us. Let's get our stuff together; they'll be coming for us any time now."

When we were conveyed to the warship by a party of sailors and brought on board, it was dismaying, but not excessively surprising, to be greeted by Captain Thatcher and Sergeant Olson. Behind them stood Rasputin, who grinned wolfishly at us and snarled something in Russian.

"He's saying, near's I can make out, that you can't be so fond of baths neither, since you give up rather than havin' to take one in the ocean," Olson told us with a derisive grin.

22

Our trip back across the Atlantic went more quickly than the one from America, the captain of the destroyer not being concerned with the comfort of his crew and passengers, but only with completing his assignment, and we were approaching New York harbor five days after we had been obliged to come on board.

Though we were prey to great apprehensions concerning our reception, the intervening time was not without its points of interest. Strangely enough, Thatcher and Olson, secure in the successful completion of their mission, became quite friendly and appeared particularly to enjoy talking with Dark, who shared many of their traits; they traded experiences of encounters in far places with evident relish.

Rasputin, now that his lust for revenge had been satisfied, appeared rather at loose ends, and spent much time striding about the deck alone. Only Olson spoke any Russian, and he was mostly occupied with Dark; in any case, the ship's crew pointedly avoided the bearded monk, as he grew hourly more unpleasant to be close to, with the salt from the sea spray and a certain tang from the coal smoke the ship's engines poured forth adding memorably to his already pungent personal atmosphere.

It was not any real fellow-feeling—for I did not think I could ever actually like Rasputin—but rather boredom that drove me to seek his company. Ari and Valmis were mostly sunk in gloom, as were Wells and Oxford, and I did not wish to spend what might be my last days of comparative freedom for some time in sharing their misery. To pass the time, I fetched out the Communicator, virtually unused since it had been employed to give us four a command of English, and adjusted it so as to perform, in a limited way, the same function for Rasputin.

This could not be done with full effectiveness, as its memory banks contained only the limited amount of English—quite enough for practical purposes, but of course nowhere near the complete language—that they had been fed, and no Russian whatever. All the same, with Rasputin's at first reluctant cooperation, in a day or so he was able to make himself understood most of the time, if without any degree of elegance, and to comprehend a good bit of what was said to him.

"What you think I can doing in Oo Ess?" he asked me, once we were on a conversational footing. "I don't think monk business very good there. Thatcher and Olson, they tell me when I help catch you, they see I be all right there, but I don't know. I so *mad* at you fellows curing Czarevitch when I can't, so Little Father throw me out, away from all good food and nice ladies, that I don't care, so long as *you* get it in neck. But now is time for cooling heads, and I am worry. Can't go back to Holy Russia, or Little Father have me struck with knout many times a day, every day, for hurting his friends. I don't think any good tell him I'm sorry, you?"

I agreed that it was unlikely that the Czar would feel that a handsome apology met the case adequately, and I suggested that one requisite to success in the United States would be a reform of his external hygiene.

"Wash?" he asked, puzzled. "Why that? Dirt has nothing to do with *soul*. Besides, women like man to smell like *man*. Countess, duchess, they go weak when I approach—I be's outside room, and their nose tell them I coming, they faint with desire." It seemed to me that he might have been right about the effect; though not the emotion involved; and I told him that in any case, from what I had seen in advertisements in the journals I had leafed through, it did not work that way in the United States.

He reluctantly agreed to allow himself to be bathed, and a party of cheering sailors hosed him down on the afterdeck, as he capered and shouted in the chilly spray. After his unspeakable robe had been scalded with live steam from the boilers and dried by being held in front of the firebox, he put it on his newly cleaned form, and said, "By God, I feel like new man! Old Grigori washed away, as in Blood of Lamb. New man for New World, not? You say ladies like clean there: they *get* clean. It work same way, clean or not." It did not appear that his exterior laundering had penetrated at all deeply.

It was as we entered New York harbor that I saw, circling the head of the symbolic statue there, a large mechanism making its way through the air. "What's that?" I asked a nearby sailor.

"One of them new Wright electric fliers," he told me. "Takes sightseers around the harbor; I went up in one when I was here on liberty a couple of weeks ago. Don't make no noise, hardly, and goes like the wind, faster'n a train, almost. I hear they'll be using 'em to carry the mail next."

"We having like that in Russia pretty soon, I bet," Rasputin said as he lounged at the rail beside me. "Fellow came to see Little Father, month, two month back, name Sikorsky, he all hot in collar about flying machines, say he got brand-new idea. No wings, but spinning thing on top keep in air. He want money to build, and Little Father say he think about it. I tell him idea from devil, so he drop, but I guess he go for it now Grigori not there. Hey, what goddam tall buildings! If that where American men work, I bet they tired at nights from climb up and down, no good to wives. Not worry, wives! Here come Grigori!"

Rasputin, of whom we lost sight after we had docked at a shipyard across the river from the main island of New York—I understood that he had been given a sum of money and escorted to a section of the city inhabited by persons formerly of his country—was the only one of our group who took our arrival thus light-heartedly. Oxford and Wells and we four Explorers were naturally subdued at the thought of what was in store for us—Wells, though not directly involved in our escape and not really subject to Mr. Edison's authority, could not hope to avoid some awkward moments at the least; Thatcher and Olson were grimly aware of their responsibility in getting us over the last leg of our journey.

"Boys," Thatcher said, as he directed us into a large, closed van, "we've got you this far, and I want you to know I don't propose to lose you between here and Glenwood. For you may as well know we're going on back to your little gray home in the East, as Mr. Edison thinks you'll be safest there. Of course, there'll be a few changes, such as the park-like grounds being enclosed with electrified barbed wire, and dogs loose after dark, and, to guard you, a full company of Marines that's seen service against the Moros and don't like *anybody* that ain't a Marine. But you won't notice that, boys, so long as you stay inside the house or lounge careless-like on the front porch of an afternoon, and do what you're told. Now, that ain't no mean setup to go back to, is it? So don't get notions about pulling any of that cute stuff, the way you done before. I like you guys, I really do, and it'd pain me to do you a lasting injury with this forty-five you will observe me holding. I believe I may safely speak for Sergeant Olson as well."

Olson agreed that this expressed his viewpoint precisely, and we began our journey into captivity.

Wells was quite interested to see our house and, with his ingratiating manner, smoothed the ruffled feathers of the servant couple (that is of course a metaphor, as they were, like almost all employees on the planet, human and not avian), who had been somewhat brusquely handled in the commotion after our hasty departure.

Oxford went with Wells to get him settled into a vacant bedroom, and the four of us took the opportunity to confer privately.

"Well, here we are again," Dark said. "And much good it did us to leave in the first place! All it's accomplished that I can see is that it's put us in the way of being shocked or bitten to death if we get a little careless in strolling around."

"I fail to take your meaning," Ari responded. "Our talks with the King, the Kaiser and the Czar were of the greatest moment. It may take a while for the seeds I have planted in their minds to bear fruit, and it is certainly a pity that we did not have the opportunity to acquaint other rulers with—"

"Ah, stow that!" Dark said violently. "Those chaps thought your top story had a 'for rent' sign up, and no tenant applying; they made that clear enough! Face it, man, they don't have the stomach to set up a war on your say-so, no matter how much Metahistory or meta-*what*ever you feed them. Your game's played out, Ari, and it's damned well time *I* took a hand."

"How do you propose to do that, *Captain?*" Ari asked coldly. "While my own poor efforts in effecting changes in the course of a planet's historical development may not seem impressive to you, I fail to see how a . . . a *mechanic* could do better. And while we're at it," he continued, turning to Valmis and me, "I suppose you two have your own notion of how to manage what we're after? Perhaps you, Raf, are carting around some splendid plan you haven't yet bothered us with? Ah, that's what I like, a nice, crisp negative shake of the head—there's Communication for you, economical of means, yet conveying accurately an admirable sentiment. And you, Valmis, have you Perceived how to use the Patterns of this planet to our advantage? *Do* let us know."

He and the rest of us were taken aback when Valmis answered mildly, "Well, you know, I think I might. It seems to me—"

"Damn your 'seems,' sir!" Ari said. "It's preposterous that you and Dark seem to think—"

While I was made quite uncomfortable by this acrimonious display, I was not especially happy to have it ended abruptly by the entrance into our sitting room of Captain Thatcher, now back in full uniform, who paused at the door, looked behind him, and said, "They're in here, sir. I'll get Oxford and the Englishman down and shoo them in, too." He gave a salute and left.

Mr. Edison came into the room and stood leaning on

214

a cane held in front of him, surveying us with unconcealed dislike. He looked older than when I had last seen him, and the lines on his face were etched noticeably more deeply.

"I'll wait 'til your friends are here before I tell you what you're going to do," he said, without any preamble or greeting, and continued to survey us in the same unfriendly manner.

When Oxford and Wells were ushered—pushed, very nearly—into the room, he acknowledged their presence by grunting. "Oxford," he remarked after a moment, "I've looked it up, and I find I can't have you shot. Not legally, anyhow. But you'd better make it your business to help me deal with these people, or you can bet you'll be looking up loopholes to see if you can find some way to rate a firing squad. You, Wells, it don't look as though I can do anything to, I'm sorry to say. But you helped this crew on their way when you knew darned well I wanted 'em here, and if you're meaning to try any lecture tours in the United States, I wouldn't advise it. I never especially wanted to be President, but, by God, now I am, and I don't take kindly to being flouted, by my own people or by foreigners."

He turned and once more let his baleful gaze rove over Ari, Dark, Valmis and me. "Now, *you*," he said. "I'm not going to bandy words with you people. You know things we can use, and you're going to give 'em to us. End of transmission. I don't know what you thought you were up to, busting out of here, but you are now darned well going to sit here and draw up plans and specifications about everything you know of, until I'm satisfied you don't know any more. We need what you've got, and we're going to get it. And if it takes red-hot pincers, or a few experiments with live wires here and there on you, why, I don't know that I'd mind that all that much."

His voice had become hoarse and shrill, and his lips drew tightly over his teeth. My uneasiness deepened into alarm. The strains of office had evidently told deeply on Edison, and he seemed to me to be approaching a condition of marked instability. I wondered what might be done to mollify him, but could think of nothing that might be effective.

"How much did you *tell* those people, I wonder?" he went on in the same unsettling tone. "That was *low*, that was, scooting off to help give those other countries a head start over us, the people that took you in—"

"It wasn't like that at all," Dark said indignantly. "We didn't tell them anything about how to make things; we didn't go there for that. It was just that Ari had this idea he could get them to start up their war a little sooner, so it'd be over quicker and everything would happen faster, you see, so that . . ." Edison, Oxford and Wells listened with awestruck fascination as Dark explained Ari's plans, each of them looking from Dark to the rest of us with expressions I could not fathom.

"But, you see," Dark finished, "it doesn't seem to have come to anything, so here we are again."

Edison had sunk into a chair during this recital. The eerily tight expression had gradually been smoothed from his face, and he looked merely extremely tired. "That was quite something to hear," he commented after a moment. "I take it, Oxford, Wells, that it came as a surprise to you?"

"Yes, Mr. President," Oxford answered, with a note in his voice I had not heard before. "We . . . it . . . yes,

216

you could say it wasn't quite how we thought things were."

Edison sighed and closed his eyes. "I feel like I'm coming out of a fever," he said. "I don't know . . . I got so caught up in thinking we *had* to have these fellows feeding us ideas, that it got to be an obsession with me. *I* don't go having people locked up, and chased and kidnapped when they get away, just so's they can work for me; *that's* not Thomas Alva Edison at all. But I've done just that, ain't I? And it took something like this—this weird, cold-blooded, crackpot notion these people came up with—to make me see it. Oxford, don't you worry about what I said before. I think you did me a favor, helping 'em escape. And I kind of wish I'd let it stay that way."

He started to rise, and then sank back again in his chair and looked glumly at the top of his cane. "But all the same, they are back, ain't they? And they do know things we can use, you can't get around that. And, as President, I'm bound to do what I can to get hold of that knowledge, though I don't have much heart for it any more. Oxford, if you're not holding any grudges and are willing to let bygones be bygones, do you think you could help me work out a way—"

"Hey!" Dark broke in. "All right, we know what you're after. So why not let's get on with it?"

"Dark!" Ari exclaimed. "You can't! It's gross interference with a planetary culture!"

"I'll leave you and Valmis to argue about the ethical difference between getting a whole bunch of people into a war earlier than they want, and giving them a few tips on things they might get some use out of *and* which would get us a lot nearer the day they can help us put

217

Wanderer spaceworthy again. Look here,'' he said, turning to Edison, ''what kind of things would you like to know?''

It would be unkind to say that Edison was gaping, but there was certainly a pronounced look of relaxation about his jaw. ''Well,'' he replied slowly, ''there's a lot of work to be done with flying machines, for a starter.''

''Ah, gravity repulsion's the thing there; I was telling those Wright fellows that last year, when we ran into them. The way you get gravity repulsion is, you . . .'' He launched into a technical description which I could not follow; Mr. Edison seemed to be able to do so sufficiently to realize that the required technology and certain vital substances did not exist on Earth.

''I can see that'd be so,'' Dark said. ''After all, if you *could* put together a gravity-repulsion unit, even if you had to be shown how to do it at first, why, then, the same thing'd hold for *Wanderer*, wouldn't it? And we wouldn't have to go to all this trouble. Let me see, what's something a bit simpler?''

He worked out a design for a standard spacesuit, very cleverly, it seemed to me, adapted to available materials and skills, but, as he had no clear idea of certain key processes in producing the metals and ceramics required for the sort of primitive spacecraft that Earth's resources might admit of, this did not appear to be of any immediate utility.

''True enough,'' Dark said with a chuckle. ''If you can't get into space, what's the use of a spacesuit? Mind you, they look pretty unusual, and there's a chance they could catch on as a fashion, so you might sell quite a few. But that's not the sort of thing you're looking for, is it?''

Mr. Edison agreed that it was not, and made the same comment on the next couple of ideas Dark came up with.

"Of *course!*" Dark finally cried. "I don't know why I didn't hit on it first off, but here's something you can *really* use. I've still got a cinder in my eye from that damned destroyer you had us picked up by, and I remember thinking just after it went in how unnecessary it was, burning all that dangerous stuff. A power source, *that's* what you want."

Edison at last began to look interested. "Well, yes," he said. "I'd admire to know about a new power source, seeing's I've made some little contribution in that line."

"Well, this'll do you very nicely, then." Dark went on to outline the construction of a form of fuel cell used in isolated areas not served by broadcast power on our home world. I was interested in following his description, as I had never concerned myself with how the things were put together. It seemed to be a simple matter and of course resulted in a very effective product at little cost, depending on the conversion of hydrogen to energy.

Edison was also fascinated, though looking less pleased than I would have expected. "Let me get this straight," he said. "*Anybody* could slap one of these things together, so long's he could read plans, handle tools, and had about three dollars seventy-five cents to buy what he needed to start off? And he could pull what hydrogen he needed out of water? And he could use one of 'em to run an auto, or a ship, or a flying machine, or a windmill, or a lathe, or a dynamo, or practically *anything* that needs power? *And* not pay more'n a cent or so a day to use it?"

"That's it," Dark agreed jovially. "I think that'll do nicely to start off with."

Edison gave him a long, careful look. "I'll tell you something," he said. "First invention I ever patented, back in 'sixty-nine, I knew telegraphy backwards and forwards, and it came natural to think up something that used what I knew. And I put this together, and it worked fine. It was for legislatures, like the Congress, and it was a machine that was set up so every time there was a vote, each member could just press a button, and whichever way he voted, yes or no, it'd be recorded instantaneously. A second after the vote was called for, it'd be down and counted, and the result known, and no hours spent in roll calls. Well, I showed that to a committee of Congress, and they turned it down flat. One of 'em was kind enough to take me aside and tell me why. Seemed that those fellows *needed* that waste of time. Gave 'em a chance to see which way the wind was blowing and change their votes if they were going to lose bad or happened to be voting the other way from some fellow they wanted to keep in good with, and so on. So something like that, that looked so good, would upset the whole applecart, and they weren't about to have it."

He looked down at the floor. "Same way with this. Nearly free power for everyone, available tomorrow, ain't that grand? No need to buy coal, gasoline, oil, wood, anything like that. *And* no need to pay the coal miners, oil people, filling stations, anybody like that. I calculate it'd take about six weeks for the country to turn into a howling wilderness of starving mobs using free power to get to places where they could steal food to stay alive."

He rose to his feet. "Gentlemen," he declared, "I

220

broke the law and I broke faith with myself to drag your secrets out of you. And then you gave them to me of your own free will, and they're ashes in my mouth. Well, that's often the way of it, that's so—I guess I forgot that there ain't much fun or profit to be had in something you don't sweat to get for yourself. No such thing as a free lunch, as they say. That business of keeping you prisoners here to milk you of ideas is out, done with, knocked in the head. I will make you another proposition. As distinguished alien visitors, or whatever damned category I can fit you under, I'll see to it that I'm authorized to grant you a handsome pension that will keep you in comfort here for as long as you're around. But only on condition that you keep your mouths shut about any such trifling boons as free power, perpetual motion and the like. That's too rich for our blood, and we'd die of it pretty quick. We're an industrious and inventive people, and I don't see any easy gifts you could let us have being worth losing that.''

When he had left, with a terse farewell, Dark looked after him, dumbfounded. ''What a fellow for not knowing what he wants,'' he muttered.

''I could have told you your idea wouldn't work,'' Valmis said comfortably. ''Edison saw right off that it was a problem of Patterns, that bringing out one of your machinery things the way you wanted would distort the Patterns so badly that they'd fall apart.''

Dark suggested Valmis do something with his Patterns that I believe he must have heard from the sailors on the destroyer.

23

Ari's confidence in the eventual results of the scheme he had at least partially set in motion was, so he maintained, unabated. "It'll start working on the King and the Kaiser and so on, you see, and they won't be able to help themselves. They'll struggle a bit and worry over it, but they'll come round to seeing it, and then we've got our war on. Just you wait and see."

There was no practical alternative course of action that we could see, so we followed Ari's. This we were obliged to do without the company of Oxford. When he returned, some days after Edison's visit, from a trip to New York to see Wells off to England, he sprawled on the couch in the sitting room and said, "Fellows, I've got news. Adieu, adieu, kind friends, adieu, yes, adieu. I can no longer stay with yieu, stay with yieu. Fare thee well, for I must leave thee, et cetera."

"You're not going *away?*" Dark asked.

Oxford gave him a sharp look. "As a matter of fact, yes, that was what I was trying to get across. Look, you can get on perfectly well without me—you've got Mr. and Mrs. Bonacker to look after you, and you're not any longer going up and down in the earth, seeking whom you may devour, so you don't need a keeper. And, while it's been interesting—I don't deny that for a moment—it's not my regular line of work. So after I put Wells on the boat, I went around to see old man Pulitzer at the *World* and put a proposition to him I've been thinking of for some time. And, in short, he's backing me in it."

Although there were a large number of journals, published at nearly every conceivable interval, from one day to three or four months, and offering news, fiction, advice, and comment in profusion, it had seemed to Oxford that there was room for yet another. This was to be a weekly magazine which would summarize the events that had taken place since the previous issue, in the brief, pithy style characteristic of the daily journals, yet in greater detail; for the further benefit of the readers, the reading matter would be arranged by topic, so that one section would be devoted to matters concerning foreign countries, another to American politics, and so on.

"Pulitzer's wild for it," Oxford said, "and I'm to start putting it together next week. I know a lot of reporters who'd give their eyeteeth to work on something like this, and I bet I can put together a staff that'd beat anything going. I've got to work up a name for it, though, something snappy. You fellows want to turn your own odd brand of logic onto that problem?"

We thought awhile, but came up with nothing useful; it was to be expected that we would not be sufficiently acquainted with the subtleties of this culture to be much help. To be polite, I offered one suggestion. "As it seems to me this new journal would save your readers a lot of time, you might call it something like *Save*."

Oxford said that he didn't quite see it, but that there might be the germ of an idea there. He took his final leave the next day, and we were on our own to await the outcome of Ari's contrivings.

From time to time he professed to find evidence in the

journals or in the news programs on the electrodiffuser that events were working out as he had hoped. He was particularly excited by the announcement of a joint visit by the Kaiser, King Edward, and the Czar to the principal nations of Europe, which he considered a sure presage of war, saying, "Just get all those fellows together in one place, and they'll be at each other's throats in no time." But months passed with no perceptible increase in world tensions.

The first anniversary of our arrival on the planet passed, and then that of Mr. Edison's election; winter closed in once more. Our long experience of interstellar flight had habituated us to inactivity, but we did find time hanging heavy on our hands, and we welcomed the purchase of an improved electrodiffusion set which carried pictures as well as sound, something like the telephone I had observed the Czar using. This instrument provided us with much diversion, though not of any very deep content. Mr. Barrymore seemed to take up a good deal of time on it, and I was interested to see some of the antics of Mr. Cohan, whom I had seen perform at Madison Square Garden.

Another year turned—it was now 1910, by local reckoning—and, some weeks into it, I noticed that Valmis was becoming increasingly edgy. "Look here," he said to me one afternoon as the last of the snow was melting on our lawn, "I don't know that I can stand this much longer, hanging on for Ari's war. He keeps saying that it's all right, that his calculations just need a little revising, but I can't see it. I was even thinking of going into stasis—"

"You wouldn't do that!" I exclaimed, shocked. It happens from time to time that an Explorer ship's warp malfunctions, and a journey that would normally be

224

accomplished in weeks stretches into centuries; as a precaution against the effects of this, Explorers are provided with the means of placing themselves in a state of complete inactivity for very long periods so that they can be aroused with no sense of the passage of time, if they should chance to arrive at a place inhabited by anyone with the capacity for doing so. As it is not actually known that the process has worked successfully in practice, Explorers regard the whole idea with a dread verging on the superstitious, even though it is required by regulations for each Captain to keep the necessary equipment by him, as Dark had.

"Well, not really," Valmis said, abashed. "It was just that I got to feeling so low that it crossed my mind. But I've got a much better notion now. Look, Ari's had his chance at getting this planet going the way we want it, and it doesn't seem to have come to much. And Dark's idea of force-feeding them technical things . . . well, we saw what happened about *that*. But, you know, I've got my own specialty, and it seems to me that it might be the way."

"How would that be?"

"Well, you see, what's in the way of these people getting on fast enough to help us with *Wanderer* is really their Patterns. What Ari's after is counting on a sudden change in the Patterns in the shape of a war. And Dark ran up against the fact that you can't work something into a world's Patterns that doesn't fit into them. But they don't know anything about Patterns, really, not like I do, and I think I've got the way to do something about these."

When he later put his proposition before the others, they were dubious. He meant, it appeared, to give public lectures, by means of which he would bring his audi-

225

ences to Perceive the Patterns relating to their lives and to their planet in general, and thus would bring about changes in their consciousness and a resultant rapid readjustment of the Patterns. "It's like I did with that Alexei boy," he explained. "I got the protein things into his bloodstream, and they altered the whole thing. It's the same, once you've got a whole crowd of people learning to Perceive—it'll spread and change everything."

"You needed my medical kit to do that," Dark pointed out.

Valmis was impatient with this cavil. "Naturally enough, if you're dealing with a mechanism, like the body, it stands to reason you've got to use other mechanisms. But with minds, you work with the mind. Look here, Raf, you've met this Cohan man, and I understand he knows his way around the entertainment business; do you think he could give me some tips on how to rent a place where I could speak and hope to draw a pretty fair crowd?"

None of the rest of us was really hopeful about Valmis's plan, but I humored him by suggesting that he go to New York and look up Oxford, who could doubtless put him in touch with Cohan.

We saw Valmis off at the Glen Head railway station, carrying a lunch Mrs. Bonacker had packed for him, as he had not yet got the knack of ordering meals in public eating places. As the train glided out on its overhead rail, Dark said, "He'll be back this evening all crestfallen, poor chap, but at least he'll have had an outing."

Valmis's return was otherwise than Dark had predicted. He strode in animatedly, humming a song I

226

recalled from the electrodiffuser, sailed his hat across the room, and sank into a chair, grinning broadly.

"So Cohan put you on to how to hire a hall?" Ari asked.

"Hire a *hall?*" Valmis repeated scornfully. "Let me tell you, that notion's down there among the remnants and markdowns! George M. says that's for soulful ladies who want to get across the latest line in theosophy, or fellows with lantern slides of the Holy Land, not a red-hot proposition like yours truly!"

"What . . . what has he in mind, then?" Ari said faintly.

Valmis produced a large cigar, bit the end off, and lit it, drawing upon it luxuriously. "Havana Perfecto," he remarked around it. "Fifty cents each, no less. George M. gave me a handful of 'em, that's the kind of fellow he is. He saw right off that the lecture dodge wasn't for mine, no sir! It isn't every day that you get a fellow guaranteed to be from another planet, and fresh from a tour of the crowned heads of Europe, ready to give forth the wisdom of the ages, and George M. means to see to it that I get a proper showcase. He's seeing to *everything:* setting up when and where I'm to appear, how I should dress—he wants me to wear the coverall from *Wanderer*, says a chap in a chalk-stripe gent's three-piece with pinched waist ain't going to cut much ice when it comes to the philosophy game—and he wants me to write down some of my material so's he can polish it up and see that it gets across."

"How much is all this going to cost you?" Dark said. Our pensions from Mr. Edison were ample for our needs and some luxuries, but would not really cover a considerable extra expense.

"Cost me? Cost *me?"* Valmis threw his head back and laughed. "Not a single simoleon, *that's* what it's going to cost me. George M.'s going to *pay* me!"

For the next few weeks, Valmis was absent much of the time, taking a morning train to New York to confer with Mr. Cohan, and returning only in the evening; he would even occasionally stay at a city hotel overnight. As presaged by his manner after his first encounter with Cohan, his speech and general attitude underwent startling changes. He would talk knowledgeably of theatrical performances and restaurants and cabarets frequented by actors, often offer to give us advice concerning wagers on sporting events, though we did not follow these entertainments at all closely, and regale us with a vast fund of anecdotes concerning persons of whom we knew nothing. One exception to our ignorance of his new circle of acquaintances was Rasputin, who appeared to be gaining a growing if in the main unsavory reputation among New York's flourishing motion picture colony. "Sharp fellow, that," Valmis remarked approvingly. "He's getting on in movie work and picking up a nice bundle of change endorsing soap for the ads. He's got a picture of himself the way he was in Russia, and they run that alongside a new one, and a balloon coming out of his mouth saying, 'Ebony soap did this for *me*—what wouldn't it do for *you?*' "

"I think," Ari observed later, "that Valmis is getting caught up in a Pattern he's not aware of."

Valmis was completely absent for some days before his first public appearance, having left word as to the time and place we should present ourselves to witness it. On the appointed day, we made our way to the theatrical district of New York. It was, I realized, at least a year and a half since I had had any close look at

228

this portion of the city, and I was struck by some changes in it. Hardly any horse-drawn vehicles were to be seen, and the many motorcars operated much more quietly than I recalled, as did the elevated railways, which were now, I understood, converted to the turbine engine in general use on trips between cities. Overhead, a large flying machine slowly drew an advertising banner across the sky, offering inexpensive air trips to a place called Florida.

At one motion picture theater, I was interested to see a large poster promising that those who ventured within would see:

MAD MONK-EY SHINES
A New Sound Feature
Starring JOHN BARRYMORE
as "Grigori the Great"
A GOLDFISH-LASKY-RASPUTIN Production
Written by GREG RASPUTIN
Directed by GREG RASPUTIN
Technical Advisor GREG RASPUTIN

The auditorium to which Valmis had directed us, an ornately decorated place, was crowded, though this was the afternoon of a working day. We found our seats and settled into them with anticipation, in spite of our reservations about Valmis's course, proud that so many Earth people had turned out to see our companion.

We were thus at a loss when he did not appear at the rise of the curtain. A lady came out and sang, to the accompaniment of an orchestra just below the stage, a long song which seemed to turn on the fact that the words "June" and "moon" end in similar sounds. She was followed by a man who obliged a dog to do a number of things which I would have thought unlikely

229

had I not seen them, and then by two bearded men whose conversation, though opaque to me, aroused great enthusiasm from the audience.

"What is all this?" I whispered to Ari. "Did Valmis send us to the wrong place?"

"It may be," Ari answered, "that this collection of oddities is meant to show the consequences of striving to live without Perceiving Patterns. Those last two, Weber and Fields, might well illustrate the principle of complete anarchy and chaos in an undetermined Universe."

"I don't know about that," Dark put in, "but the native term for this is three-a-day."

After two more people had come out and thrown each other into the air for some time, a placard was pushed onto the stage reading: THE AMAZING VALMIS— THE MAN FROM THE STARS.

"Ah," Dark said, "now we get down to it. I wonder what this crowd'll make of a lecture on Patterns after they've been worked up by all these other acts?"

The orchestra struck up a brisk tune, and Valmis, the spotlight gleaming on his white coverall, sauntered onto the stage. I was surprised to see him carrying a light walking stick, and hoped that he had not suffered an injury.

He assumed a negligent attitude, leaning on the stick, and, in time to the music from the orchestra, *sang*. I was later able to obtain a copy of the words of this song from him, though he insisted that any reproduction of them was strictly forbidden without mention of the fact that they were copyright 1910 by Co-Val Music Corp.

When singing in the bathtub or walking in the rain,

he warbled in a high, nasal voice,

230

Do you ever think to wonder what gives pleasure and what
    pain?
Why East is East and West is West, and never twain do
    meet?
Why sky is blue and grass is green, and honey mighty
    sweet?
Well, folks, I've got the news on that, and now you'll have
    it, too:
You've got to make your mind go blank, and let the Pat-
    terns through!

At this point, the tempo of the music became faster,
and he executed a series of intricate steps, which had
the effect of causing him to rotate about the walking stick
as he continued to sing.

It's the Patterns! The Patterns!
In rabbits and their habits, in stars and Christmas trees,
In toads and frogs and puppy dogs, in hives of bumblebees;
It's the Patterns that all make 'em—
It's the Patterns, you can't break 'em—
Once you see 'em, you can shape 'em—
It's the Patterns that make all things as they are!

It was, I was obliged to admit, a catchy tune, and as
Valmis accompanied succeeding verses with ever more
imaginative steps, the performance was well received
by the audience.

When he left, to be succeeded by an individual who
announced his intention of divining the thoughts of any
person in the audience, we quitted our seats and made
our way to an area behind the stage, as Valmis had
previously requested us to do.

We found him in a small room, seated in front of a
mirror, removing some colored substance from his face.

231

"Didn't it go well?" he asked. "I thought I really had 'em after the verse, and once I swung into the chorus and did that sort of shuffle around the cane, they were in the palm of my hand—right, George?"

I now saw that Mr. Cohan was seated on a chair in the corner of the room. He nodded approvingly and assured Valmis, "You killed 'em, boy. You just want to watch your timing toward the end—you nearly kicked the cane out from under you and took a pratfall."

"Well," Valmis said, "don't you think a bit of comedy might in fact go well just there? It would, I don't know, give it a sense of—"

"Hey!" Dark strode over to Cohan. "You were supposed to be giving our friend here a chance to get some deep stuff across to the public, right? So what's this business about making him into a vaudeville turn?"

"I'll tell you," Cohan replied, looking up at the towering Captain. "I thought about it some, after Valmis came to me, and it just didn't seem to me that he would get any kind of a hearing, doing what he planned. So I worked out how he could at least draw an audience. And say," he added, glaring at Dark, "where do you get off knocking vaudeville turns, anyhow? Can you think of anything *else* you fellows are good for?"

24

We all knew after that, I think, what the future held for us, though the ingrained dread of which I have spoken caused us to avoid facing it for a very long time.

Valmis, though he insisted on playing out the engagement to which Mr. Cohan had bound him, had no heart to continue further when the disparity between his intention and the reality of his performance had been made clear to him. He spent much time in his room, looking morosely at a collection of signed photographs of theater people he had mounted on his wall, and sighing.

Ari, with an increasing lack of conviction, scanned all journals for signs of the oncoming war.

Dark sought relief in busying himself with mechanical matters; he participated in several automobile races and did quite well. During the latter part of this period, he was aided by Sergeant Olson, as mechanic, and Captain Thatcher, as manager, they having retired from the Marine Corps. But to an Explorer Captain cut off from his ship, automobile racing prizes are only a palliative, they do not cure; and the passage of time only deepened his gloom.

I quite enjoyed my trips to the Roslyn tavern, in spite of an occasional return of my fatigue, but these also could not make me forget that we were where we ought not to be, with little prospect of leaving . . . at least not during our normal life span.

Thus, the word "stasis," while unspoken among us, began to loom larger in my mind and, I now know, in those of my companions.

The events of that time held moments of occasional interest for us, even of high excitement. I shall never forget, for instance, the *Titanic* disaster, as we saw it on the color electrodiffuser. The scene of the great ship, mortally ripped by a piece of floating ice, slowly slipping under the sea, was eerily impressive, and contrasted dramatically with the darting movements of the rescue fleet of Wright fliers and Sikorsky ornithopters which had been dispatched from the American and European shores within moments of the arrival of the news of the ship's plight. After all the passengers and crew had been removed, one lone aircraft in the service of the electrodiffusion company remained, floodlighting and relaying the scene until, with a sudden boiling movement of the ocean, the ill-fated liner vanished. All of us were shaken, recalling *Wanderer*'s disappearance in just such a manner . . . four years before, now.

It was in the same year that we saw and heard President Edison's unexpected speech in which he announced his decision not to run for a second term, as he wished to get back to work. "There's more going on than I ever dreamed possible," he declared, "and I mean to show the world that I'm up to getting in on it."

Mr. Roosevelt's triumphant return to office was also a reminder of our first days here, when our hopes had been so high.

One afternoon in July of 1914, Ari burst into my room in high glee. "It's late, but it's coming!" he announced. "I just heard on the electrodiffuser that somebody's shot the heir to the Austrian throne in Europe, and that's just the stuff to set them off. You wait, there'll be

234

ultimatums and mobilizations and I don't know what else, and then, bang!''

"Well, that's nice,'' I said, not being able to rouse any real enthusiasm, for I had been through many such moments with Ari. And of course I was correct in this, the shooting, in the usual way of such crises, resulting in nothing more than the standard conferences of heads of government and some political readjustments.

A year or so later, for some reason, the papers, Oxford's magazine, and the electrodiffuser gave a great deal of coverage to Czar Nicholas's installation of one Vladimir Ulyanov as Minister-President of the Russian Democratic Empire; according to the electrodiffusion commentary, delivered, curiously enough, by Rasputin, who appeared to have spread himself over much of the communications and entertainment industry, this signaled political changes of great moment.

"An historical day, ladies and gentlemen,'' we heard him say, as the screen showed a view of the Winter Palace at St. Petersburg. "Vladimir Ilich now kneeling before Little Father—all that about Siberia forgotten now, by damn!—and giving homage. On platform I can seeing Emperor from China, Kaiser, King Edward. Bells in cathedrals ringing now—that banging you hearing is twenty-one-gun salute from battleship *Potemkin*. When it finish, is sign that Holy Mother Russia be changed, all legal and by vote, to democratic monarchy! This Greg Rasputin, bringing you scene I *never* expecting to see!''

Ari switched the set off and regarded it glumly. "Everything's going on, and we're left out of it. I'm beginning to have moments, you know, when I almost lose my faith in Metahistory. I know it backwards and forwards, and everything I ever learned about it tells me that there *should* have been a war by now, even if I miscalculated about being able to do something to bring it on faster. But, damn it, it's as if we weren't here, as if we were ghosts or something, unable to get anybody to hear us or pay any attention to us. It's almost enough . . .''

All the same, we put off making the decision for another two years, watching the months come and go at what seemed to be an ever-increasing pace, and ourselves becoming less and less active.

It was Valmis who voiced our thoughts openly, on a bright autumn day. "Damn it, we might as well *be* in stasis, for all the good we are to ourselves, each other, or *Wanderer*. Your war is *not* coming on, Ari, and that means there's no telling when this planet's going to be up to helping us. I don't know what went wrong—maybe that Ford man was right about Metahistory being metabunk—but in any case that's a dead end. And the same about anything else the rest of us have tried. If we're not just going to sit around here until we wither, the only thing to do is face it and go into stasis for as long as we need to."

Our protests were a half-hearted ritual, for we had each privately arrived at the same conclusion some time before, though not yet daring to act on it.

Once the decision was taken, we took a melancholy pride in carrying it out quickly and efficiently. We consulted Oxford and were granted an interview with President Roosevelt (who had persuaded the voters in 1916 that the next term would not, if you looked at it the right way, actually be his fourth). Both were disconcertingly quick to agree that stasis would be a good solution.

"You just get off to sleep, then," the President said heartily, "and we'll have you woken up when we're

236

ready to help you on your way, by Godfrey! Not before, mind you; we wouldn't want you cooling your heels any longer and thinking about getting wars started, eh?''

He agreed to have a stasis chamber constructed according to our specifications in a corner of a military cemetery at a place called Arlington. "Might as well," Ari muttered morosely. "The way things are going, it's not going to be used for much else."

Oxford agreed to set up, with the assistance of Wells, an organization that would oversee our period—perhaps centuries—in stasis and ensure that when the time came we should be awakened. Both the method of going into stasis and the process of awakening were quite simple, so that there would be little likelihood of the necessary instructions being garbled by the passage of years.

Soon the time came for us to leave the house at Glenwood, to return no more. We bade farewell to Mr. and Mrs. Bonacker, to whom we had deeded the place in appreciation of their services for almost precisely ten years, and took the train to New York.

"Look," Dark said, "why don't we put this off for a day or so and have one last look around Europe? There were some nice places there, and the fliers can get you across within a day. It'd be fun, wouldn't it?"

But, having made our decision, the rest of us agreed that it would be unnerving to defer its execution, and we proceeded to Washington and thence the next morning to the chamber prepared for us at Arlington.

We set out the stasis-inducing equipment and prepared it for use, and we stowed the reanimation instruments in a prominent place, not wishing them to be overlooked when the time came. We made all the preparations we could before sealing the chamber, and we stood for a moment at the half-opened door. It was a clear day, with the sky a deep blue and a touch of frost in the air; we heard the sound of a distant bell giving several slow chimes.

"Eleven o'clock," Dark said, counting them. "Well, that's a bit of a Pattern for you, Valmis. Eleventh hour of the eleventh day of the eleventh month. If we'd had the sense to do this seven years ago, it'd have been the eleventh year of the century, too. Well, let's get on with it—we haven't been able to do anything with this place, so the sooner we're out of it the better."

He pulled the door to and sealed it.

25

All the information we had been given on stasis was firm on the point that there was no subjective awareness of the passage of time, that the interval between entering that state and leaving it would seem no more than a blink. As I have stated, this was mainly theory, based only upon limited experimentation, since volunteers to test the proposition that this effect would hold true over a period covering several normal life spans were not forthcoming.

I thus expected at the time I awoke to be somehow conscious that a number of years had come and gone, but the theory turned out in fact to be true after all. When I found myself aware of my surroundings again, it seemed to me so soon that I could almost fancy I heard the echo of the chiming bell still ringing in my ears.

Light flooded our chamber, and I looked up curiously to see what manner of future man might have awakened us. I felt an eerie chill as I saw in the two figures who now stood among us an uncanny resemblance to Wells and Oxford. These were men of more advanced years, but close to identical to them in feature and bearing. The clothing they were wearing, though substantially different in cut, was also sufficiently close to twentieth-century garments to suggest a bizarre idea.

Could it be, I wondered, that the "sleeping space-men" had become the object of a cult, as decade followed decade and century followed century into the past? Had Oxford and Wells become the founders of a hereditary priesthood, passing their genes down the years to their successors? It would follow, then, that the prescribed ritual garments would be modeled after those of the original priests, or keepers. If such were the case, it boded little good, it seemed to me, as the level of superstition it suggested would not be compatible with the technology we required. It was in no easy frame of mind that I sat up and looked at my companions.

"Wells? Oxford?" Dark said. "What the *hell* are you doing here? We've only just got set to . . . in fact, somehow, I thought we had . . . and what are you wearing those funny clothes for?"

"Good to see you again, fellows," the "Oxford" one said. "Why don't you stretch a bit and then get up? You might be a bit stiff after all this time."

"You mean we've *been* in stasis already?" Dark demanded. "But then who are you, and how long has it been? What year is this, anyhow?"

"Nineteen thirty-three," answered the "Wells" one— and then, of course, I realized that it was not, so to speak, a "Wells," but Wells himself!

"That's nice," Dark said heavily. "Do you plan to bring us out of stasis every fifteen years to let us know the time? Kind of you, I'm sure, but we really don't need it. It's bad enough to go into this sort of thing once, let alone over and over again."

"You won't have to go back into stasis," Oxford explained. "Not unless your warp drive goes out on the way home, which I don't think it will, as we've had it checked over pretty thoroughly. The Wrights' people have made some changes in the atmosphere control surfaces which I think you'll find useful, too."

240

If we were stiff after our period of stasis, I do not believe we were aware of it. In an instant we were on our feet, surrounding the two Earthmen and bombarding them with questions.

Oxford and Wells soon made it clear to us that in spite of the absence of war during the entire fifteen-year period of our stasis, to say nothing of the years immediately preceding it, there had been a great worldwide flowering of science and technology, together with many social and political changes, and that this had resulted in the locating, raising, and refitting of *Wanderer* within the past few months.

"Everybody pitched in, you see," Wells told us. "Scientists and technicians from all over the place came to help. We had some most valuable contributions from the new universities in Africa, and Einstein himself came in from Berlin to see that the calculations for the warp drive were done properly. Oh, it was an international effort, right enough."

"Well, that was decent of them," Dark said. "But, look here, how come? I mean, before, well, we could hardly get anybody to pay attention to us. We just got sort of pushed aside, until there wasn't anything to do but put ourselves out of it for a bit. So how does it happen that there's this great rush to help us?"

"And I should take it kindly," Ari continued with some asperity, "if you could make it clear to me in what way the principles of Metahistory have come to such grief in dealing with your planet. What you tell us is impossible by any Metahistorical precepts, and I'm not at all sure you're not giving us some fanciful story for purposes of your own."

"Come on outside, fellows," Oxford said gently. We followed him and Wells from our chamber into the sunlight. At some distance, we could see the city of Washington in the clear air. I could recognize many of the buildings, but there were others, some of a shimmering white hue and graceful shape, others somewhat partaking of the qualities of a rainbow. A long ovoid sped through the sky high above us; somewhat nearer the ground, brightly colored winged machines, each with a visible passenger, darted and swooped silently in apparent play.

"All right," Ari said after a moment. "It's there, I can see that. You *have* come a long way, then. But how? We tried so hard to . . ." He stopped, apparently a little embarrassed at recalling the method by which he had attempted to speed Earth's progress.

"You did a lot, you know," Oxford said. "I don't know that anybody could ever trace everything, but you left quite a trail of surprises. I don't know what Metahistorical teaching's like, but doesn't it take into account things like what happens to a man when he's been a crippled megalomaniac all his life, and then all of a sudden he's not a cripple? Or a father who has the fear that his son's going to die any minute lifted from him? Metahistory doesn't consider that giving those fellows a whole new idea of what life can be like might have a little effect here and there?"

"It is the nature of Metahistory to deal with probabilities of increasing refinement," Ari replied. "Thus the inescapable tendencies are clearly established."

"Well, I guess your probabilities were pretty unrefined," Oxford retorted. "And if you really wanted that war, why on Earth did you go and tell the King and the Czar and the Kaiser what it'd be like? Couldn't you see they'd bust their crowns to avoid it?"

"I was counting on their rationality," Ari said.

242

Both Wells and Oxford threw their heads back and laughed. "Oh, *my!*" Wells exclaimed delightedly.

"You mean," Valmis said slowly, "that what Ari did to change things worked just the wrong way? I *knew* there was a reason why we weren't supposed to meddle in other planets' affairs."

"That was some of it," Oxford said. "But the main thing, I guess . . . the big effect you've had, was just the *fact* of you. Once we all knew that there were other worlds, that there were people pretty much like us some place else, why, when that sank in, it gave everyone here a whole new way of looking at things, you see. For ten thousand and some years, we've been free to consider our neighbors, the fellow next door or in the next country, as somebody *else*, a foreigner, and likely an enemy. This planet was all there was, and there was plenty of room for suspicion and jealousy and shooting people in the head on the off chance they might be a bother to you. But that doesn't hold up any more. It took a while, but when you fellows showed up, it kind of took the heart out of things like that. For the first time *ever,* people started getting a clear notion of what it was to be human and to live on a planet in space."

"So we didn't need the wars to get on," Wells continued. "Within a few years after you went into that place"—he gestured at the dark chamber behind us —"there was a new age of science, literature and art, and advances in economics and social progress, like nothing there's ever been, and it's been buzzing along like mad ever since."

"Well, I could have given you a start on that, only Edison told me to shut up about it," Dark said sullenly.

"He was right, d'you see!" Wells exclaimed. "Right as rain. He finally saw that it was the *idea* that something could be done that counted, not getting the plans as a gift. He didn't invent electrodiffusion by dissecting that hearing-aid thing you gave him, Raf—he saw what was there, and then he worked out how electrodiffusion *had* to be done. And the same with the Wrights and the others—once they learned something about the sorts of things you had, once they knew there was something great to get at, why, then, they could go and do it. And, by God, haven't we just done it!''

"So," Ari said after a moment, "it is in gratitude for our completely involuntary services—our blundering and our ignorance, not to mince matters—that we are being assisted on our way by a considerable number of your population. It is not an easy thought to accept.''

"If it gets me back behind the controls of *Wanderer,* I don't mind a bit if I'm made to look something of a fool,'' Dark declared.

Valmis looked rather pale, and I wondered if he were still troubling himself about his so-called use of the Probability Displacer, ten—no, twenty-five—years before. If he persisted in clinging to that delusion, he would be bound to be somewhat shaken by Oxford's and Wells's description of the changes we had occasioned.

We spent one more week on Earth, the greater part of it occupied with a tour of the planet, it being thought that we ought to see how it had got on in our absence.

The first evening after our awakening, we dined with President Roosevelt—not our old acquaintance, who had perished tragically some eight years previously when an early moon rocket launch he was observing failed in a spectacular explosion, but a cousin of his—who insisted on taking us on an extensive tour of the White House and its grounds, walking at a pace that

244

quite tired us. "Uncle Ted was right," he called back to us over his shoulder. "The strenuous life, that's the thing—in this job, you can go stale awfully quickly if you don't keep moving."

The news of our revival had been kept secret until after its accomplishment and, in fact, until very nearly the time of our departure for Europe the next day. We thus avoided a crush of newsmen and electrodiffusion people, but were able to take with us on the sleek Wright flier that carried us over the ocean—hardly recognizable as a descendant of the electric-powered dragonflies that had darted over the *Titanic*—an armful of journals relating the event.

These made interesting reading, as there were not only news stories, but what Oxford called "think pieces" and other sorts of literary effort presented.

I was struck by one of these, a verse by a person named Seeger. Its opening lines:

> We have a rendezvous with Life
> At some still-distant planetfall

seemed to suggest that Earth was setting about an endeavor in space which might bring our peoples into contact. I was not sure that this would be a good idea, and made a note to mention to the Explorer directorate when we arrived home that it would be well to keep an eye out for this unpredictable race.

I retain few clear impressions of the world tour, as reception followed reception with dizzying swiftness. We were greeted in London by King Edward's recently crowned successor, George the Fifth, who had a remarkable resemblance to Czar Nicholas, and by the Poet Laureate, Sir Rupert Brooke, who composed a

245

rather florid ode in our honor. I transcribed part of this as well, as I do not believe any residents of other planets have written verse about Explorers, and thought it worth preserving as a curiosity, especially as it seemed intended to represent a personification of the planet itself.

Earth's Farewell to the Starmen

And when you leave, think only this of me,
That there's some planet of a foreign star
That is for ever your world; there shall be
On this rich Earth a heritage by far
More splendid than we ever dared to hope. . . .

It went on for some time in this vein.

In St. Petersburg, Czar Alexei, now quite a strapping young fellow, received us handsomely; he had little recollection of Valmis's intervention in the matter of his health, but had been told of it often enough by his late father, he said.

It was a melancholy thought that the passage of fifteen years had taken so many of those we had encountered only recently, as it seemed to us; we were pleased that Kaiser William himself, quite white-haired now, was present when we touched down in Berlin. We accompanied him through the streets of the city in an open vehicle that appeared to have no wheels; the Kaiser told us that it rested upon a cushion of air, which Dark found implausible. At one spot where the crowd was dense and our machine therefore slowed somewhat, a dark-haired man darted from the crowd, thrust an object into the Kaiser's hand, shouted something, and withdrew. "Ha!" the Kaiser commented. "Not bad. He said he wanted you to have it as a souvenir—it would be nice to think his name and work would travel to other worlds.'' He handed it over for us to examine. It was a detailed, if lifeless, portrait in colored inks of the four of us, apparently radiating from our heads a strong light which fell upon a representation of the planet placed in front of us.

"I've seen his work,'' the Kaiser remarked. "He illustrates for some trashy magazines my grandsons read. Well, I daresay you'll be the only Explorers with a genuine Hitler drawing for your private gallery!''

The Sultan of Turkey, the President of India, the Emperor of China . . . these dignitaries, their lands and their cities, are all a blur to me now. We came, were greeted and displayed to the crowds, and we went on, day after day.

I remember asking Wells, who was also showing the strain of the journey, how it was that in the face of the changes he had described in the world, so many of the old political entities remained unaltered.

"There wasn't any need to alter them,'' he told me. "When everybody got to working together and understanding that we all had to fit on the same planet, why, it just sort of bypassed the old business about revolutions and independence and such. Since governments are responsive to the needs of the people, the forms and the boundaries don't much matter now, and the people're perfectly content to leave matters of that sort as they are and get on with things that really interest them.''

The last leg of our journey was over the same body of water that *Wanderer* had traversed in its final descent; it was with a thrill that I saw the coastal features of San Francisco emerging ahead. Then, as the aircraft circled before landing, I could see below us a familiar gleaming shape.

"That's *Wanderer* down there!'' Dark bellowed. "By

247

God, there she is, sleek as ever and ready to take us home!"

And so she was. There was no official ceremony, just a hasty farewell from Wells and Oxford. "It's been quite a time, fellows," Oxford said. "I wouldn't have missed it for anything. But . . . you're not planning on coming back, are you?"

We assured him that we had no such intention.

"Good," he remarked, stepping back to allow us to enter *Wanderer*. "I kind of think once was enough. So long."

With this last cryptic example of Earthly conversation, we took our departure.

When the globe was dwindling behind us, sparkling blue and white against the darkness of space, I observed that Valmis and Ari were looking back at it, as I was, their expressions ambiguous. Dark was peering ahead as well as from side to side; he muttered gloomily, "If they've been up to all that they said, no telling *what* we might run into without expecting it before we can get into warp."

"Raf," Ari asked, his eyes still on Earth, "have you started composing your Survey Report?"

"In a sense, yes," I replied. "I've got down pretty well all that happened, at any rate. But . . ."

"Precisely," Ari said. "Though Recording is your province and none of us would presume to suggest how you ought to handle it, there is still the fact that a *total* Recording would present certain problems for all members of this team. There is much that happened during our extended sojourn there which, considered by over-worked bureaucrats in the Directorate, would have an aspect that would not be conducive to the most tempered—"

248

I was beginning to wonder whether Ari had embarked on a sentence to which there was no possible ending and which might therefore go on until he wore out, but Dark interrupted him:

"You mean we're in the soup if we let it get out that you tried to start a war and kept one of their rulers alive past his time, and that I put that Kaiser man's arm straight and did what I could to turn their technology on its head, and that Valmis laid 'em in the aisles with his Patterns patter number, right? Well, we don't tell them, see? It's that simple."

"I imagine," I said, "that the normal process of editorial compression would—"

"You'll fudge it, then? Good," Dark said. "Whoo! That was a damned big *something* that just went by, and no mistake! Lights flashing all over it. My word, these chaps *have* been up to something while we were out of the swim."

"My own opinion," Ari remarked, "is that Mr. Oxford's and Mr. Wells's remarks were, though well-intentioned and appreciative, wide of the mark, and reflected a certain primitive bias typical of Level Four cultures—though they do seem to have got to Level Seven rather quickly. Therefore, any moderate infractions of the directives which we may have fallen into must be seen as actually having no effect on the planetary culture, and therefore are hardly worthy of being brought to the attention of—"

"Of *what*?" Valmis asked, turning away from the ever-smaller globe visible in the rear viewport. "Don't you see, it's not *the* Directorate we're going back to, but another one. One that didn't exist until I used the Displacer twenty-five years ago. Maybe none of us can tell the difference, and maybe *they* can't, but it's there all the same. I *did* that to save our lives, and at least we're here to worry about it. . . ."

Dark, Ari and I did not normally find ourselves in accord on any given question, but the looks of disapproval, boredom and long-suffering patience which we turned toward Valmis bore a substantial resemblance to one another.

"Back there, twenty-five years back," Valmis mused, "I made a cowardly choice. I kept us from crashing into that place you found out about, Dark—Siberia, was it? And we landed, and we met all those people and did all those things, and I wrote that rather nice song—though I don't suppose I'll ever see any royalties on it. And . . . things turned out as we saw, and the people back there don't seem too bad off, I suppose. But, you know, there would have been a world, almost like that, in which a spaceship hit the Tunguska region in 1908, and probably blew up like a meteorite, and so no Explorers talking to Roosevelt and Oxford and Wells and mending the Kaiser and the Czar's son and all that. They'd have been left to find their own way, don't you see? And it almost tears me apart to think about it. My using the Displacer, and all those other things we did . . . we shouldn't have, you know. Because they had the right to their destiny; we can only have diminished them by our meddling! For the rest of my life I'll be haunted by wondering . . ."

He cast a glance backward at the last blue-white glint in the encompassing darkness.

"What might they not have become—without us?"